The Psychoanalytic Study of the Child

The Psychoanalytic Study of the Child

VOLUME II   1946

AN ANNUAL

INTERNATIONAL UNIVERSITIES PRESS

NEW YORK   NEW YORK

Copyright 1947. International Universities Press, Inc.

Second Printing, 1950

Third Printing, 1955

Fourth Printing, 1959

Fifth Printing, 1962

Sixth Printing, 1968

Manufactured in the United States of America

The Psychoanalytic Study of the Child

VOLUME II   1946

MANAGING EDITORS

ANNA FREUD   HEINZ HARTMANN, M.D.   ERNST KRIS, PH.D.

CONTENTS

III. GUIDANCE WORK

IV. PROBLEMS OF EDUCATION AND SOCIOLOGY

V. HISTORY OF CHILD PSYCHIATRY

COMMENTS ON THE FORMATION OF PSYCHIC STRUCTURE

By HEINZ HARTMANN, M.D., ERNST KRIS, Ph.D.,
and RUDOLPH M. LOEWENSTEIN, M.D. (New York)

I. *Introduction*

Concern with clarification of terms is unpopular amongst psycho-analysts and rare in psychoanalytic writing. This is partly due to Freud's example. Semantics could hardly be the concern of the great explorer and some inconsistency in the usage of words may well be considered the prerogative of genius.[1] It is a different matter when a generation or two of scientists assume a similar prerogative; then scientific communication may tend to suffer and controversy to dissolve into soliloquies of individuals or groups. The latter conditions seem to prevail in recent psychoanalytic writing and clarification of terminology may well be one of the means to counteract it.

Psychoanalysis has developed under social conditions rare in science. Small teams of private practitioners everywhere formed the nuclei of larger professional groups. During the early stages of team work, written communication was supplemented to such an extent by personal contact on an international scale—mainly by training analyses with the few instructors—that mutual understanding was not endangered by uncertainties of terminology. With the increase of the number of psychoanalysts, that condition was bound to change. The situation of the 1940's is hardly reminiscent of the period of early team work; large groups of psychoanalysts work in ever looser contact with each other and the diffusion of psychoanalytic concepts in psychiatry, their extension into psychosomatic medicine, social work and various educational and psychological techniques opens up new vistas of development. Every step in this development, every new context in which psychoanalytic propositions are being tested or used raises anew the problem of adequate communication. Since scientific

1. See also E. Kris (1947), a contribution written at the same time as this paper.

11

communication is impaired by ambiguity of meaning, the need for clarification has become urgent.

Psychoanalytic hypotheses have undergone far-reaching modifications in Freud's own work and in that of his earlier collaborators. The importance of some of these reformulations was in many instances underrated at the time of their publication; and we believe that the importance of the most radical and farsighted ones, suggested in Freud's *Inhibitions, Symptoms and Anxiety,* has not yet been fully appreciated. Briefly, since a structural viewpoint was introduced into psychoanalytic thinking, hypotheses established previously must be reintegrated. The task of synchronization is larger than it might seem at first. For the newcomer the study of psychoanalysis will remain cumbersome until this is accomplished: he can hardly turn to any one book or any one presentation. While psychoanalysis has reached the "handbook stage", no handbook exists.[2] In order to grasp the systematic cohesion of psychoanalysis as a theory, the student has to study its development. This detour alone seems to guarantee full understanding; it is a detour which only a few devoted workers choose. Yet without it, there is some danger that part of what has been presented in many years of psychoanalytic writings is lost to the student, that rediscoveries of what once was discarded for valid reasons may occur ever more frequently, but also that the degree of relevance of various hypotheses may not always clearly be established and a systematic understanding of hypotheses seems to indicate that shifts in emphasis are unavoidable. Without these shifts, progress in insight tends to be retarded at a moment which otherwise lends itself uniquely to concentrated efforts of research. In restating some of the most general propositions of psychoanalysis, we have such concentrated efforts of research in mind.

In the writings of Freud and of other psychoanalysts, a large number of assumptions are tacitly implied, partly because the atmosphere of team work made full explicitness seem unnecessary; partly because the novelty of the clinical phenomena suggested global rather than detailed explanation. Thus, in turning to any one statement in the literature on a given subject, the student is likely to find incompletely stated hypotheses, and those who rely on random quotations from Freud's work have an easy time obscuring his meaning. When verification of hypotheses is at stake, incomplete statements are bound to encumber the way. Yet verification is essential in many areas; in none

2. This point was made by H. Hartmann at the Symposium on Present Trends in Psychoanalytic Theory and Practice, at the Psychoanalytic Congress in Detroit, 1943.

so much as in genetic questions (Hartmann-Kris, 1945). In the present paper we attempt to formulate just those propositions that are concerned with the formation of psychic structure; and within this group we select some that may be considered as models; i.e., many parallel hypotheses are being used in other areas of psychoanalytic theory. Our selection of propositions is also guided by consideration of actual or potential misunderstandings. We are therefore less concerned with problems of libidinal development, its stages and its manifestations, and more with some problems of ego development and superego formation, and with the part played by maturation in these developments.

II. *The Structural Concepts*

Precursors of structural concepts appeared in Freud's work when, at the end of the nineteenth century, he implemented his first startling discoveries by explanatory concepts which his subject matter had forced upon him. That subject matter was the study of psychic conflict.

The concept of a psychic conflict is integral to many religious systems and many philosophical doctrines. Ever more frequently since the days of enlightenment had the great masters of intuitive psychology, had writers, poets, and philosophers described the life of man as torn between conflicting forces. Freud's contribution conquered this area for the rule of science. The study of psychic conflict in general, and more specifically that of the pathognomic nature of certain conflicts, suggested that the forces opposing each other in typical conflict situations were not grouped at random; rather that the groups of opposing forces possessed an inner cohesion or organization. These impressions were undoubtedly stimulated by a topic that in the 1880's and 1890's played a considerable part in French psychiatry: that of multiple personality.[3] The intermittent eruptions observed in these cases supported the idea that other less dramatic manifestations of mental illness could be understood in terms of "man divided against himself".

Freud's first approach to this division and his first understanding of its implications was guided by the physicalist school in the German physiology of his time (Bernfeld, 1944), and by the evolutionist thinking of Darwinism. Under these influences he tentatively suggested his first formulations on the nature of "the psychic apparatus" whose complex functions would account for the kind of bewildering phenomena that had emerged: disturbances of memory, indirect expression

---

3. See in this connection Azam, Binet, Bourru and Burot, Camuset, Dufay, Paul Janet, Pierre Janet.

of impulses in symptoms or symbols, the nature of dreams, fantasy and delusion; all these appeared in a new context, once the limitation of psychology to consciousness had been abandoned; all had to be explained in the light of the clinical study of conflict situations.

We shall not describe in detail here how, in a set of reformulations, the first hypotheses concerning the psychic apparatus were gradually modified; how step by step the concepts emerged which in the early 1920's Freud introduced under the names of "id", "ego", and "super-ego". These three psychic substructures or systems are not conceived of as independent parts of personality that invariably oppose each other, but as three centers of psychic functioning that can be characterized according to their developmental level, to the amount of energy vested in them, and to their demarcation and interdependence at a given time. Under specific conditions one of the centers may expand its area, and another or the two others may recede; more correctly, we should say that functions exercised by one of the systems may temporarily be more or less influenced by one of the others.

Thus, three of the foremost functions of the ego, *thinking, perception* and *action,* are frequently put into the service of either the id or the superego.

Thinking may be used for the gratification of instinctual as well as self-critical tendencies. In pathological cases, e.g. in compulsive thinking, it can become a substitute for masturbation. In psychoses, e.g. in paranoic delusions, it is overwhelmed by id and superego functions.

Perception may be used for the gratification of instinctual wishes in scoptophilic activity. In pathological cases, it might lead to hysterical disturbances of vision. In dreams and in psychoses perception is modified in a different sense; hallucinatory phenomena are perceptions without objects in the outside world. The perceptual function in these cases can be used by both the id and the superego.

Normal actions may serve instinctual gratification or superego demands, completely disregarding the interests of the ego. In pathological cases, interference of these systems may lead to hysterical symptoms, e.g. paralyses. In extreme cases, in catatonic states, for instance, motor activity loses even residues of ego functions—its coordination into deliberate acts.

In using more precise formulations, we have indicated the criteria used in defining the three substructures: the psychic systems are defined by the functions attributed to them.

A word need be said here as to how these definitions were arrived at. Definitions are matters of "convenience", and convenience in science consists of an adequate relation to the observed facts. Freud established his definitions of the psychic systems after careful and repeated scrutiny of his clinical material. That material suggested that in a typical psychic conflict one set of functions is more frequently on "the one side" than on "the other side" of the conflict. Functions that we find "together on one side" have common characteristics or properties. The relatedness is one of frequency.

Functions of the id center around the basic needs of man and their striving for gratification. These needs are rooted in instinctual drives and their vicissitudes (we do not here deal with these drives themselves and the theory of instincts as developed by Freud). Functions of the id are characterized by the great mobility of cathexes of the instinctual tendencies and their mental representatives, i.e., by the operation of the primary process. Its manifestations are condensation, displacement, and the use of special symbols.

Functions of the ego center around the relation to reality. In this sense, we speak of the ego as of a specific organ of adjustment. It controls the apparatus of motility and perception; it tests the properties of the present situation at hand, i.e., of "present reality", and antici-pates properties of future situations. The ego mediates betwen these properties and requirements, and the demands of the other psychic organizations.

Functions of the superego center around moral demands. Self-criticism, sometimes heightened to incentives to self-punishment, and the formation of ideals, are essential manifestations of the superego.

In adopting the *functions* exercised in mental processes as the decisive criterium for defining the psychic systems Freud used physiology as his model in concept formation. However, this does not imply any correlation of any one of the systems to any specific physiological organization or group of organs, though Freud considered such a correlation as the ultimate goal of psychological research. Psychological terminology, he assumed, has to be maintained as long as it cannot be adequately substituted by physiological terminology.[4] It seems that the time for such substitution has not yet come. We therefore do not dwell, in the following, on parallels between the psychic systems in Freud's definition and certain organizations of the central nervous system.

4. *Jenseits des Lustprinzips*, Gesammelte Werke, XIII, p. 65. The English transla-tion (*Beyond the Pleasure Principle*) by omitting one word, fails to render Freud's meaning.

The structural concepts of psychoanalysis have met with much criticism. It has been said that through their use clinical description has been obscured, since the terms were dramatic in an anthropomorphic sense (Glover, 1930; Masserman, 1946). Clearly, whenever dramatization is encountered, metaphorical language has crept into scientific discourse and that there is danger in the use of metaphor in science hardly needs to be demonstrated; danger, it should be added, to which Freud (1933) himself drew our attention. However, it remains a problem worth some further discussion, under what conditions the danger outweighs the advantage. The danger obviously begins if and when metaphor infringes upon meaning: in the case in point, when the structural concepts are anthropomorphized. Then the functional connotation may be lost and one of the psychic systems may be substituted for the total personality. There are cases in psychoanalytic literature where dramatizations have led to anthropomorphisms of this kind. To quote one conspicuous example: in Alexander's *Psychology of the Total Personality* (1927), the id, ego and superego have indeed become exalted actors on the psychic stage.

In order to illustrate the vicissitudes of meaning in this area, we select as an example the Freudian sentence: "The Ego presents itself to the Superego as love object." The metaphor expresses the relations of two psychic organizations by comparing it to a love relation between individuals, in which the one is the lover and the other the beloved. However, the sentence expresses an important clinical finding: self-love can easily and does, under certain conditions, substitute for love of another person. Self-love in this formulation indicates that approval of the self by the superego concerns the self in lieu of another person.

We replace the word "ego" in Freud's text by the word "self". We do so since the ego is defined as part of the personality, and since Freud's use of the word is ambiguous. He uses "ego" in reference to a psychic organization and to the whole person. Before we can attempt to reformulate Freud's proposition, it is essential to go one step further. In a more rigorous sense, we find it advisable not to speak of "approval" or "disapproval" by the superego, but simply to speak of different kinds and degrees of tension between the two psychic organizations, according to the presence or absence of conflict between their functions. Approval would be characterized by a diminution of tension; disapproval by its increase.

There can be little doubt that a reformulation of this kind that tries to restrict the use of metaphors, considerably impoverishes the plasticity of language, as compared to Freud's mode of expression. Man frequently experiences self-satisfaction as if an inner voice expressed approval, and self-reproaches as if the inner voice expressed reprobation (Loewenstein, 1938). Thus the metaphorical expression comes closer to our immediate understanding, since the anthropomorphism it introduces corresponds to human experience. Our reformulation shows that not the concepts which Freud introduced are anthropomorphic, but that the clinical facts he studied and described led us to understand what part anthropomorphism plays in introspective thinking.

When the French psychiatrists of the nineteenth century turned to the clinical study of human conflict, they used a metaphorical language of their own. Their descriptive skill lives in the papers of Pierre Janet and others; it has rarely been emulated in the descriptive psychiatry of other schools. But the metaphorical language of descriptive psychiatry did not permit in the nineteenth century, and no reformulation in terms of existential psychology will permit in the twentieth century, the step from empathy to causal explanation. This step became possible only after conceptual tools had been adopted which permitted a more generalized penetration of the phenomena; a penetration that becomes possible only at some distance from immediate experience. This was the function of Freud's structural concepts. If we use these concepts in a strict sense, the distance from experience grows. Freud's metaphorical usage of his own terms was clearly intended to bridge this gap. It might thus be said that Freud's usage bears the imprint of the clinical source from which the concepts were originally derived, the imprint of the communication with the patients. Requirements of communication may ever again suggest richness of metaphor, but metaphors should not obscure the nature of the concepts and their function in psychoanalysis as a science. That function is to facilitate explanatory constructs. Briefly, the structural concepts are amongst our most valuable tools, since they stand in a genetic context.

III. *The Formation of Psychic Structure*

Whenever in psychoanalysis we use biological concepts, we are faced with one of three cases. First, the case of immediate borrowing: we refer to a biological or physiological phenomenon and use the terms current in these sciences; for instance, when we refer to the physiological changes within the personality at the age of puberty as distinguished from the concomitant psychological processes of adolescence. Second, a term may be borrowed, but its meaning may be changed by the context in which it is used and new properties may accrue. A case in point is the term "regression". Through its use in psychoanalysis, it has acquired meanings far transcending those in its original neurological setting. Third, biological terms may be used in a different context. Their definition is taken over from the old context, since the requirements of the new are similar to those in which they have originated.

In describing developmental functions, child psychology and psychoanalysis use the concept of differentiation and integration.[5] Differentiation indicates the specialization of a function; integration, the emergence of a new function out of previously not coherent sets of functions or reactions. The terms maturation and development are not always so clearly distinguished. We use both terms here in the sense that maturation indicates the processes of growth that occur relatively independent of environmental influences; development indicates the processes of growth in which environment and maturation interact more closely.

The relation between stimulus and response becomes, during growth, ever more specific. One might say that a specific structure of stimulus-response correlations is characteristic of a specific phase through which the child goes. Thus a stimulus that was of little relevance in one phase of its development may be of decisive relevance in another. The best known examples of this correlation can be found in the way children react to sexual experiences. Their reactions depend upon both the nature of the experience and the stage of the child's development. The "Wolfsman's" observation of the primal scene at the age of one-and-a-half became of pathogenic importance only at the age of three when specific conflicts reactivated this memory (Freud, 1918).

Differentiation and integration in the child's early phases of development are partly regulated by maturational sequence, but even where they are influenced by environmental conditions, we are compelled to assume a principle regulating their interaction (Hartmann, 1939). Thus acceleration of certain integrative processes may become pathological. Premature ego development, for example, may in this sense be considered as one of the factors predisposing to obsessional neurosis. The regulation of this interaction can be attributed to a principle of balance, one that does not work in the cross-section only,

5. For closer definitions see Allport, 1937.

but that regulates balance of development.

a) The undifferentiated phase[6]

We assume that the essential elements in the structure of personality exist in children of our civilization at the age of five or six. Developmental processes occurring after that age can be described as modifications, as enrichment, or, in pathological cases, as restriction of the then existing structure. Developmental processes before that age can be described in terms of formation of this structure. In introducing his concepts of psychic structure, Freud speaks of a gradual differentiation of the ego from the id; as an end result of this process of differentiation the ego, as a highly structured organization, is opposed to the id. Freud's formulation has obvious disadvantages. It implies that the infant's equipment existing at birth is part of the id. It seems however that the innate apparatus and reflexes cannot all be part of the id, in the sense generally accepted in psychoanalysis. We suggest a different assumption, namely that of an undifferentiated phase during which both the id and the ego gradually are formed. The difference is not merely one of words. The new formulation permits a better explanation of some of the basic properties of both id and ego. During the undifferentiated phase there is maturation of apparatuses that later will come under the control of the ego, and that serve motility, perception, and certain thought processes.[7] Maturation in these areas proceeds without the total organization we call ego; only after ego formation will these functions be fully integrated. To the degree to which differentiation takes place man is equipped with a specialized organ of adaptation, i.e., with the ego. This does not mean that there do not remain in the id certain elements that further the "maintenance" or preservation of the individual (Loewenstein, 1940). However, the differentiation accounts for the nature of the instinctual drives of man, sharply distinguished as they are from animal instincts. One gains the impression that many manifestations of the id are further removed from reality than any comparable behavior of animals. The instincts of the animal (Lashley, 1938) mediate its adjustment to the reality in which it lives and their properties determine the extent of the possible adaptation. With man, adjustment is mainly entrusted to an independent organization. One may raise the question whether, early in the infant's life, a residual equipment of "instincts" exists, that later loses its function of adjusting to the environment.

6. This section follows Hartmann (1939).
7. For a somewhat divergent discussion of these problems see Hendrik (1942).

b) The self and the environment

We have refrained from indicating at what time during early infancy the successive steps leading to structural differentiation take place, and from what time the psychic systems of id and ego oppose and supplement each other. While we do not wish to draw rigid chronological lines, we shall summarize some of the steps in the child's growth, which lead to the formation of the ego and partly represent its earliest functions. The first and most fundamental of these steps concerns the ability of the infant to distinguish between his self and the world around him. At birth, environmental circumstances have suddenly changed; the organism grows no longer under conditions of total shelter from all disturbances from outside, and no longer, comparatively speaking, under conditions of total gratification of all basic needs. The most essential part of the new environment is the infant's mother; she controls the physical properties of the environment, providing shelter, care and food.

The nature of the biological equipment of the infant, and the nature of its environment account for the fact that the infant's first reactions are related to indulgence and deprivation experienced at the hands of its mother. Freud assumes that as long as all needs are gratified, i.e., under "total" indulgence, the infant tends to experience the source of satisfaction as part of the self; partial deprivation thus is probably an essential condition for the infant's ability to distinguish between the self and the object. The classical example concerns the child's relation to the feeding breast or its substitutes. To the extent to which indulgence prevails, comprehension of the breast as part of the self is dominant; to the extent to which deprivation is experienced, or indulgence delayed, the distinction becomes possible. That distinction, however, seems to become impossible unless a certain amount of gratification is allowed for. There is some reason to believe that the neutral term "distinction" may be preceded by or cover a number of highly significant experiences: they may range from expectation of or longing for gratification, to feelings of disappointment, and even rage against the source of frustration.

Deprivation, we have said, is a necessary, but clearly not a sufficient condition for 'the establishment of the distinction between the self and the object. The process of distinguishing has a cognitive or perceptual side; it is thus dependent on the maturation of the child's perceptual equipment. Moreover, psychoanalysis works with the hypothesis of another necessary condition, which concerns the distribution of psychic energy. Freud assumed that with the newborn, psychic energy is concentrated upon the self (primary narcissism). When we state that an object in the external world is experienced as part of the self, we imply that the object partakes in its narcissistic cathexis. When we speak of a distinction between the self and the external object, we assume that the object which is experienced as independent from the self has retained cathexis in spite of the separation; we infer that primary narcissistic cathexis has been transformed into object cathexis.

These processes we here describe are not accomplished in one step; they proceed in ever repeated trial experiences. Some of these trials follow a pattern established by the physiological organization of man; predominant modes of this pattern are incorporation and ejection; its psychological counterparts are introjection and projection.

These processes seem to accompany the earliest sequences of indulgence and deprivation in the child's life.

". . . the course of gratification of instinctual needs during the period immediately following birth can be presented as follows: the instinctual need —crying—gratification. The next possible step in the course of the process would be: instinctual need—hallucinated gratification which does not suffice— crying which brings on the real gratification; the child can then sleep again." (Benedek, 1938)

We have no means to assess what might happen if even under such early conditions indulgence were maximized; no conditions of infancy have been observed in which nursing procedures occur that could be described in these terms; they do not exist in human society, and would have to be created for the purpose of an experiment. We are better informed on consequences of intensive deprivation, and have learned recently that the prolonged absence of maternal care, or the lack of adequate stimulation (from the first quarter of the first year of life) tends to produce irreversible retardations that even affect maturation (Durfee and Wolf, 1933; Spitz, 1945). It seems reasonable to assume that the infant's apparatus of control and adjustment are given their best training chances at a distance considerably closer to the maximum of indulgence than to that of deprivation. As the maturation of the apparatus proceeds, the child shows signs of expectation and recognition; he turns his head towards the mother's breast, searches for the breast when put in a feeding position, and between the third and fifth month of his life, he learns to anticipate the feeding situation without crying. He recognizes his mother while she prepares his food. (For a good summary, see Benedek p. 207.)

As the child learns to distinguish between himself and the mother, he develops understanding for her communications. Little is known about the detailed processes by which this understanding is established; reactions to the actual handling of the child by the mother, to touch and bodily pressure, certainly play a part; gradually, the understanding of the child for the mother's facial expression grows. It seems probable that experiences concerning emotive processes and expressive movements in the infant itself form the basis or are a necessary condition for the infant's understanding of the mother's expression (Freud, 1905; Schilder, 1935). But the cognitive side of the process, the understanding of signs of communication, is part of the libidinal tie existing between the two. The identification of the child with the mother that we assume to exist at an early stage, gradually develops into an object relation.[8] The mother, as the first love object, is the object most highly cathected in the child's world, and the child's earliest learning proceeds partly by identifying with this object.

In this connection we mention Freud's latest suggestion on the subject, communicated in 1940 in a paper by Ruth M. Brunswick: Freud indicates the possibility that the development of the child's activity is decisively influenced by the identification with the nursing mother.

Maturational changes proceeding during the second half of the first year give the child further control of his own body and enable him partly to master the inanimate objects in his life space.[9] Some kind of anticipation of future events plays its part in each of these operations. They represent a central function of the ego; that which makes the transfer from the pleasure principle to the reality principle possible. The two regulatory principles of mental functioning express two tendencies of man. The one strives toward the immediate and unconditional gratification of demands; the other accepts the limitations of reality, postponing gratification in order to make it more secure (Freud, 1911).

Various theories have attempted to explain the relation of the two principles (Ferenczi, 1926; French, 1936). No explanation is satisfactory unless we assume that the transition from one principle

8. Balint (1937) and others assume, in addition, the existence of an early object relation in the newly born infant. We do not decide how far this assumption is warranted. Freud's theory of "primary narcissism" seems still best to account for facts observable immediately after birth.

9. We do not however follow Hendrick (1942) in assuming the existence of an "instinct to master".

to the other is rendered possible by the formation of the ego, which enters the process as an independent variable (Hartmann, 1939; see also Mahler, 1945).

c) Some influences on ego formation

The development of the ego proceeds along with that of the child's object relations. Amongst the factors that threaten object relations and thereby endanger the stability of the child's ego functions, we here discuss ambivalence. Theories on the origin of ambivalence are in part identical with those concerning the origin of aggression. Thus Freud (1930) considers the possibility that ambivalence arises as a necessary protection of the individual against destructive impulses bound within the self; their externalization would then be a prerequisite of survival. Some of the characteristics of ambivalence, the rapid oscillation from manifestations of positive to manifestations of negative attitudes in infant and child suggests another possibility: one might assume that the intermittent changes between projection and introjection, which were necessary concomitants of the infant's trials to establish a distinction between the self and the environment survive as a tendency towards and away from the human object. Better founded in observable fact, and not necessarily in contradiction with these assumptions, is another explanation: without discussing the problem whether or not instinctual drives tending towards destructive aims are part of the original equipment of man, one may be satisfied to assume that in the earliest phases of the infant's life any transition from indulgence to deprivation tends to elicit aggressive responses. The child's ambivalence towards his first love objects, one might say, corresponds to their position within the continuum leading from indulgence to deprivation (Ferenczi, 1926). All human relations would, according to this suggestion, be permanently colored by the fact that the earliest love relations in the child's life were formed at a time when those whom the child loves are those to whom it owes both indulgence and deprivation.

However tempting it might be to assume a correlation between the frequency and intensity of the infant's deprivational experiences, and the frequency and intensity of the child's aggressive impulses as manifested in his ambivalence, evidence does not support such simple conclusions. Too many variables exist that tend to obscure the issue, except possibly in extreme cases such as described by Bender, Schilder and Kaiser (1936), who were exposed to neglect and hostility, in an environment hardly interested in their survival. In less extreme cases, the complexity of the emotional processes can hardly be overestimated. Deprivations in earliest infancy are unavoidable in that the rising intensity of demand of the crying child waiting for the mother is experienced as deprivation; deprivations on this level are, as we have said, essential incentives for the distinction of the world from the self. At a later stage, when the child learns to exchange immediate for future indulgence, he is again exposed to a deprivational experience, one that, as we shall see, is a prerequisite for the formation of the world of thought and the further development of his ego. The child delays his demands in order to comply with the mother's request. There can be little doubt that the better assured the child is that indulgence will follow the postponement of demands, the more easily will the deprivation be tolerated. (Benedek, in this connection, stresses the importance of the element of confidence.) And yet one cannot overlook the fact that each of the basic demands of the child, the fulfillment of which is postponed, contain both libidinal and aggressive impulses. They are linked to every one of the dominant biological functions, to the nutritive as well as the eliminative, and both libidinal and aggressive tendencies find their expression on the oral and anal level of libidinal development. Any attempt to study the child's reaction to deprivation should therefore take at least three aspects into account: the nature of deprivation, its timing, and the modes of its administration.

The situation seems clearest where the third point is concerned. The mother's role is a double one. She sets the premium on learning: in order to retain her love, the child has to comply. Secondly, once the ego organization is established, by the consistency of her requests the mother supports the child's ego in his struggle against his impulses. Both roles are best fulfilled if education is conducted in an atmosphere of loving attention, i.e., if no conscious or unconscious manifestations of aggression on the part of the adult elicit counter-aggression of the child. We do not discuss here the problem of how the child senses the adult's hostility—even when it is carefully controlled—but we assume that the child's capacity to perceive it is greater than has been assumed until recently, and that this capacity develops at an extremely early age.[10]

The effect of the adult's attitude upon the child when administering deprivation has been studied in the set-up of restraint situations.

10. For problems later in the child's life, see Burlingham (1935).

The child does not only experience deprivation when one of his demands is denied—the demand for food, care or attention—but also when the adult interferes with one of his spontaneous activities, whether they serve the gratification of a drive or the solution of a problem. In the child's life, various types of activities tend to be not as sharply delimited from each other as they normally are with the adult. All action is closer to instinctual drives; problem-solving and fantasy play tend to interact; even the older child eats while it plays, and may at any moment shift from one type of gratification to the other. Many attempts to "stop the child from doing something" restrict, therefore, processes that are highly cathected. In order to characterize these manifold occurrences, we speak of restraint situations.

By and large, the child tends to react to restraint by some manifestation of aggression. However, that response is not regular. Infants swaddled during long periods of the first year of life are said not to show any more pronounced proclivity to aggression than infants who could move their bodies freely (Greenacre, 1944). This finding seems to suggest that early swaddling, especially if it is a part of a cultural tradition, and not the expression of an individual preference of the mother, does not stimulate aggressive response, since it does not interrupt an activity but prevents one (Buxbaum, 1947).

The assumption that early in childhood the interruption of activity rather than the prevention, may be a crucial experience—though the point should be generalized only with care—leads us to the hypothesis that many kinds of "practising" activities are highly cathected, and thus indirectly to the proposition that interruption of practice, prevention of what one calls "completion of the act" is likely to upset the balance in psychic energy. This proposition is generally true of man's life; a host of experiments on act completion with normal adults and one set of experiments with obsessional patients has given ample evidence in this area (Zeigarnik, 1927; Hartmann, 1933; Gerö, 1933). The similarity in the behavior of child and adult extends even to those cases where the completion is prevented by failure: a child who fails in handling a toy properly, or who fails to solve a problem he has set himself, may turn from activity to rage-like reactions. Frustrations imposed upon adults by unsolvable problems elicit a similar response—except that their frustration tolerance is greater.

However, the relevant point in our context is that the child's tendency to aggressive outbursts when he experiences restraint can easily be modified by the behavior of the restraining adult: friendly restraint tends to reduce aggressive response. One distracts a child best by loving attention. Cathexis directed towards action is thus transformed into object cathexis. The importance of this area of problems is considerable, since the sequence of restraint of the child's spontaneous activities and decrease of aggressive impulses in the child affects many learning situations.

We do not here attempt to enter into the question of what contributions psychoanalysis might make to a general theory of learning, or how the presentation of certain psychoanalytic hypotheses could profit in general, if formulated in terms of learning. We briefly note that learning processes may lead to the gratification of instinctual impulses, since they make the mastery of reality possible, but that, at the same time, they represent an essential requisite for the development of the child's defenses against danger. As far as the child's early experiences in learning are concerned, psychoanalytic hypotheses tend to take mainly four factors into account: first, the stage of maturation of the apparatuses; second, the reaction of the environment; third, the tolerance for deprivation; and fourth, the various types of gratification afforded by the processes of learning and the satisfactions that can be obtained as consequences of mastery. Among the specific learning situations that tend to become crucial for the child's life, as a sort of model in which ego control is developed, we wish to discuss habit training.

There are plausible reasons of a physiological and psychological order to which we may refer in an attempt to account for the extreme importance of this specific situation in the child's life. The demand for control of habits has two phases; it involves the demand for retention and for elimination. Compliance therefore involves two opposite innervations of both the voluntary urethral and anal sphincters. On the other hand, the same innervation may at various times express opposite things—compliance at one time; defiance at the other.[11]

Compliance is facilitated when the child understands the adult's request, and when the muscular apparatus itself is fully developed. The recent tendency to postpone habit training to the second year of life takes these factors into account. But not only the intellectual capacity and the muscular apparatus have matured: another maturational process, that of the libidinal cathexis of the anal zone, takes

11. A somewhat similar viewpoint has been suggested by Erikson (1940).

place approximately at the same time. Learning takes place at a time when the stimulation of the anal passage is likely to create intense sexual experiences.[12] The situation of the child during the period of toilet training represents in a nutshell the nature of its conflict situation at that age. That conflict situation is threefold: first, there is the conflict between two instinctual tendencies, that of elimination and retention (instinctual conflict); second, there is the conflict between either one of these tendencies, and the child's attempts to control them and to time his function: it is a conflict between the id and the ego (structural conflict); and third, there is the conflict with the external world that has made the structural conflict necessary: the mother's request for timing of elimination.

The power of this request rests in the premium which the mother offers: approval or disapproval in all their manifold intensities. Approval may range from the mother's smile to caresses or gifts, disapproval from the disappearance of the smile to spanking. But again, it is not the intensity, or not only the intensity of approval or disapproval that is relevant; not the tangible manifestations of indulgences and deprivation, since whatever the intensity of manifestation, the threat of disapproval embodies the greatest danger in the child's life.

At the end of the first year, in the early phases of ego development, the child has formed lasting object relations; his attachment can outlast deprivation, and libidinal energy directed toward the love object has been partly transformed into aim-inhibited libidinal energy, transient into permanent cathexis.

As long as the demand for immediate indulgence prevails, any absence of those on whose care the child depends is experienced as a threat; gradually, as ego development proceeds, abstraction from the concrete situation becomes possible. The threat becomes, to some extent, independent of the presence or absence of the mother. These two stages coexist in the child's life for a long time and are embodied in a variety of highly complex situations. Freud (1926) comprehended these situations in the formulation that the fear of losing the love object is supplemented by the fear of losing love. Thus, one might say that the child in acquiring this new security acquires also a new kind of vulnerability; anxiety may now invade its life under new conditions.

The meaning of fear itself undergoes parallel transformations: it has been integrated into the child's structural equipment. Originally,

12. It is possible that "premature" toilet training could accelerate the libidinal cathexis of the zone.

fear is a reflex-like response to danger, i.e., to changes that tend to evoke feelings of helplessness; later, it acts as a signal that warns of changes to come. It is only when the ego cannot act upon the warning of the signal, that the intensity of anxiety grows and the state of anxiety may develop. That change in the function of anxiety is another instance of what we shall call later the extension of the inner world: anxiety as a signal can operate only when the child has learned to anticipate the future.

Only since in 1926 Freud introduced the concept of the danger situation, has the full impact of the problem of the child's defense against danger been studied in some detail. In the present context, two aspects of the problem of defense deserve our particular attention: we have said that in order to retain the love of his environments, the child learns to control his instinctual drives: this means that the differentiation between id and ego becomes ever more complete as the child grows, and that those of the child's defenses that are directed against the power of his drives serve to maintain that differentiation. The vicissitudes of these conflicting forces can be studied in the instances of regressive behavior, and of sudden eruptions of instinctual impulses in the child's early life: we do not here enter into this area of problems, since they require a discussion of the functions and the strength of the ego.

The term "defense" should not suggest the misapprehension that the process here referred to is either pathological or only of a negative importance. Rather is it correct to say that the human personality is formed by psychic mechanisms which serve, also, the purpose of defense. Some of these mechanisms first operate in other areas; thus projection and introjection are used in order to establish the distinction between the self and the non-self; regression, as a regular and temporary transformation of psychic functioning, accompanies the daily cycle from awakeness to sleep; and denial of the unpleasant represents probably an initial phase in the elimination of all disturbing stimuli. These and other mechanisms, which in the infant's life serve the function of adjustment and may be rooted in the reflex equipment of the newborn, may later function as mechanism of defense and thus produce changes in the child's personality (Hartmann, 1939). Some of these changes are only temporary, others may become permanent. The ego may develop a preference for one or the other kind of defense, use it in coping with both the id and the outer world, and later the superego; thus in all, or many, of its functions, the ego may bear the imprint of the reaction to early danger situations (Anna Freud, 1936). Certain mechanisms of defense regularly leave their traces in a permanent modification of the structure of personality: repression and identification are cases in point.

There is no reason here to state anew Freud's hypotheses concerning repression (1915) and its consequences for the dynamics, the economy and the structuralization of the personality. Suffice it to say that with the existence of repression the demarcation between id and ego is drawn more sharply and maintained by counter-cathexes.

It is different with identification. Whereas repression is a specific mechanism, not previously operating—unless we assume the tendency to denial to be its precursor, as we well may—identification has been one of the major, if not the major mechanism contributing to the child's early formation of personality; secondly, and under the pressure of danger, it can also be used for purposes of defense. But the two functions, the primary function of identification, its part in growing, and its secondary function, as a defense against danger, can hardly ever be sharply distinguished. The roots of identification can be traced to those impulses of the id, which strive towards incorporation; the psychological mechanism of identification is a correlate of and is built upon the model of this striving. In the earliest phases of the child's ego development, the child relies upon the adult in his dealing with the external world; he participates in their reactions and thus acquires their methods of solving problems and coping with emergencies. The impact of identification on the child's ego development is not known in detail. Our impressions are clearest in regard to moral behavior.

In taking over the parent's attitudes, the child strengthens his resistance against the onslaught of instinctual demands that he has learned to consider as undesirable. He pays for this greater security with the sense of guilt in case of failure, and acquires the precarious faculty of using the archaic mechanism of turning the drive against the self for auto-punitive purposes. The siding with the parents' requests, the acceptance of their demands as part of what the child wishes himself strengthens his ego against id impulses. This security also plays its part in the organization of the child's intellectual world.

The maturational sequence of the child's growing intellectual capacities is known in great detail. There is an interrelation of this maturation with the formation of psychic structure; the maturational factors in this connection concern the apparatuses that the ego controls.

The relationship of the child to the world around him changes in character when the reality principle, at least in part, replaces the pleasure principle. That "replacement" may be described as a process of learning. The child gradually becomes aware of probable changes in his environment; the anticipation of the future centers on considerations such as these: "When I behave in a certain way, my environment will react in a certain way"—and thus behavior can be regulated in order to meet expectations.

This step becomes possible only if and when the urgency of demands can be reduced, when, as we said, future gratification can be substituted for immediate gratification. As a consequence, experience with those whom the child loves is no longer exclusively in terms of indulgence or deprivation. The child's attachment to them can outlast deprivation and they gain characteristics of their own that the child tries to understand. In studying this process with respect to the distribution of psychic energy, we have said that libidinal energy has been transformed into aim-inhibited libidinal energy; with respect to the child's ego functions, we may say that the child has learned to establish objective criteria and to use them in action and thought.

The child's thoughts are not only concerned with the problem of finding new ways in order to gain formerly valued gratifications. This clearly plays a part; the child "learns" in order to obtain the candy and in order to elicit the parents' caresses. But there are new pleasures corresponding to each level of development. Moreover, the mastery of difficulties, the solving of problems, becomes a novel source of delight. And thinking itself yields gratification. Thought processes can operate on various levels; thought and fantasy interact. The child can imagine and pretend; he can, in his fantasies, reenact his relationship with his environment; he can play at being an adult—briefly, the child has created a world of his own.

His independence from the outer world, his resistance to immediate reactions to stimuli, has led to an enlargement of his inner, his intellectual world.

d) Superego formation

The processes of differentiation and integration in early childhood show the constant interaction between maturational and developmental factors. The processes leading to the formation of the third psychic organization, the superego, are to a higher degree independent of maturation. There is no specific apparatus whose maturation is

essential for the growth of conscience; only a certain stage of development of intellectual life forms an essential precondition. But though
the formation of the superego is the result of social influences and of
processes of identification, these processes take place under the pressure
of a specific situation in the child's life that is brought about by
maturation.

The child reaches the phallic phase of its sexual development
usually in the third or fourth year. (We here discuss these problems
only as they concern the male child.) The manifestations in behavior of
the cathexis of and the interest in the genital zone are manifold; the
higher frequency of genital masturbation, the greater desire for physical
contact with others, particularly with members of the opposite sex, and
the predominance of tendencies towards phallic exhibitionism are outstanding examples. Other manifestations frequently interacting with
those of behavior pertain to fantasy life. That interaction has best been
studied where masturbatory activity is concerned. The link between
fantasies of sexual activities with incestuous objects, and of fantasies of being prevented from or punished for such activities (by
castration or its equivalent) account for the fact that masturbation
during the phallic phase frequently acquires a crucial significance
for symptom- and character-formation.

The reaction of the environment to the manifestation of the
boy's demand during the phallic phase is no less decisive than the
reaction to his earlier strivings. As far as incestuous demands are
concerned, deprivation at this stage is regular. The boy's reaction
to the new deprivational experience, however, can as a rule not be
sharply isolated from his previous experiences in indulgence and
deprivation. The intensity of his reaction to deprivation is at this
stage partly under the shadows of the past. This relation is in many
cases, if not regularly, sharpened by the phenomena of regression:
under the pressure of the oedipal conflict, the boy tends temporarily
to return to earlier phases of his libidinal development.

The oedipus constellation itself, best studied under conditions
of western civilization, is replete with a series of unavoidable conflicts: the phallic demands of the boy directed against the mother
are not only doomed to meet with partial rejection or restraint on her
part, but they involve the boy in inescapable conflict with his father.
That conflict represents a complete structure: there is the boy's hostility against the rival and his fear of the father's retaliation; the
climax of this fear is the fear of castration. There also is the fear

that the boy's hostility may actually endanger the father, who outside the area of conflict is a love object of paramount importance.

Freud originally stressed the idea of a phylogenetic factor, predisposing the individual to castration fear. Hartmann and Kris (1945) have formulated alternative views, as follows:

". . . Freud argues that the intensity of the fear of castration experienced by the male child in our civilization is unaccountable if we consider it as a reaction to the actual threats to which the boy is being exposed in the phallic phase; only the memory of the race will explain it. To this, we are inclined to reply with Freud's own arguments. While in many cases the child in our civilization is no longer being threatened with castration, the intensity of the veiled aggression of the adult against the child may still produce the same effect. One might say that there always is 'castration' in the air. Adults who restrict the little boy act according to patterns rooted in their own upbringing. However symbolic or distant from actual castration their threats might be, they are likely to be interpreted by the little boy in terms of his own experiences. The tumescent penis with which he responds in erotic excitement, that strange phenomenon of a change in a part of his body that proves to be largely independent of his control, leads him to react not to the manifest content but rather to the latent meaning of the restriction with which his strivings for mother, sister, or girl-playmate meet. And then, what he may have seen frequently before, the genitals of the little girl, acquire a new meaning as evidence and corroboration of that fear. However, the intensity of fear is not only linked to his present experience, but also to similar experiences in his past. The dreaded retaliation of the environment revives memories of similar anxieties when desires for other gratifications were predominant and when the supreme fear was not that of being castrated but that of not being loved . . ."

The importance of castration fear in the economy of man's anxiety is best illustrated by the fact that it even affects man's attitude to death. Like all higher organisms, man fears death, but this fear is colored by all previous conditions that have evoked anxiety; particularly by the fear of castration and by the "fear of the superego". The formation of the superego and its specific relation to the situation of the child during the phallic phase has been frequently discussed. We approach the problem from one point of view: we ask ourselves to what degree earlier experience in the same area, i.e., that of moral conduct, can be related to the formation of the superego. The identification with the parents and the compliance with their demands exists, as we have said, at an earlier stage of the boy's development. So does the feeling of guilt in case of failure to comply with the parents' requests; and even actions as a result of hostility turned towards the self occur in the younger child. In order to differentiate the functions of the superego from their precursors, we sharply distinguish two aspects of the process of superego formation.

First, the child identifies with the parents in a new way in order to escape the conflict between love, hate and guilt and the torments of anxiety. He does not identify with the parents as they are, but with the idealized parent, i.e., the child purifies their conduct in his mind and the identification proceeds as if they were consistently true to the principles they explicitly profess or aspire to observe. Hence Freud's formulation, the child identifies with the superego of the parents.

It would be erroneous to assume that idealization of the parents starts at this age; it rather reflects the concomitant stage of the child's mentation and is possibly linked to its original ambivalence. All primitive mental operations tend to sharpen contrasts and to "agglutinate values" (Hartmann, 1947). The child's proclivity in this area has been repeatedly studied. However, it seems that at the pre-phallic stage, idealization is predominantly concerned with the area of puissance: the child aggrandizes the parents in order magically to partake in their protection and power. At the end of the phallic phase, under the pressure of the fear of castration, idealization concerns moral behavior.

Second: the process of identification that takes place is different from previous processes of identification, through the concomitant change in the economy of psychic energy. The newly acquired identifications of the child retain permanently part of the cathexis previously attached to the objects. The relative independence from the objects on the one hand and from the ego on the other constitutes the superego as an organization, distinct from either the id or the ego.

In the course of this process, libidinal energy is desexualized: the dangerous, or sexual part of the boy's attachment to the mother is sublimated and partly used in idealization. The aggressive attitudes towards the father are internalized; they become the force with which the demands of the superego are equipped.

The clearest manifestation of the existence of the newly formed organization is that as a consequence a new anxiety situation is introduced in the child's life. The fear of loss of the love object or of loss of love, in the pre-phallic phase, the fear of castration in the phallic phase, are supplemented, but naturally not supplanted by a new fear; the new factor, that of superego anxiety, creates the possibility for the child's moral independence of his environment. Man has acquired an inner voice.

The development of personality is not concluded at this point, and we feel that the potentialities of its transformation throughout latency and adolescence have for some time been underrated in psychoanalytic writings. But it seems that the basic structure of the personality and the basic functional interrelation of the systems have been fixed to some extent. The child does not stop growing and developing, but after that age both growth and development modify an existing structure. The newly formed superego organization is exposed to many conflicting demands. At first, it tends to be over-rigid. It does not compromise—it rather yields. The over-rigidity expresses itself in its "moral absolutism" (Piaget, 1932). Psychoanalytic observation adds that at this stage, early in latency, obsessional symptoms are highly frequent amongst children.

Throughout latency, one can watch a gradual adjustment of superego functions. That adjustment is partly due to the growth of intellectual comprehension, and educational or religious indoctrination, but partly also to the fact that the function of the superego is less endangered; therefore it needs less protection. The pubertal change creates new dangers; they reactivate the situation that once led to superego formations. The ensuing polarization of behavior between asceticism and indulgence has repeatedly been described (Anna Freud, 1936). Less clearly has it been realized that at this stage a new set of ideals is frequently chosen. They become part of the adolescent's conscious moral equipment (ego ideal). Again, that choice is not sudden. Throughout latency, the child has identified with many models—teachers; friends; policemen; leaders in battle, state or community; and the whole set of images that his culture makes available. But during adolescence, identifications gain a new impact; they become more compelling, and the need for support from outside is greater.

Hence the obvious importance of cultural conditions for the function of the superego. We do not enter into the area of problems that exist here; we do not discuss under what conditions idealism and cynicism tend to develop as transitory phases of development, and how gradually balance is reestablished. We only point to one alternative: if social values rapidly change, if new values do not fully substitute for old ones, if no new conduct ideals supplement the older structure of the superego, then we may be faced with behavior in the adult that maximizes compliance with what "the neighbors" do. The intensity with which ideals are invested in a society assured of its social values may manifest itself then in a compulsory drive to be exactly like "the others are". Conformity then has become the supreme good.

IV. *The Data of Observation*

The genetic hypotheses here discussed represent a selection from those formulated by psychoanalysts in order to explain the formation of psychic structure. Without saying so explicitly, we have also frequently implied dynamic propositions; in the context of the system of psychoanalytic psychology, as in any other scientific system, hypotheses support each other, and where support is at default, there is room for doubt. Whether in science one retains any one hypothesis, a set of hypotheses, or even the assumptions and concepts that hold the system together, depends on their usefulness as tools in the causal explanation of the phenomena studied.

Freud, and those with him, who based upon the assumptions and concepts of psychoanalysis definite genetic propositions, were, on the whole, faced with four sets of specific data that they attempted to integrate. We enumerate these data according to their probable importance at the time:

1. The reconstruction of life histories in psychoanalytic observation.

2. The study of regressive phenomena in normal, but mainly in pathological behavior, largely in the study of neuroses and psychoses.

3. Observations on child development.

4. Data from history and anthropology mainly interpreted in the light of evolutionism and used for the formulation of "prehistoric" **constructs.** These constructs were then linked to ontogenetic observations.

In partially reformulating some of these hypotheses, we have not only tried to eliminate terminological impasses and certain contradictions within the systematic cohesion of hypotheses. We have also attempted implicitly to reevaluate, to some extent, the contributions of the data. The difference can be stated as follows:

We have avoided all connection between ontogenetic hypotheses and prehistoric constructs; we did so not because we doubt the importance of such constructs as sources of valuable clues, but because we doubt their value within the more rigorous set of hypotheses that aim at verification by empirical procedures. On the other hand, we tried to allow for a better integration between the three other types of data, those gained from the study of regressive phenomena in general, from psychoanalytic reconstructions and from direct observation of the growing child. All three are essential and their interrelation in the formulation of psychoanalytic hypotheses deserves some more detailed discussion.

In order to explain the earliest processes of differentiation and integration, we turn to the study of phenomena that we attribute to regression to these stages. Thus, the loss of the distinction between the self and the non-self is familiar from many psychotic processes. The schizophrenic experience of the emptiness of the external world, and many other hallucinatory and delusionary processes, as well as the psychological aspect of sleep, are explained according to Freud's hypothesis as a withdrawal of cathexis from the world to the self. These phenomena and their opposites supply the models for the hypothesis of transformations of object cathexis into narcissistic cathexis, and vice versa.

On the other hand, the fact that the distinction between the self and the outer world gradually develops, and the ways and time intervals in which it develops, belong to a series of data which can be ascertained by the study of infant and child behavior. The importance of these latter data is, we believe, indicated by some of our reformulations, for instance, by those that stress the importance of maturational processes.

Only in exceptional cases have we directly referred to the data themselves; their systematic integration with psychoanalytic observations and hypotheses represents a task for monographic studies in many areas. The data now available will not suffice. Only studies in child development, guided by these psychoanalytic hypotheses, can supply a better empirical foundation. As far as studies in this area proceed, they prove to be of great value. That value will increase when they fully deal with the communication between the child and the mother in the pre-verbal stage, or in the earliest verbal stages. What we need is an observational check on our hypotheses concerning object formation. Similarly, hypotheses concerning the reactions of mother and child to toilet training, and many other hypotheses concerning early childhood, could be formulated more concretely and probably more correctly if observational data were more ample.

Observations of this kind will still not replace the findings of psychoanalytic reconstruction. In the observation of the behavior detail, the potential importance of one experience cannot always be seen. Retrospective investigation alone can elucidate that importance.

Thus we repeat what has been said elsewhere, that the systematic study of large numbers of life histories from birth on, based on an integration of many skills of observation, permits the greatest chance for verification or falsification of hypotheses. There are areas in which objective observations cannot, as yet, contribute to the formulation of hypotheses; but they are often eminently useful in excluding hypotheses that are in contradiction to observation.

BIBLIOGRAPHY

Alexander, F. 1930. *Psychoanalysis of the Total Personality.*
Allport, G. 1937. *Personality, a Psychological Interpretation.*
Azam. 1876. "Histoire de Félida", *Comptes Rendus de l'Académie des Sciences Morales et Revue Scientifique.*
Balint, M. 1937. "Fruehe Entwicklungsstadien des Ichs. Primaere Objektliebe", *Imago*, XXIII.
Bender, L., Schilder, P. and Kaiser, S. 1936. "Studies in Aggressiveness", *Gen. Psychol. Mon.*, XVIII, 5, 6.
Benedek, T. 1938. "Adaptation to Reality in Early Infancy", *Psa. Quarterly,* VII.
Bernfeld, S. 1944. "Freud's Earliest Theories and the School of Helmholtz", *ibid.* XIII.
Binet, A. 1892. *Altération de la Personnalité.*
Bourru and Burot. 1888. *Variations de la Personnalité.*
Burlingham, D. T. 1935. "Child Analysis and the Mother", *Psa. Quarterly,* IV.
Buxbaum, E. 1947. "Activity and Aggression in Children", *Amer. J. Orthopsychiatry*, XI (in print).
Camuset. 1882. "Un cas de Dédoublement de la Personnalité", *Ann. Med. Psychologiques.*
Dufay. 1876. "Lettre sur la Notion de Personnalité", *Rev. Scientifique.*
Durfee, H. and Wolf, K. M. 1933. "Anstaltspflege und Entwicklung im ersten Lebensjahr", *Zeit. f. Kinderforschung,* 42/3.
Erikson, E. H. 1940. "Studies in the Interpretation of Play", *Gen. Psychol. Mon.,* XXII.
Ferenczi, S. 1926. "The Problem of Acceptance of Unpleasant Ideas — Advances in Knowledge of the Sense of Reality", *Further Contributions.*
French, T. 1936. "A Clinical Study in the Course of a Psychoanalytic Treatment", *Psa. Quarterly,* V.
Freud, A. 1937. *The Ego and the Mechanisms of Defence.*

Freud, S. 1905. *Wit and its Relation to the Unconscious.*

Freud, S. 1911. "Formulations Regarding the Two Principles in Mental Functioning", *Coll. Papers*, IV.

Freud, S. 1915. "Repression", *ibid.*

Freud, S. 1918. "From the History of an Infantile Neurosis", *ibid.*

Freud, S. 1923. *The Ego and the Id.*

Freud, S. 1926. *Inhibitions, Symptoms and Anxiety* (American transl. 1936 as *The Problem of Anxiety*).

Freud, S. 1930. *Civilization and its Discontents.*

Freud, S. 1933. *New Introductory Lectures.*

Gerö, G. 1933. Review of Dembo, T. "Der Aerger als dynamisches Problem" in Psychol. Forschung, XV; *Imago*, XIX.

Glover, E. 1930. "Introduction to the Study of Psychoanalytical Theory", *Int. J. Psa.*, XI.

Greenacre, P. 1944. "Infants' Reactions to Restraint. Problems in the Fate of Infantile Aggression", *Amer. J. Orthopsychiatry*, XIV.

Hartmann, H. 1933. "Ein experimenteller Beitrag zur Psychologie der Zwangsneurose", *Jahr. f. Psychiatrie u. Neur.*, 50.

Hartmann, H. 1939. "Ichpsychologie und Anpassungsproblem", *Int. Zeit. f. Psa. u. Imago*, XXIV.

Hartmann, H. 1947. "On Rational and Irrational Action", *Psa. and Social Science*, ed. G. Róheim (in print).

Hartmann, H., and Kris, E. 1945. "The Genetic Approach in Psychoanalysis", *this Annual*, I.

Hendrick, I. 1942. "Instinct and the Ego during Infancy", *Psa. Quarterly*, IX.

Janet, P. 1876. "La Notion de Personnalité", *Rev. Scientifique.*

Kaiser, S. See Bender.

Kris, E. 1947. "Methodology of Clinical Research", Contrib. Round Table Discussion, *Amer. J. Orthopsychiatry*, XI (in print).

Kris, E. See Hartmann.

Lashley, K. S. 1938. "Experimental Analysis of Instinctual Behavior", *Psychol. Rev.*, 45.

Loewenstein, R. 1938. "Les Origines du Masochisme et la Théorie des Pulsions", *Rev. Franç. de Psa.*, X.

Loewenstein, R. 1940. "On Vital and Somatic Drives", *Int. J. Psa.*, X.

Mack-Brunswick, R. 1940. "The Pre-Oedipal Phase of Libido Development", *Psa. Quarterly*, IX.

Mahler, M. S. 1945. "Ego Psychology Applied to Behavior Problems", *Modern Trends in Child Psychiatry*, ed. Lewis and Pacella.

Masserman, J. H. 1946. *Principles of Dynamic Psychiatry.*

Piaget, J. 1932. *The Moral Judgment of the Child.*

Schilder, P. 1935. "The Image and Appearance of the Human Body", *Psych. Mon.*, 4.

Spitz, R. A. 1945. "Hospitalism: an Inquiry into the Genesis of Psychiatric Conditions of Early Childhood", *this Annual*, I, II.

Wolf, K. M. See Durfee.

Zeigarnik, B. 1927. "Das Behalten erledigter und unerledigter Handlungen", *Psychol. Forschung*, IX.

THE CHILD'S LAUGHTER

Theoretical and Clinical Notes on the Function of the Comic

By EDITH JACOBSON, M.D. (New York)

Unquestionably child analysis has proved its value as a method that has yielded remarkable scientific contributions in the field of child psychology. With due respect to the work done by Anna Freud and other outstanding child analysts it must be admitted, however, that the scientific harvest has not wholly fulfilled the hopes that Freud himself pinned on child analysis at first. If we but compare the results of analytic investigation of children, and of experimental and observational work, to the material outlined in *The Three Contributions to the Theory of Sex,* we are amazed at the amount and depth of knowledge of child psychology that was first gathered merely through reconstructive analysis of adults—by someone with Freud's vision, to be sure.

Bearing in mind the discussion and the evaluation of the "genetic propositions" of psychoanalysis (10) we may be able briefly to define the potentialities and shortcomings of child analysis as a research method, in comparison to the analysis of adults.

Unfortunately, the child analyst can only observe cross-sections and stages of development, rather than the vicissitudes of instinctual drives and ego trends, from childhood to maturity, i.e., over the whole life span. In the first place, he rarely succeeds in reconstructing a complete genetic picture of the past development from child patients through the recovery and analysis of memory material, as is frequently possible in the analysis of adults. For such work the mind of a child is not equipped. The child is concerned mainly with present and future, and is neither willing nor detached enough to turn back to and search in the past. Secondly, the child analyst's field of vision is limited, as he cannot look beyond the age level of his patients nor follow their development longer than a few years at most.

These handicaps are counterbalanced, though not fully, by a number of advantages: the child analyst can gain more convincing evidence and deeper understanding of the unconscious, and of the primary process, than the analyst of adults. As Anna Freud has shown in *The Ego and the Mechanisms of Defence,* he may be able, moreover, to apprehend the mechanisms of symptom-formation, the development of defenses, ego attitudes, sublimations, etc., *in statu nascendi.* However, the observation of emotional processes at such close sight involves the danger that usually arises with insufficient distance: the child analyst is overwhelmed and confused by the variety of instinctual, emotional, and ideational trends which may simultaneously arise in a child, may quickly change, be given up or be replaced by new ones, until definite lasting trends may eventually develop. This richness of the picture, which Berta Bornstein recently demonstrated[1] in a discussion on child analysis, may prevent the analyst from watching the child patient from that bird's eye view that is necessary for him to recognize the leading genetic lines and trace them back to their origin.

All these factors which are here only intimated may account for the fact that in many cases analysis of adults can not only trace adult personality traits back to their roots in specific childhood experiences, but can even clarify the underlying mechanisms of such early reactions, dynamically and genetically, more completely than is possible through the direct analysis of children. This paper may furnish evidence for the validity of such a statement by two clinical examples dealing with the problem of laughter and the development of humor in children.

I.

The psychological literature on laughter and related phenomena such as wit, humor, the comic, is so extensive that instead of giving a full bibliography, I refer to two tables found in "A Study of Laughter in the Nursery School Child", by Blatz (2). One table lists authors who have developed theories on laughter; the other is a review of observational and experimental work on laughter and smiling in children of different ages.

In the psychoanalytic literature some fundamental papers on the comic have appeared. It was Freud who initiated the discussion of this subject in *Wit and its Relation to the Unconscious* (7), which considers mainly economical and topological perspectives. Freud showed that laughter provoked by wit originates in the saving of psychic ex-

---

1. Meeting of the Faculty of the New York Institute of Psychoanalysis, Dec. 16, 1945.

penditure, and that the element of pleasure in laughter is derived from regression to infantile happiness. Later Freud and others called attention to the role of ego and superego in comical productions and in humor. Reik (18) investigated the role of introjection and projection in Jewish jokes by comparing them with manic-depressive mechanisms. Freud (7) interpreted humor as a spiteful triumph of narcissism and the pleasure principle over the miseries of life, effected by a momentary change of cathexis from the ego to the superego which, looking down from a bird's eye view, comforts the frightened ego as a father comforts a child in harmless trouble. Kris (15) supplemented Freud's economic theory on laughter and wit by pointing to the importance of "speed at which tension is relieved", to the "element of suddenness in this economic process" which "is responsible for the nature of comic pleasure". He suggests that most comic phenomena are bound up with past conflicts of the ego, that "they help it to repeat its victory and in doing so once more to overcome half-assimilated fear". It should be possible to confirm this and other analytic theories by clinical investigations, in particular of laughter and the comic in children.

Some special psychological studies on smiling and laughter in infants, preschool and school children have been published by Brackett (3), Blatz (2), Dearborn (5), Enders (6), Justin (11), Kenderdine (13), Washburn (20). Bühler (4), Gesell (9), and many others, have also touched upon the subject. Most of these authors have merely collected useful data about smile and laughter-producing stimuli, from the observation of physical, social, and ideational experiences. No contributions to this problem have thus far been made by child analysts.

In studying the material referring to children up to three years we can clearly group the various stimuli according to common elements: this is worth while because it suggests hypotheses on the infantile origins of smile and laughter reactions.

The table given by Blatz shows in the first place that especially smiling, but also laughter, occurs in infants and babies as a general reaction to or in anticipation of intense gratification of any kind. The table reveals, furthermore, that smiling—and much more conspicuously, laughter—are at a slightly higher age level (2.2) bound up with a great number of experiences, all of which are connected with the motor system.

Recent studies by Spitz (19) which are based on the research work of Kaila (12) show that smiling is elicited from infants as a social response to an approaching person, by the horizontal-vertical configuration of the face combined with the rhythmical nodding of the head toward the face of the child. This itself points to the significance of movement as a laughter-producing stimulus.

Omitting the purely emotional and ideational stimuli in Blatz' table, we see that laughter is elicited from children of two months up to two years by three groups of stimuli:

1. By short, especially rhythmical, exteroceptive stimuli: tactile (tickling), visual (bright color, artificial light), auditory (loud noises).

2. By proprioceptive stimuli: induced or voluntary fast motor activity of the whole body or parts of the body, at first particularly by rhythmical movements (e.g., first, shaking of hands and arms, swinging or tossing to the arms of another; later, active play, physical and verbal movement, etc.).

3. By observation of sudden or fast movements of persons or objects (e.g., first, gestures, rhythmical hand-clapping or knee-dropping, peek-a-boo, quick movements of toys or bright objects; later, conspicuous or absurd mimic expressions, such as grimaces, laughing, funny talk, etc.).

Stimulation by sound, light, or color is mostly described in combination with observation of fast movement: shaking of a rattle or bright toy, rhythmical hand-clapping, droll sounds, prattle, laughter, funny talk—all of which go along with conspicuous gestures or expressive movements of the face. Hence noise and light stimuli may be listed under groups 1) and 3).

It may be assumed that observation of expressional movement, as in 3), has an "infectious" stimulating effect on the motor system, as for instance in the yawning, crying, laughing itself, etc., of adults. This means that the child who observes fast movements participates in the experience not actually, but emotionally, and finds release in laughter instead. Since the stimuli of group 3) are mentioned among those responded to earliest and most frequently, between the third and twelfth month, it may not be too daring even to assume that this very inability of the baby to respond to the stimulating observation with corresponding motor activity may help bring about restriction of motor release, and achieve instead a release in laughter, which merely involves a muscle group—that which is the first in life trained to function. We recall in this connection that Kris (16) points out that as gesture language is, in the development of mankind, replaced by verbal language, so in laughter archaic motor pleasure is revived and socially permitted.

Before investigating the three groups of stimuli further, we must question whether there is any link between the smile as response to or in anticipation of intense gratification, and laughter provoked by stimulation of the motor system. As all infantile cravings seek relief through the motor system it is not difficult to understand that any intense gratification may elicit smiling, the mild twin of laughter, while the latter as a much stronger reaction becomes more specifically tied up to experiences in the realm of the motor system itself.

Since stimulation of the motor system as such does not produce laughter, we have to search for the specific elements which are responsible for this effect. What appears to be of greatest importance is speed—the suddenness of the stimuli and the fastness of the movements, which has been stressed by Kris. There are, besides, certain affective prerequisites for the production of laughter.

The observational material suggests that even in very early simple laughter experiences—such as "tossing or swinging a child to arms of another" or "sudden reappearance of examiner from under a table", a sequence of affects develops in two phases, coordinated to the stimulation and to the final discharge, which may alternate rhythmically and bring about waves of laughter.

There is first the initial phase of "thrill", i.e., of anxious tension mixed with quickly increasing pleasure which dissolves the fears. The fear elements stem apparently from the speed, the suddenness of the stimulating movements, i.e., the intensity of the motor experience. The pleasure is partly direct motor pleasure. Partly it seems to be purely emotional enjoyment derived from an awareness of the harmlessness of the procedure and from anticipation of a most pleasurable end. The source of these last significant emotional prerequisites for the production of laughter are either memories of previous similar laughter experiences or of social factors: the gay joyful promising attitude of the person who handles or is observed by the child. In the earliest smiling reaction, as studied by Spitz, we find the element of anticipation represented by the visual impression gained from the configuration of the approaching face.

The second phase, the final discharge, often comes as a surprising climax, evidently brought about by the sudden slowing down, or stopping, of the movement; there is a sudden relief, with intense pleasurable convulsive motor discharge in laughter.

These two phases, and the affective and emotional components involved, may be exemplified in a typical laughter game which can be performed with children under one year:

A person lets his hand move up along the body of the child who is in a lying position. This movement up toward the face is made with increasing speed and is accompanied at first with slightly threatening sounds and facial expressions; then it is ended suddenly by tickling the child's neck and laughing. The child, after a first stage of thrill, bursts out laughing.

In this and other similar laughter experiences the surprise factor plays an important part and is effective in provoking a sudden outburst of laughter. Incidentally, the example given is hardly different from laughter experiences in amusement parks, e.g., in the roller coaster. The speedy sliding down representing the first phase of thrill is followed by a second phase of slowing down during which laughter occurs; this is followed again by another quick "risky" ride down, provoking a new wave of laughter, etc.

Summarizing the elements common to the three groups of early laughter experiences as distinguished above, we come to the following formulation:

When intense, especially rhythmical, stimulation of the whole or a part of the motor system produces a sudden or surprising fast enjoyable experience which, though first suggesting danger, arouses pleasant anticipation of relief, laughter comes about as a final intensely pleasurable motor release. The original close relationship between laughter and motor experience paves the way for later stages in the development of laughter from a reaction to complex experiences of body mastery to, finally, a victory of the ego over the outer realistic and the inner instinctual world.

Blatz, from his observations on laughter in nursery school children, has offered an interpretation that comes rather close to psychoanalytic theory: "Laughter and probably smiling may be considered as socially acceptable tics or compensatory motor mechanisms accompanying the resolution of conflicts that have, for a shorter or longer period, kept the individual on the horns of a dilemma." The experimental situations described in his paper show precisely the nature of these conflicts as hinging on physical control or on other ego achievements. Some of his examples of physical activities are: the child laughs after having reached the bottom of a slide; after having jumped into a pool; after a toy thrown by the child has landed in the water. All of these examples represent likewise intense fast motor activities but, at the same time, purposeful actions, physical achievements. In other words: laughter, produced in the previously described group by sudden or quick rhythmical movements or intense playful purposeless activity, is brought on here by successful motor functioning, in the service of the ego. And as another series of experiments by Blatz shows, may finally be tied up with ego achievements which need no longer be associated with physical activity.

Blatz calls these generally "completion of events", and concludes that in most cases of laughter it may be assumed that ". . . the child foresaw the conclusion of the event . . . he has learned by experience to expect this result". But also ". . . he has learned that there are elements of danger in such a procedure".

The observations and conclusions of Blatz correspond, on the one hand, to the above given formulation, and on the other, to the hypothesis of Kris (15).

The decisive difference between complicated and simpler types of laughter-producing stimuli lies in the shift—caused by the part of the ego in the experience—to narcissistic pleasure components. They gain increasing importance the more the experience is bound up with ego achievements in physical functions and with the mastery of instinctual conflicts, rather than with expressive motor activity only. The fears provoked by the speed of movement stimuli are replaced, as the ego gets more involved in the experience, by fears of failure of the ego to master outer realistic or inner instinctual dangers. In both cases laughter comes about only if the fears are quickly dissolved by the anticipation of pleasure, which in the later complex experiences means the expectation of a victory of the ego, founded on the awareness of having learned how to master such a dangerous situation.

In complex comic phenomena, especially in comic art presentations, the categorical factor, i.e., the awareness of comic phenomena, such as the expectation of a joke that is going to be told, of a picture meant to be funny, of the happy end of a comic performance, etc., contributes largely to the "anticipation of amusement" which counteracts the fears.

The laughter occurs in all cases apparently "after completion of the event". In the case of stimulation by fast movement it comes about when the movement stops; in complex laughter experiences, when the achievement is secured at the moment of success. It seems that one must here consider the role of the superego, which permits the laughter as a well-deserved reward; the successful ego can afford now to let down the defenses, regress to uncontrolled infantile pleasure, and find relief through the harmless channel of laughter.

With regard to wit it might be said that wit seduces the ego to spite the superego, and out of the awareness of its strength to permit regressive infantile gratification through laughter. With regard to humor it might be said that the experience starts with a feeling of real failure—or identification with it—which is overcome by part of the ego detaching itself, climbing up to the height of the superego and undoing the failure by setting its strength against it, as if saying: the "real" core of myself is invulnerable, whatever happens elsewhere.

One significant point must furthermore be stressed: the simpler and more primitive the laughter-producing stimulus is, the more does the laughter express "pure uncontrolled motor pleasure" only. The more complex the stimuli, the broader becomes the margin for the variety of affects and emotions that can be discharged through laughter, and the richer become the shades of laughter, e.g., from subtle tender amusement, on to bright and joyful, to mildly ironical, to grim sardonic or triumphant laughter. However, as most complex stimuli develop, simpler primitive types of stimuli remain partly effective, and adult laughter experiences may come from sources that combine all kinds of stimuli.

A special role in the stimulation of laughter in the adult is played by observations which, as mentioned above, are also most effective and most frequent in stimulating the laughter of the child. A comparison between early simple laughter experiences of this type, such as laughing at observing quick movements, with later ones such as laughing at another person's physical or moral failure, and with most complex ones such as laughing at jokes, cartoons, comic art performances, etc., is highly interesting. Complex experiences of this kind are discussed in the next part of this paper. At this point I limit myself to the comparison between laughter at observing quick movements and laughter at observing physical failure, e.g., when a person stumbles and falls on the street.

In the first case, as discussed above, the child laughs apparently as he participates in the movement. In the second case he laughs in reaction to the other person's "ridiculous" failure in regard to body control. In view of what has been said above we may interpret the emotional process which arouses the laughter as follows: the observer feels at first tempted to participate in the observed uncontrolled movement but in doing so experiences fright. (Children often mimic laughingly the gait of drunkards or similar "failures".) The observer's fears are quickly overcome by the realization of his own body mastery. Having thus established his feeling of superiority, he may now relax and permit himself to participate in the experience again through a similarly uncontrolled but socially accepted and harmless motor release, the outburst of laughter, which represents both, pleasure and narcissistic triumph, and in addition is an outlet for aggressive impulses (Schadenfreude).

II.

The part of instinctual conflicts in the production of laughter in children has nowhere found special consideration. No clinical psychoanalytic papers have been published that might verify the correctness of analytic theories on this subject.[1] As indicated in the introductory remarks above, the clinical material presented here has been gained not from the analysis of children but from adult patients. It refers, nevertheless, to laughter provoked in children by observations that mobilized instinctual conflicts.

However, I should first like to insert some information, received in a personal report from a psychoanalytically-trained observer in a nursery school, concerning the giggling and laughter of preschool children in response to situations of instinctual danger. These observations are as follows:

"Two-, three-, and four-year-old children of both sexes respond with a great deal of giggling to anxiety situations. At the age of two and three they giggle frequently in situations which cover observations of sex differences. They do not giggle when actually noticing the anatomical differences—they react rather with intentness, surprise, puzzlement, and other expressions. At the same time, however, they giggle about 'absurd' displacements otherwise. For example, they use the words that have to do with genitals or with toilet functions, apply them to other objects, and laugh uproariously; or they change the word somewhat and use it out of context, as for example, a child who refers to his stool as 'po-po' may call some other child's penis 'po-po-pony', and make a great joke of it. Similarly, they laugh inordinately at all absurd (i.e., displaced) situations: one child puts on a rubber without a shoe, and

1. Annie Reich read an unpublished paper on "The Structure of the Grotesque Comic Sublimation" at a meeting of the New York Psychoanalytic Society in the winter of 1941.

an epidemic of giggling goes through the nursery group. A child puts on another one's hat or shoes, and this provokes giggling, whether it was done originally as a clowning trick or by mistake. It is at three and four that the children giggle about sex differences directly."

At first glance these observations seem to contradict the thesis of Kris that "comic pleasure refers to a past achievement of the ego which has required long practice to bring it about". Children of two to four years have hardly achieved complete mastery over their toilet functions and are just beginning to cope with the dangerous problem of sex differences. However, it appears that this contradiction is resolved by considering that the above reported reactions were observed in a group situation. It may be assumed that when they are in a group children draw sufficient mutual ego support from each other to feel momentarily masters of situations which would certainly produce anxiety if each of them were alone. The report indicates, moreover, that over a long period (age two to three) the children need defensive measures such as displacement, word-distortion, symbolism, in order to bring about the giggling reactions, before they can laugh in response to anxiety situations directly (age three to four).

Considering this, we are justified in assuming that the observations do not contradict but rather confirm the thesis of Kris. The fact that group reactions are more complex and differ from individual reactions gives special importance to the analytic investigation of individual cases.

The two childhood memories reported below were brought up by adult patients in connection with the analysis of their striking sense of humor, which in their treatment played an important part as an effective defense.

The first patient, Mrs. O., was a fifty-year-old college teacher. After a few years of disappointing married life she had divorced her first husband and married another divorcé who had made her rather unhappy again. In her climacterium she fell ill, and had severe depressions which were precipitated by a lung infection of her only child, a son by her first husband. It is not her depression which will be discussed, however, but a personality trait that came to the fore when she was in normal or slightly hypomanic states.

As soon as the patient would emerge from her depressions, she would turn into a different person: a charming and brilliant woman who would impress people by her excellent sense of humor. With a great capacity for perception—particularly of human weaknesses—Mrs. O. would make strikingly good, dry remarks about other persons as well as about herself, which would precisely "hit the point". Her characterizations of people were astoundingly subtle and witty, varying between "tender ridicule" and sharp attack, according to her state of mind. One might say that she was a born caricaturist, her medium of expression being words. She herself was not much of a laugher, even when well; in fact, she rarely laughed aloud.

In normal states, her humor would be good-natured and would serve, for instance, to help her students over painful situations of exposure. With the onset of a depression her humor would turn grim and would gradually get lost in bitter criticism and complaints. Her smile and her laughing, losing their spontaneous quality, would at first become strained, and later on, compulsive. During such periods her unnatural, embarrassed, or aggressive-apologetic laughing would obviously point to the defensive function of her humor; such laughing occurred whenever unconscious anxieties were touched.

In her analysis Mrs. O. told a childhood memory which shed light on the unconscious origins of her sense of humor. It was an incident that occurred when she was about four years old, when she watched a little boy urinating. The little girl had reacted with a "profound feeling of inner amusement". Thinking back on this incident, Mrs. O. felt sure that her amusement had expressed a feeling that this was "a pretty funny way for an inferior little boy to function". She did not remember feelings of envy of him. It was characteristic of her, indeed, that as far as she could recall there had never been any definite overt desire to be a boy or a man, such as is frequently associated with a purer type of penis envy. Mrs. O. thought, though, that she was "inwardly tickled" by the performance, and that "the tickled reaction was the shadow of envy". There was a fusion there of the jeopardy to her ego and of some erotic stimulation, and the inward laughing was the substitute even then for the outer demonstration.

The boy had been one of the sons of a neighbor of a much lower class, socially, and a member of a minority group. Vaguely she connected these boys with dirty and sexual activities. Her family, in contrast, was then one of girls only. She had three older sisters and a younger one. The only boy was born when she was seven years old.

Her father, the only man in the family when she was a young child, came from a socially lower and less cultivated background than her mother. Moreover, he, as well as two of the older sisters—one of whom was a "tomboy", the other known to have "masculine brains"—were afflicted with hernias, i.e., physical deformities. Accordingly, Mrs. O. had identified being a boy or like a boy with moral and physical as well as social, national, and racial inferiority.

Later on, the choice of her husbands and of professional friends corresponded to this concept. Her first husband was of German extraction, the second a Jew, whereas she was of Anglo-Saxon descent. Especially her first partner had behaved in many ways like an inferior little boy rather than like a man.

Her disparaging attitude toward boys appeared at first to include her father. Material coming up during the first period of analysis indicated that her oedipal attachment and her admiration of men had revolved around the figure of her grandfather. Her feelings toward her father, a queer paranoid personality of doubtful character, who had rejected and ignored her, had been a mixture of resentment, hurt, and contempt, from childhood on.

It was not until the last stage of analysis that we uncovered very early sexual experiences with him which had left deep traces in her emotional life. They were touched upon for the first time in association to two dreams. One was a dream of being involved in a trial for having killed a child— a crime she felt innocent of. In the other dream a baby fell off a table while she was preoccupied with professional work; again her feeling was that that this was not her fault.

Both dreams reflected the recurrent and slightly paranoid complaints of Mrs. O. about being exploited, misjudged, or blamed for wrongs committed by another. The first dream was linked up with a recent experience: the trial of a professional friend of her husband, a school principal, for having seduced and ruined his pupil, a minor. Mrs. O. had openly expressed her condemnation of his deed. When he was exonerated she felt stupefied —as if she were condemned instead of him. The second dream referred in particular to her first husband. His behavior had been so irresponsible that it fully justified her contempt for his moral weakness. He had expected her to be the head of the family, wanting her forever to be the giver and never letting her be the receiver. At the same time, he had always blamed and wronged her, projecting, as it were, his own faults on her. Mrs. O. suspected him correctly of being jealous of her higher intellectual achievements. Whereas she actually shied away from any competition with either men or women, he had treated her as a masculine competitive type of woman which, in fact, she was not, either in appearance or personality.

Their conflicts had come to a peak when Mrs. O. had her baby. Her husband had accused her repeatedly of being a career woman rather than a mother. Actually, her difficulties at that time had not been caused by her unwillingness to accept motherhood, but by the complete failure of her husband to take over the part of a father and to support his family. She had to go back to work soon after delivery. She blamed him bitterly for having deprived her of the happiness of motherhood which otherwise she would have enjoyed tremendously indeed. He had, in reality, behaved almost as if getting a child was a crime for which she had to pay.

The neurotic attitude of her husband made Mrs. O. feel unjustly accused of aggressive masculine as well as of overpossessive feminine desires; whereas, as indicated, the role of a man and of an ever-giving mother had actually been imposed on her as a penalty for faults that were not hers but his.

The material showed that Mrs. O. had unconsciously fused the figure of the unethical school principal with that of her husband, and that both men represented her father. She had always blamed her father, who was a judge, for having only legal instead of true ethical codes. From early childhood she had been aware that he, a representative of law, had maintained a secret love relationship with a cousin who was a regular guest in their home. As a little girl, Mrs. O. had shifted her curiosity about sex activities of adults from her parents to her father and cousin. Her suspicions were covered by a screen memory from the age of four or five: she was going with her sister to call on the cousin. She carried a package containing a toothbrush which the cousin had left on a visit to the household. When the cousin playfully asked what was in the package the child replied, "Your toothbrush." The cousin then made a laughing wisecrack about a great big package like that containing only a toothbrush. The child had felt this as ridicule and been very much hurt. This and another recollection, probably based on a real observation, covered fantasies about her cousin performing fellatio with her father. Further associations showed that Mrs. O. had unconsciously identified with this girl in relation to her father who, later on, left his mistress alone in misery with an illegitimate child.

The patient had recurring dreams of abdominal tumors. The dreams were associated with worries about her fatness which had developed since her first school years. This otherwise very sincere patient tried to conceal her weight like a shameful fact. Further material coming up when the patient fell ill with attacks of colitis, unearthed eventually fantasies of an "unborn second child" and of oral impregnation causing malignant stomach diseases. All these fantasies, which at first seemed to relate to observations of her father and cousin, turned out to stem from even earlier childhood experiences.

Mrs. O. had been a sick weak baby with feeding problems. Her mother, a conscientious but over-strict and cold woman, had never given her love but had taken good care of her mainly to spite the father, who regarded the child as unfit to live. Having a delayed development, the little girl had been much ridiculed by her family as a little dumbbell until she went to school, where she turned out to be a brilliant student. The second sister, her father's favorite, stood out in her memory as the one who teased her particularly by flattering her at first and then ridiculing her for having been taken in by the flattery. Between three and four years of age, prior to the incident of "inner amusement", the patient had suffered a severe attack of typhoid fever and pneumonia. Once when she was very sick in bed she had overheard her father saying that it might be better if she would die. The child recovered, and never forgot this "sentence of death".

The last period of analysis brought evidence that during her first years of life, when none of the girls were yet at school, the children had indulged in many instinctual activities: in mutual exhibition, masturbation, and anal and genital play. This period reached its climax during a long visit of a little girl cousin and her brother. In many dreams these group activities were represented as "mass parties", in which Mrs. O. played mostly the role of a neglected outsider. Although there were sufficient indications for assuming that the patient had experienced pregenital and genital over-stimulation and some form of vaginal masturbation before the age of three, this must have been a stage of intense envy of her older sisters with regard to their superior sexual organs and functions. She had believed that she possessed "no clitoris— well, hardly any" and for this reason could not masturbate manually the way her sisters did.

It is noteworthy that in this case where older sisters were the first objects of observation, the "clitoris envy" preceded the "penis envy" and was later on fused with it. During the early childhood years the "clitoris girls" were the superior children whom later she identified with the "little penis boys", as opposed to big men. This accounts, by the way, for the profound difficulties which Mrs. O. had to overcome later in life when having to compete with both men and women.

Her stage of uninhibited sex experiences ended, earlier than is common, with her severe illnesses, between three and four. It was followed by a period of complete suppression of sex and aggression, accomplished by building up very strong and over-strict reaction-formations.

Further associations about girls being impregnated against their will, or in a state of unconsciousness, revived vague memories of having been seduced to sexual activities by her older sisters and her boy cousin, when she was still a baby, "too dumb to know what she did". As the analysis progressed, the material pointed more and more to very early sexual incidents with the father himself, prior to her severe illnesses. It became clear that she had observed a sexual scene between her father and a German housemaid— possibly also an abortion performed on the same girl—all of this before the age of four. A dream of lying in a crib and seeing a big penis in a beam of light focused on it was linked up with the memory of her father clamping his big hand on her mouth as she lay crying in bed. The associations suggested that Mrs. O., as a little girl of about two or three, must have at least watched her father's genital. She herself felt, with great inner evidence, that she had actually been seduced by him to touch his penis. According to further material connected with her father, it seemed likely that once as a baby, when in bed with her father, her face must have come close to his genital, whereupon she had a bowel movement, for which her father beat her. As in these memories the penis of her father appeared to be fused with her mother's breast, they may refer to her mother rather than to her father. However far her experiences with her father went, they had evidently thrown her into panicky sexual excitations. Their specific nature was clarified by associations to the above-mentioned screen memory of his clamping his hand on her mouth. These excitations brought to the fore defensive wishes to bite off his fingers; these covered deeper oral aggressions against his genital and, deepest of all, impulses to bite the breasts of her aggressive mother. It appeared that watching and touching her father's penis, and probably observing a fellatio performance—all of this happening at the pre-oedipal stage, as it were—had aroused overwhelming visual as well as oral impulses fusing with panicky vaginal excitations.

Consequently, the kernel of her fantasies of oral impregnation and the "unborn second child" turned out to be the illusion of an incorporated intra-anal or intra-vaginal baby-phallus. Her illusory concept of a penis hidden inside of her body was supported, as is often the case, by the early arousing of anal as well as vaginal sensations.

It became clear now that the little girl had considered the rejection and ridicule of her family as well as the typhoid fever and pneumonia as consequences of her early sexual fantasies and experiences. She regarded them, as later on in life she regarded her bad marital and professional experiences, and the sickness of her child, as punishments unjustly imposed on her; in particular, by her father, the cruel judge, who condemned her to death while being the real culprit himself. This was the unconscious core of her complaints of being always blamed or punished for "crimes without guilt", crimes which the accuser himself had indeed committed. It is understandable that these complaints should revolve around feelings of being accused of castrative masculine and feminine strivings, of aggressively craving a penis or a baby.

We now turn our attention back to the childhood memory, her observation of the little boy's urinating. The uncovering of earlier sexual experiences with her father sheds light on the unconscious background of the little girl's reaction of "inner amusement". The view of the little boy, leading to a comparison between their genitals, was bound to have a traumatic effect. It would stir up envy and fear of the penis, oral and genital castrative wishes, urinary impulses, and anxieties about her own being castrated. This is her way of overcoming the emotional upheaval: reviving earlier scenes of watching, her observation conjures up the far more impressive picture of her father's genital and leads to a comparison between previous and present experience. To put it in the words of the patient, "Compared with what I had seen before, this was nothing."

The comparison of past and present situations suggests various implications. The superficial realistic ones refer to her own different position and the difference between her partners in the two experiences: in the past she was a helpless baby, dumb enough to be seduced and overpowered by her father's big genital; since then she has grown up and changed; there is no reason to get excited or scared at nothing but a little boy's small penis. On a deeper, irrational level, however, her own unconscious fantasies lead the comparison farther beyond reality: "Compared with the big penis I took in, not only with my eyes, but in fantasy through mouth and genital, the little boy's penis is inferior. His performance is a 'ridiculous show'." Her conclusion leads to a reversal of the frightening present—and underneath, the past—situation: "It is not I who lack the penis, who am castrated and ridiculous. He is, whereas I possess a powerful genital inside of my body."

Since the patient's narcissistic inflation, and the projection of her own deficiency on the boy, are based on objectionable fantasies, she needs justification through further projection of her guilt on her partner. Using past experiences again, in particular her secret knowledge of her father's and sisters' forbidden sexual activities, her train of ideas ends like this: ". . . . and it serves him right to be laughed at, because not I have been doing wrong. He—and my father and sisters—are the real culprits." Thus exonerated and in righteous amusement, the little girl can permit herself to indulge in watching and inwardly laughing. In the same emotional act she rids herself of sexual and aggressive tensions and, for the moment, successfully overcomes the castration trauma. That she reacts with "inner amusement" rather than with overt laughter, expresses the superiority of her "inner penis" and of "inner experiences" over the little boy's external genital and his "showy" demonstration. This attitude Mrs. O. maintained through her whole life.

Her "inward laughter" represents both emotional discharge and triumph of the ego which feels free of guilt and fear, at the expense of the little boy; and, in a deeper layer, of the father. The little girl can be all the more amused, since the sight of the boy proves to her at the same time that he is not really castrated: he does have a little penis, after all.

Mrs. O's. childhood experience with the little boy shaped the pattern for her future sense of humor. It may be mentioned that in depressive periods the projection mechanism which in humorous moods would effect so much pleasure and narcissistic gain, was partly sustained; but with the changed economic function, it was sustained as a defense only, in her paranoid complaints and criticisms. These would sometimes be accompanied by unnatural and strained laughing. Yet frequently it happened that the patient, when depressed, would identify in dreams or associations with the same persons who would otherwise be targets of her ridicule.

Another patient reported a similar infantile memory of laughing in which the underlying mechanisms resemble in some ways those of the first case.

Mr. M., a forty-year-old bachelor, showed a charming talent for telling good jokes and funny anecdotes. However, his humor had less pleasant aspects, and would occasionally be rather grim or sardonic. I may give one especially interesting example. Mr. M. was extremely musical without being really creative, which he resented very much. His greatest hobby was to select the most imperfect work of a great composer and transcribe it for two pianos. He would do this with great mastery, but in such a way that it would produce an overwhelmingly funny effect on his listeners.

Mr. M. was in treatment for phobic fears and difficulties in his love life. A typical Don Juan, he had maintained, besides innumerable escapades with promiscuous girls, long-lasting secret relationships with very respectable married women. He was constantly harassed by fears that the husbands of his mistresses, with whom he would always keep up cordial personal or even business relations, might discover his love affairs and retaliate by ruining him financially and socially.

The way Mr. M. selected his women friends, and the set-up of his triangle affairs, pointed clearly to his infantile incestuous fixations. One of his favorite sexual fantasies, which he eventually acted out, while in analysis, was to have another man perform intercourse with his mistress while he watched, focusing his sexual interest on the observation of the woman having an orgasm. The analysis of his perversion took a long time because of the complicated vicissitudes of his instinctual drives. There was an interesting childhood memory associated with it, of a watching experience which appeared to be a forerunner of his later perversion as well as of his sense of humor.

As a boy of about seven he had spent his vacation with his mother at a fashionable summer resort. Lacking suitable company, he had felt lonesome. The other children around him belonged to a socially higher milieu.

They were better dressed and better behaved than he. Their parents were respectable and distinguished, unlike his mother, who was a divorcée. Gradually, though, he was accepted by this group and took part in their activities. Once a game was arranged by the boys and girls which ended in a general kissing scene. The boy did not participate. Surprised and stupefied at first that these "nice" children would do such things, he suddenly got into an elated state. Laughing and clapping his hands, he goaded them excitedly to continue and go further in their sexual amusements.

Associations to this screen memory revolved around his masturbation conflict. All during the summer the boy had been preoccupied by sexual fantasies involving the "nice and innocent" little girls around him. His thoughts had made him feel very guilty, as if he "polluted" or "raped" the girls in his mind. He was sure that the other "fine" boys of "good American stock" never masturbated or had fantasies such as his. Full of admiration and envy of their social as well as moral superiority, he had tried hard to maintain a façade, at least, of being a well-bred boy of moral integrity, and their equal.

The kissing episode caused the breakdown of his illusion. His discovery that these boys and girls behaved worse than he did revived earlier childhood memories, in particular of situations where he had felt caught in sexual activities himself.

The leading memory went back to an incident when, at the age of five, he was caught in sexual activities and when, at the same time, he had heard rumors about the bad morals of his parents. His father, though originally engaged to his aunt, had seduced her sister; when the latter became pregnant, he had to marry her. His wife divorced him after two years. When the boy, who was born before the marriage, was discovered by the aunt in sexual play with her little daughter, she started a violent scene with him and his mother, hinting at the bad morals of his parents as the reason for his naughtiness.

The boy had never gone through a true latency period, because his belief in the moral standards of his parents had broken down too early. Feeling doomed to be bad as they, he had however built up reactive ideals, which he would pin on such superior immaculate families as those in the summer resort. But unable to really identify with them, he instead made an effort to imitate them. This caused a growing split in his personality, which reflected the hypocrisy of his parents. He developed an outer façade of being a good innocent baby, but led a secret, well-concealed inner life, absorbed by aggressive, sexual fantasies. His "secret" made him shy and timid at home and with other children, and constantly scared him of being "found out". When he entered school, it was his outer appearance of an over-protected, over-good child that caused the other children to ridicule him as a "sissy". His reaction to the ridicule was shown by the recollection of a scene in which he had urinated in the presence of his parents. His mother had pointed to his genitals and laughingly said to his stepfather, "Look how cute!" The boy had felt very ashamed, as though caught masturbating.

The sexual performance he witnesses, the boys and girls kissing each other, repeats his previous disillusionment in his parents, but now only in relation to the children, and not to their parents. The children, though they have such wonderful superior parents, are unmasked as being not better but worse than he, the son of bad parents. As they act out what, since the seduction of his little cousin, he has done only in masturbation fantasies, it is they who deserve to be laughed at. His amazing discovery, depressing at first, quickly brings about a tremendous relief from guilt feeling, and inflates his ego. His elation indicates that he has suddenly scored a moral triumph over the others—in the deepest layer, over his parents. Remaining a harmless passive onlooker, he can now secretly gratify his own sexual desires by watching, and discharge his affects by applauding and laughing.

A summary comparison between the two childhood memories shows that they have much in common on the surface as well as in the unconscious kernel. In both patients, analysis revealed that they were frequently ridiculed, prior to the given incidents, supposedly because of sexual sins. At the same time both made shocking discoveries about the sexual life of their parents, or parent-substitutes, in their early childhood. In both cases the memory is that of witnessing a sexual performance of other children which, coming as a surprise to them, suddenly arouses instinctual impulses, in particular envy and the desire to participate in the performance; but, at the same time, great anxieties. The central conflict is in the first case more distinctly than in the second case, the castration conflict. Both children ward it off by a successful projection mechanism which leads to their laughing at the other parties. For this purpose they utilize earlier childhood memories: on the one hand, of knowledge of the sexual sins of their parents; on the other, of sexual incidents, similar to the present ones, in which they were actively involved. The comparison of past and present situations enables both children to project their own sinfulness on their partners and to retaliate for having been exposed and ridiculed by reversing roles. In this way they gain superiority over their seducers and over the present temptation, as well as over their guilty past. In the role of only passive observers both children feel free to participate in the sexual performance through watching and laughing at the others the way they have been watched and laughed at before. In both cases the laughter or amusement response expresses a triumph of the ego and the pleasure principle, which relieves them of objectionable aggressive and libidinous tensions.

Evidently the present situation, fusing with and utilizing earlier events, has afforded an opportunity to master the present as well as the past experiences. The successful outcome appears to be guaranteed by the fact that the ego of the children has developed since the period of the previous experiences. Looking back, the children feel strong enough to do now what they could not do then: to control sufficiently their own instinctual impulses. This enables them to unmask, condemn, and laugh at their seductive partners, or parents, respectively. Besides, the incident which provokes their reaction occurs with persons other than their parents, and, as it were, not with adults. The sinners whom they unmask and laugh at are children, equals in age, though admired or envied as superiors. It has been emphasized that the boy depreciated the other children in terms of bad offsprings of respectable parents, i.e., maintained an idealization of the latter while he unmasked the sins of the former.

It is also of interest that the laughter reaction of the boy, like the "inner amusement" of the girl, seems to be favored by the awareness that "nothing really bad or serious had happened to the other party, after all". The girl realized that the little boy did have a little penis, the boy was aware that what he saw was only a game approved by a group of children who, despite what they did, remained what they had been before: immaculate little girls and "fine American boys".

When later on Mr. M. reenacted the triangle scene, he was disgusted at his girl friend for "taking it seriously" instead of regarding it as an "amusing little game only".

In accordance with Freud's views, analysis uncovered in both cases the change of narcissistic cathexis, the elation of the ego, and the victory of the pleasure principle, as well as "the saving of psychic expenditure", at the moment of laughter. However, the amusement of the two children was not yet a truly humorous reaction, but a forerunner of the sense of humor which both patients developed later on in life as characteristic personality traits. Being an infantile reaction, it lacked the precious wisdom and mild superiority of humor. The laughing of the children meant a narcissistic victory at the expense of their partners, a triumphant retaliation, achieved by projection mechanisms which were induced by comparison with past experiences.

What is characteristic of the memories presented is that the patients behaved like an audience at a comical (funny) performance. It is this that has challenged the author to end this paper with a short excursion into the field of comic art.

The type of comic art briefly discussed here is represented best by the American comic film in which the hero goes through an endless series of calamities, disasters, and persecutions which provoke roaring laughter in the audience. The comical effect resembles that achieved by the clown, who does everything wrong and is beaten up constantly, or by the funny dwarf of past centuries, whose misshapen figure, in grotesque caprices, amused his master.

Kris (14) speaks of the clown as a figure related to caricature. He explains the art of caricature by tracing it back to its origin in primitive magic charms and to the belief that the picture is identical with the depicted object. Caricature, though related to past customs of punishing distorted pictures of adversaries in effigy, is not however supposed to affect the enemy but the onlooker. Magical thinking, the primary process, does not control the artist; he masters and uses it for his artistic goals.

What distinguishes the clown and his modern offspring, the typical primitive comic film hero, from caricature, is that he is a living, gesturing, speaking and acting figure. While caricature produces a short-lived effect, that of a clown or comic film performance is prolonged. As in caricature, the clown or the comic film hero are endowed with certain exaggerated characteristics which "unmask" their inferior personality and make them ridiculous. This is precisely what in our cases the two patients did in fantasy to the other children whom they were watching. What they accomplish by a complicated emotional process, the transformation of the scene into a performance that is funny, from their subjective point of view only, the artist achieves by the comic art presentation. Apparently he stimulates psychic mechanisms in the audience similar to those that made the two children laugh.

Let us call to mind the comic film hero who in pursuit of some ridiculous goal meets with catastrophes, falls and hurts himself, is persecuted or beaten up. Whereas normally the spectacle of such suffering and calamity would invite unpleasant identifications arousing anxiety and aggression, disgust, or sympathy and pity, the audience roars with laughter. Yet, on closer observation, one discovers that there are waves of laughter, interrupted by minutes of tension, which is discharged again in new outbursts of gaiety. These interpolated tensions indicate what has been pointed out above, in relation to the laughter reaction to seeing a person stumble and fall: identification with the hero, participation in his actions, does not obviate completely but on the contrary induces the comical effect (16).

The audience, tempted to identify with the unfortunate hero, immediately escapes from such painful sympathy by having a good look at him. Seeing this caricature of a hero, his grotesque gestures and actions, the onlooker can say to himself, "This cannot happen to me. I am a different person, in fact, a wonderful person compared with such a misfit."

In other words, the comic film permits the onlooker, after a tentative identification, to quickly detach himself from the suffering hero again by unloading on him—as did the two patients—all the inferiority he dreads having himself, the sins and weakness of the past which he has long since mastered. As he succeeds in warding off the danger of painful sympathies, he withdraws them from the victim and switches to the pursuer. Like the two children, he feels: being punished serves this impossible fellow right; and he discharges his affects and his own mobilized infantile impulses in laughter and "Schadenfreude" —pleasure in the hero's being hurt. He can do so all the more freely because he is certain of the "happy end". Nothing serious is going to happen, anyway. "Lachen heisst: schadenfroh sein, aber mit gutem Gewissen" (Nietzsche).

Those who know the German humorist Wilhelm Busch, painter and poet, may recall the last rhymes of "Pious Helen", one of his best creations. "Uncle Nolte", who represents the reader and onlooker, is pictured learning about the tragi-comic death of his sinful niece Helen: at first mourning, then moralizing, and at last looking up to heaven hypocritically, with a broad grin. These are the accompanying verses:[2]

> When Uncle Nolte heard the news
> He was distressed and had the blues.
> But having mourned enough and cried,
> He said, "I told her so, all right!
> Good deeds—this principle is true—
> Are bad ones that you fail to do.
> Well, well—I'm really glad, my friend,
> Because, thank God, I'm different!"

> (Als Onkel Nolte dies vernommen,
> War ihm sein Herze sehr beklommen.
> Doch als er nun genug geklagt:
> "O!" sprach er, "ich hab's gleich gesagt!
> Das Gute, dieser Satz steht fest,—
> Ist stets das Böse was man lässt.
> Ei ja!—Da bin ich wirklich froh!
> Denn, Gott sei Dank! ich bin nicht so!")

2. Author's translation.

BIBLIOGRAPHY

1. Bergson, H. *Laughter. An Essay in the Meaning of the Comic*, Macmillan, 1921.
2. Blatz, W. E., Allin, K., and Millichamp, D. "A Study of Laughter in the Nursery School Child", *Univ. Toronto Studies, Child Dev. Series*, 7, 1936.
3. Brackett, C. W. "Laughing and Crying of Pre-School Children", *J. Exper. Educ.*, 2, 1933.
4. Bühler, C. *The First Year of Life*, John Day, 1930.
5. Dearborn, G. V. N. "The Nature of the Smile and Laugh", *Science*, 2, 1900.
6. Enders, A. C. "Laughter of the Pre-School Child", *Papers of the Michigan Academy of Science, Arts and Letters*, 8.
7. Freud, S. *Wit and its Relation to the Unconscious*, 1905.
8. Freud, S. "Humour", *Int J. Psa.*, IX, 1928.
9. Gesell, A. L. *The Mental Growth of the Pre-School Child*, Macmillan, 1925.
10. Hartmann, H. and Kris, E. "The Genetic Approach in Psychoanalysis", *this Annual*, I.
11. Justin, F. "A Genetic Study of Laughter-Provoking Stimuli", *Child Dev.*, 3, 1922.
12. Kaila, E. "Die Reaktionen des Säuglings auf das menschliche Gesicht", *Turku*, 1932.
13. Kenderdine, M. "Laughter in the Pre-School Child", *Child Dev.*, 2, 1931.
14. Kris, E. "The Psychology of Caricature", *Int. J. Psa.*, XVII, 1936.
15. Kris, E. "Ego Development and the Comic", *ibid.*, XIX, 1938.
16. Kris, E. "Laughter as an Expressive Process", *ibid.*, XXI, 1940.
17. Reik, T. "Psychoanalytische Bemerkung über den zynischen Witz", *Imago*, 2, 1913. pp. 573-588.
18. Reik, T. "Zur Psychoanalyse des jüdischen Witzes", *Imago*, 15, 1929. pp. 63-88.
19. Spitz, R. A. and Wolf, K. M. "The Smiling Response: A Contribution to the Ontogenesis of Social Relations", *Gen. Psychol. Mon.*, XXXIV, 1, 1946.
20. Washburn, R. W. "A Study of the Smiling and Laughing of Infants in the First Year of Life", *Gen. Psychol. Mon.*, VI, 5 and 6, 1929.

TWINS

Observations of Environmental Influences on their Development

By DOROTHY T. BURLINGHAM (London)

Before attempting the psychological study of the relationship of twins to each other, it is necessary to examine, as far as possible, outside circumstances which might have a bearing on the subject of twins and therefore have an indirect influence on them. The mother's relationship to twins must be investigated for influences dissimilar to those which she has on her other children. The brother and sister relationship towards twins may have components which are not present in their relationship otherwise. The investigation includes not only close emotional ties but the more casual and general contacts, which make up the world in which twins live. Here the influence may not only work through direct contacts but through more subtle and indirect ones, as for instance through the general view that all twins love each other. There is still another aspect to keep in mind, the effect of twin fantasies on twins. As I have recently shown[1] many people have had a period in their lives when they enjoyed the fantasy of having a twin. It would be interesting to know how far their fantasies determine the behavior of these persons when they meet twins in reality; whether these fantasies are not played out on twins, encouraging and perhaps enforcing them to take over the fantasied roles. As a result the twins might find the compelling character of these fantasies even more powerful than the effect of their own twin relationship.

The Impression of Twins on Adults.

To observe adults when they are unexpectedly confronted by a pair of boy or girl twins gives striking evidence of one form of outside influence on twins. Adults generally show surprise and interest when they meet twins of a young age. They gaze from one twin to the other, making mental comparisons. Often their observations are accompanied

---

1. "The Fantasy of Having a Twin," *this Annual,* I.

by remarks and exclamations to the person who accompanies the twins, such as, "How charming," "How interesting," "How odd," "What a trouble they must be;" and questions follow: "Are they alike?" "Can you tell them apart?" "How do you manage?" The twins as a pair are made to feel different, unique; and the fact of their twinship is continually forced upon them in the form of comparisons.

Children with deformations also call forth reactions of surprise and interest from the outside world, but these feelings are quickly followed by pity and often disgust. The child feels these reactions as painful. The impression that twins create is almost always pleasurable.

It would seem natural for adults, who have had twins in their own families, or as playmates or schoolmates, to have different reactions from adults who have never been in contact with twins before. They would have impressions already formed from former experiences and find twins familiar and more ordinary. It is therefore astonishing to find that twins have as great a fascination for these individuals as for those who meet twins for the first time. The fascination apparently is not produced because twins are rare, but because two like individuals have a sudden appeal. A spontaneous identification with the twins probably sets in, initiating the absorbing train of thought, "If I had a twin." The fascination decreases as twins grow older. Adult twins who remain identical in looks, and especially those who stress their similarity by dressing alike, are stared at as oddities and curiosities but they have lost their appeal as twins. They cannot be fitted into the "fantasy of having a twin", since the desired twin of that childhood daydream is definitely a child.

The Impression of Twins on Young Children.

The following examples show how little children notice the identity of twins and desire to stress this fact.

Examples taken from the Hampstead Nursery:

When Josephine, one of non-identical triplets, was put into her shelter bed, a child called out from one of the other beds "Other Ronnie" (the name of the boy triplet). At another time these same two triplets had been separated due to illness and when Josephine reentered the toddler nursery the other toddlers of about two years showed surprise, calling out, "Two Ronnies." Lydia, two years, two months, said: "Not want two Ronnies."

Another example of an older child of three-and-a-half years: She saw her twin playmates Margaret and Anne in the garden. She called to Margaret: "Other Anne, other Anne, come here." As Margaret did not respond she got cross and called even louder. When asked what was the matter she complained, "The other Anne won't hear when I talk to her." And on being asked why she did not call her Margaret she replied, "Because she is another Anne."

Little children who come in contact with twins for the first time express their astonishment and show that they are fascinated. They stand still and point from one twin to the other. Often another element is added, one of consternation.

Richard, a little boy of three, confronted with twin boys for the first time, a little younger than himself, pointed first at one and then at the other. "Boy, boy," and then added, "me not two Richies." The idea that he might not be one entity was definitely a shock.

It is perhaps not astonishing to find that twins themselves are fascinated by other twins.

Twin boys of ten years met a nurse wheeling a baby carriage with twin boys of eighteen months. The boys stopped and observed the twins with the greatest interest, asked the nurse many questions about them and remained with them for a long time. From then on whenever these twin boys met the twin babies on the street they would join them and remain with them as long as they could. It was quite clear how attracted they were by the fact that these babies were twins, two individuals who were in the same situation as themselves and with similar problems.

The Relationship of Brothers and Sisters to Twins in the Family.

An elder child will have very much the same reactions of jealousy when his mother has twins as he would have if only one baby were born. The jealousy is caused by the mother's preoccupation with the new babies and the withdrawal of the accustomed attention and love from the older child. The fuss and excitement over the twins not only by the mother but by everybody who comes in contact with them can only increase the jealousy.

A mother writes of her boy of three realizing his suffering because of the attention the twins received.[2] (The twins are fifteen months younger than the boy.)

2. This and the following letters are answers to an inquiry sent out by *The Nursery World,* a weekly periodical for mothers (London).

"In Bob's interest I gave them the minimum attention. Whenever I took them out the pram was surrounded by admirers, all admiring the twins of course; few people had the sense to say a word to Bob. So I usually came home furious! I have a huge pram, and the babies were together at one end and Bob the other. He seemed such a forlorn little creature, I always made a point of talking to him and fussing him while people enthused over the twins at the other end."

The fact that there are two babies, twins, that this is an unusual occurrence, that they are two while the elder child is only one, must increase emotional reactions.

A five-year-old girl knew that her mother was going to have a baby and she hoped that it would be a girl. When she heard that twin girls had been born, she was heard to murmur, "Three girls." A few days later she came to her mother and asked her if she could not have another baby, hesitated, realizing that this would not solve her problem, and then added: "I will go back in your tummy to be born again." It is likely that she wanted to be twins too. She probably felt that she was at a disadvantage in being only one.

A child who has twins as elder brothers or sisters may feel that it is quite natural and usual that there are two children in the family of the same age. He will gradually observe the extra attention paid to the twins, notice the remarks about their likeness, and realize it is because they are two. But above all the younger child will be impressed by the fact that the twins always have each other as companions, that they are never alone, and that they make an intimate pair just as the parents do. The child may believe that the world is made up of couples, feel left out, and decide that he is lacking something and at a great disadvantage in consequence. He may feel his oneness as a castration and have one more situation on which to play out his castration complex. The intention to look for other objects to make up for this deficiency either in substitute relationships or in fantasy relationships will be very great for these children. Parents, too, may react to the loneliness of their child and try to produce a playmate for it.

The Spontaneous Wish for Like Beings in Children.

Children are not only eager to find substitute twin relationships for themselves when in contact with twins; they also seem to have spontaneous desires that induce them to look for beings similar to themselves at a very early age.

When a little child is first introduced to a baby brother or sister he is often surprised that the baby is not as old as himself and is bitterly disappointed to find it so tiny. The idea that the baby should be similar to the child himself is probably brought about by remarks made by the parents: that they would like to have another child; that it would be nice for the child to have a playmate. The child then thinks of himself and imagines another like being. It has often also been observed that school children make spontaneous friendships with children who have the same birthdays as theirs, or with children who have names similar to their own. It is as if the slightest reminders of identity were often the greatest attraction to them.

Under the domination of another fantasy children like to pretend that they are their mothers' twin. They like to dress like her, imitate her in voice and gesture and even say to her, "I am your twin." Similar dresses for mother and daughter were sold in American stores for awhile and were very popular. This fantasy, under the domination of the oedipus complex, is a method of attracting the father; the child attempts to be like the mother.

Other twin fantasies have already been mentioned in my former paper.[3] Children in the latency period are overcome by feelings of loneliness and solitude when they have been disappointed by their parents in the oedipal stage of their development. Some children imagine a twin as the inseparable companion, who will give them the understanding and love they are missing and longing for. Other children, overcome by their limitations and ineffectiveness—owing to the castration complex—imagine a twin as an addition to themselves, who will give them double the strength and courage that they need to overcome their inferiority.

For all children who imagine other children or adults as their twins, or fantasy a twin to overcome their loneliness, the sight of real twins must appear as the prototype of what they had imagined for themselves, a relationship in every way superior to the one they had painstakingly built up and artificially created for themselves. Thus twins are made to feel that they possess something which is most attractive and interesting to other children, in some way superior to ordinary friendships; and that they are envied for their twinship.

3. Loc. cit.

The Mother's Reaction to Bearing Twins.

A mother, before she has given birth to twins, will already have had a certain attitude towards twins as a result of her own life experiences. She may have had twins in her own family, or met them outside her home, or had a fantasy of possessing a twin herself. These factors will influence her thoughts and determine her behavior towards her own twins. This may even overshadow the importance of her position in her own family constellation, which so often is a determining factor in influencing a mother's behavior towards each of her children.

Twins will be a great shock to a mother, if she lives in straitened circumstances. There is only a quantitative difference between two unwanted babies and one unwanted baby. Twins mean more care and more worry not only because there are two babies, but because twins are often very delicate. Without help the mother must find them a very great burden. A mother of good circumstances who had just borne twins and was delighted with them found herself in a maternity ward with women all poorer than she. She was very surprised when the mothers in the ward one after the other came to her with words of consolation and sympathy.

A mother writes: "I felt dismay that I should be inflicted with twins, when it was my first pregnancy and I should be single handed."

Another mother writes: "How perfectly frightful. We had no domestic help or prospect of it, the thought of additional expense horrifying and to add to our troubles, I had absolutely no experience of babies."

For the father twins can only mean more responsibility, more mouths to feed.

A wife writes: "I was thrilled to bits. My husband was furious with me and refused to speak to me . . . He persisted it must be all my fault and none of his."

There are some fathers however who feel very proud of what they have accomplished.

A wife writes: "My husband was very proud of himself."

By some parents, whether rich or poor, to produce twins is felt as something to be ashamed of. They consider it lowly. For some women even the idea of having twins is revolting and disgusting.

There are, however, many mothers who are pleased to have twins, even if taken aback for the first moment when told of the possibility. They also show great pride in their achievement.

Three mothers of twins write:

(1)   "My husband and I were both thrilled and full of anticipation."

(2)   "If there was a way of guaranteeing the conception of twins, I should undoubtedly be one of the first to try it."

(3)   "When I knew that I was going to have twins I was very pleased and naturally proud of myself."

The mothers adapt with pleasure to this event and enjoy the preparations and the planning for the future of their babies. The mother, beside having maternal feelings which arouse love for her babies, enjoys the extra fuss and attention that she receives because of her twins. She responds to this with pleasure and pride and delights in showing them off. Through the reaction of the outer world to her twins she gains a feeling of importance. She herself has achieved something unusual and her twins have become precious possessions which other people are interested in, wonder at and even envy. The curiosity and interest that twins create affects not only mothers who have accepted the twins gladly but all mothers of twins. Even if having twins has appeared to some mothers as a narcissistic injury, they all find that in reality it affords a narcissistic pleasure.

This may be one of the reasons why mothers have a tendency to increase the similarity of twins. Twins are often given like-sounding names, are dressed alike, have their hair cut and arranged in the same style, and have everything done by their mothers to "increase" their twinship. This is so with non-identical as well as identical twins as long as they are babies and toddlers; later, as the non-identical twins look less alike and develop individual personalities, the mothers respond to this change in them and treat them more as individuals. Identical twins are kept alike much longer. If a mother hears remarks about a dissimilarity of her identical twins she will often behave as if a disparaging remark had been made about them and react by pointing out their likeness. Their similarity has become an object for her exhibitionism.

But mothers have the opposite tendency as well, that is, to look for differences in their twins. This may start immediately after their birth. The mothers search for any dissimilarity in looks, in behavior, in character. They consider that one twin looks like the father, one like themselves; one is more beautiful, one is more intelligent, one cries more, one is more greedy. The mother will often be convinced that she can tell her twins apart because of some such peculiarity that she has noticed, though in reality she often confuses them. In the Hampstead Nursery where there were four pairs of twins and a set of triplets it was observed how very often the twins and the triplets were mistaken one for the other by the mothers, as well as by the nurses. A mother is likely to be mortified when she realizes her mistake. It is as if she feels that a mother should be able to distinguish between her babies, and that it is a serious failing on her part when she cannot do that—it shows a lack of love.

Love and hate are outgoing emotions which are directed primarily towards a single individual. A responding emotion is expected showing that the original emotion has achieved its aim. It is therefore very disconcerting and disturbing as well as inhibiting for a mother not to be sure which child is to get the emotion and whether the right child is getting the emotion destined for it. Until the twins are distinguished one from the other there can be no feeling of close contact. Several mothers have expressly said that it was impossible to love their twins until they had found a difference in them. The search for distinguishing marks, on the part of the mother, is therefore of significance. She feels that it is necessary for her to find a difference in order to express her emotions freely towards each of her twins, so that she can love them. When a teacher takes over a class of children, she feels she has no real contact until she knows the children by name, that is, until she can tell them apart, and they have become individual personalities for her. In the army, officers take great pains to know their men individually, realizing that the men will work better for them when they do.

The problem of distinguishing one personality from the other is a very important one for the animated sound pictures. It is necessary to keep the figures on the stage individual and distinct so that there is no confusion in the mind of the spectator. In an interesting book on the *Art of Walt Disney*[4] Robert D. Field describes, in the chapter on the "Right to Live", how animated sound pictures are created. He writes:

"Each person, each thing must live his own private life and behave according to his own nature. The moment the window of the screen is

4. Collins, London, 1944.

opened, there must be no room for any question. With the first intimation of vitality the character must establish his identity once and for all. However insignificant may be his role, he must be unique to the occasion."

He goes on by giving examples:

"How, for instance, was it possible to keep under control all the animals that shared the housecleaning in the dwarfs' cottage, and at the same time to endow each of them with such a unique personality that no confusion could arise as to which rabbit was which?"

And in "Snow White":

"Seven little men must be created. Seven little men, approximately the same size; they must all have the same ethnical characteristics, yet all must be personally different. There must be no possibility of confusing one with another when all were on the screen together."

The reason for this is that it would otherwise be impossible for the spectator to identify with the various characters on the screen. The mother of twins must be faced with very much the same problem as she watches her babies. She needs to be able to identify with each of them in order to love them. If the twins are alike she finds this impossible and as a result her emotions cannot have free play. She considers that she is not giving the children what is their due and at the same time fears that she will provoke their aggression because they are unloved.

Mothers with non-identical twin babies soon have no difficulty in telling the babies apart, they often not only look different, but have different temperaments or habits—in sleeping, for instance, which makes for different routines.

A mother writes:—

"They have always slept in different rooms, and when they were tiny in different prams in the garden, as their sleeping habits were different."

And another mother:—

"From the first Alice cooperated. From the first Mary fought and objected. She was the weakest, and had more time spent on her than the stronger Alice. Mary screamed when you picked her up to bathe her, then got used to it and screamed when you put her down. Alice had a regular motion, Mary never did."

The mother therefore treats these non-identical twins from the start as individuals with personalities needing individual opportunities.

It is interesting that mothers of non-identical twins often say they wished to treat their twins equally or alike as a matter of principle but that for some reason they were unable to do so:

"I have often tried to treat them equally. We feel they should be treated alike in the early years, but allowed to develop on individual lines later, if they show special aptitude for certain things."

On the other hand mothers with identical twins, even though many in theory plan and wish to give the twins individual treatment and individual opportunities, find it difficult to do so.

A letter from a Nanny about twins of three years ten months expresses this:—

"Both their mother and I find it quite impossible to favor one more than the other. This is probably because they are so alike."

From a mother of twins, four years old:

"I certainly feel that twins should be allowed to develop on individual lines . . . I think it is a good plan to dress twins differently, but am afraid I found it easier to dress mine alike, because if one of them has a certain dress or coat, or any other article of clothing, the other one wants one just like it. Sometimes, however, they will choose to wear different dresses or cardigans, and I always allowed them to do so."

From a mother of twins, seven years:

"I remember reading advice somewhere to let twins go their separate ways as much as possible and to dress them individually. I think myself this might lead to jealousy, as my own seem to resent any different treatment from outsiders."

From a mother of twins, twenty-one years old:

"We gave a great deal of thought as to whether they should be educated together or sent to separate schools, and discussed with masters, etc., the advisability or otherwise of trying to give them a chance to develop on individual lines. It has ended however, that they have been together, and I am sure now that it has been best. They are a complete unit and would never have been happy apart. They are taking up the same careers and are terribly keen about everything they do."

Mothers often say that twins hate to be separated, that they cannot do without each other, that they like to be treated alike and for this reason the mothers seldom separate them from each other.

"In my experience the twins themselves virtually dictate to you how to treat them; at the moment we have to dress them alike (twenty months) and give them identical toys because they are so very apt to be envious of the other's possessions. And I don't think they are able yet to understand that their own thing, though different, may be as valuable as the thing the sister has."

A mother states that at an earlier stage it was not possible to treat them identically, for instance, in feeding.

Twins (one year nine months):

"I found that even from the beginning they would not be parted. At first I had only one cradle, but bought another and tried to part them, but no, I did not get any sleep at night. As soon as they were put back together they were contented.

"I find that they each like to have a toy of their own, so we always endeavour to get two toys exactly alike. In fact I think the twins like to be treated alike, after all they are so near and dear to each other, and I know from experience that mine are miserable if they are separated."

Identical twins when they grow up often fail to develop into two separate human entities. It remains a matter of conjecture whether this is due to the twinship itself or to the attitude of the mother who in their infancy could not tell them apart, who was driven by an inner urge to give them the same opportunities and experiences thus treating them as one being and not as two.

Conclusions.

On the basis of the pleasure principle babies respond to whatever gives them sensations of pleasure and look for opportunities to repeat these pleasures. As they gradually become aware of the mother's presence they respond with pleasure to her handling and later when the mother reacts with interest to each of their newly acquired accomplishments they try to repeat them so as to increase this interest as well as to enjoy the pleasure they have created for her. Twins in this early stage of development react to the mother just as single children do. It is only in a later stage of development that they become aware of the mother's pleasure in both of them, and in the comparisons she makes of one with the other. In this way they become conscious of each other and of the mother's pleasure in them as a unit. They meet this reaction not only from the parents but from practically every one. As twins they may create interest far greater than any interest they may get as single individuals. They will therefore wish to please in this way in order to attract attention. Their desire for individual attention and praise will not be less, perhaps it will be even greater because they receive it more rarely, but the second desire will be there as well, and of great importance for them: the desire to please à deux.

With non-identical twins, if they are not very alike this "interest à deux" will gradually fade as they make contacts on their own and gain interest because of their individual personalities. But with identical twins the similarity in looks and the confusion this creates may make them feel that nothing is personal or unique about them. They have therefore every reason to feel misunderstood, lonely and angry, for they never can be sure that even their own mother is not taking one of them for the other. There is only one person for whom they are unique: that is, their own twin. This situation continues throughout their childhood unless they are separated. This may be one of the determining factors of their close relationship, that is, they turn to each other for certain missing elements in the mother relationship and in all other relationships of their childhood. In a former paper on "Child Analysis and the Mother",[5] this author has stressed the fact that some children are prone to read the unconscious thoughts of their mother. It seems probable that the closeness of the tie in twins enhances this same ability to read each other's thoughts.

I have indicated that it makes an unpleasant impression on twins when they watch the surprise that their appearance causes in other children. They may thus realize that other children value their singleness and may fear the loss of their identity.

On the other hand the great interest and envy shown by brothers, sisters and friends for their twin relationship heightens the value of the latter and to a certain extent makes up for other frustrations.

We have discussed how the parents', especially the mother's, own problems in regard to the twins are a factor in determining the development of twins. The mother's feelings towards her babies and her consequent behavior are powerful influences in the children's lives. Therefore the mother's problems that arise in regard to bearing twins and rearing them are certain to affect them. Whether she feels her twins as a narcissistic injury or a narcissistic pleasure; whether she uses

5. *Psa. Quarterly*, IV, 1935.

them as objects of her exhibitionism or struggles against this tendency, will cause reactions in the children. Her feeling of guilt when she is unable to tell them apart and her resulting inability to identify with them will, similarly, have their repercussions in the personality structure of the twins themselves.

THE PRE-OEDIPAL PHASE IN THE DEVELOPMENT OF THE MALE CHILD

By JEANNE LAMPL DE GROOT, M.D. (Amsterdam)

Not in all phases of the psychoanalytic study of infantile development were data drawn from the analysis of male and female patients equally important. The first insight into neurotic mechanisms in general derived from the treatment of women; in the *Studies in Hysteria* (2) by Breuer and Freud only female patients were described. The case of Dora (3) gave us the first insight into the importance of infantile events for development.

In a later phase, our knowledge of infantile sexuality was gained in the analysis of patients of both sexes. However, more was known about boys than about girls. The growth of the oedipus complex and its relation to the phases of pregenital libidinal development and the early object relation to the mother was first described for the male child, but the parallel processes in the girl remained in the dark for some time. Similarly, the development of the superego as it relates to the termination of the oedipal conflict and the castration threat, was understood as part of the boy's development before the sequence of analogous events in the development of the girl was understood.

Freud's paper, "Some Psychological Consequences of the Anatomical Distinction Between the Sexes" (4), discussed some differences of male and female development and demonstrated that the latter is more complex. The castration complex of the little girl does not obliterate the oedipus complex, but proves to be its forerunner; the content of the castration complex of the girl, the penis envy, pushes the girl into her sexual position as a female. But the earlier history of these developments remained obscure.

At this point, insight into the development of the girl preceded that of the boy: the pre-oedipal phase was first studied in connection with female patients. In 1927 this author (6) tried to point out that the female castration complex, and therefore the normal oedipus complex of the woman, was preceded by a negative oedipal constellation.

In these studies stress was laid on the libidinal development, on the object-relation towards the mother insofar as she is indispensable for the fulfillment of the needs and the desire for love of the child. Freud's study on female sexuality (5) taught us how full of content, how rich and decisive, the pre-oedipal attachment to the mother is in the development of the little girl into womanhood. We have since succeeded in getting more detailed knowledge about this period, both in relation to the id of the little girl and to her ego development. Especially many of the peculiarities of the woman's object-relation and of her adult love life are now better understood.

This paper deals with the influence of the pre-oedipal relation to the mother on the development of the boy, especially from the point of view of the sexual life of the adult male. In approaching this subject we have two sets of expectations. First, as the earliest mother-child relationship is physically as well as mentally, the closest possible between two individuals, traces of it must be found in adult life; and second, the difference in the development of boy and of girl must play its part: the little girl has the more complicated development; she has to abandon her early attachment to the mother in order to develop into womanhood, whereas the boy need not part from his original love object. Hence we may expect that the influence of the pre-oedipal phase on the development of female sexuality may be more decisive and overwhelming than on the development of male sexuality. Yes, we may well expect this influence to be of such importance that its closer study is justified.

All further considerations must start from one insight: the direct development of male sexuality from the infantile oedipal attachment to the mother to the love life of the adult is threatened by the fact that a negative oedipus complex regularly exists in childhood, in addition to the positive one. At one time or other in their development, all boys develop a more or less intense loving attachment towards the father and a more or less intense rivalry with and hostility against the mother. In this position the boys tend to behave in a way similar to little girls in their normal development. The attachment to the father is, as a rule, a passive feminine one; (we can also speak of a homosexual attachment).

The existence of these passive libidinal tendencies must have a pre-history. Our findings indicate that during the pre-oedipal stage of development these passive libidinal tendencies are satisfied by the mother, who at the same time satisfies the boy's active strivings. In normal development these active strivings predominate and the passive ones are subordinated to them; it is well known that they are of great importance in the social adjustment of the normal male. In cases of pathological development, these passive tendencies manifest themselves in three ways. First, they may influence the adult's sexual life as potency disturbances, in the guise of feminine masochistic behavior; or, in extreme cases, they may lead to homosexuality. Second, they may lead to neurotic tendencies. Third, they may cause abnormal character formation.

The analytic exploration of such cases shows that the continuation of the passive relation to the father is due to a fixation in the negative oedipus complex. In prolonged analysis we reach the earlier history of this fixation, and we are able to observe the residues of the original passive attachment to the mother. We may therefore say that the passive feminine relation to the father is with the male a second edition of his primitive passive love relation to the mother, in a similar way as with the girl. The difference is obvious. With the girl, passive attachment falls within normal development; with the boy, it contributes to pathological trends which may later disturb his normal sexuality.

But there is another consequence of the early attachment of the little boy to the mother, which can be of decisive importance. Not only the negative oedipus complex, but also the positive oedipal relation, has its forerunner in the pre-oedipal phase, in the active turning of the little boy towards the mother. A fixation on this stage or a regression to it has equally important consequences in the later development of the boy. His sexual life does not become a truly active and manly one; it rather repeats his early relationship to the mother. Various signs of this relationship can easily be discerned. Its stigmata are the infantile aggressive forms of the object relation, which is less libidinal and more narcissistic, intensely ambivalent, generally fluctuating. When passivity plays a considerable part, potency disturbances may occur. Peculiarities of pregenital libidinal development may be persistent. Oral and anal gratifications may be preferred and may lead to perversion. Males of this type behave like infants, whose love for the mother is egoistic, and claim indulgence of their own needs without respecting the needs of the partner.

A specific form of sexual behavior, the separation between tenderness and sexuality, which Freud first described, now seems easier to understand. Men whose behavior takes this form worship one woman whom they dare not possess as a sexual partner; their sexual partner must always be degraded. Freud explained the genesis of this attitude in the following way: The revered and unreachable woman is the beloved mother; since sexual activity has become degraded through prohibition, and has become bad and dirty through its link to masturbation, the sexual partner has to be a degraded person. We are now in a position to add to this explanation: the admired and honored woman is the mother-image of the period of the oedipus complex. She is the heiress to the great love of little Oedipus for Jocasta. The degraded sexual partner, on the other hand, is heiress to the image of the mother of the pre-oedipal phase; she has inherited the intense hostility that the little boy may have felt for her. That hostility, in turn, partly stems from his early ambivalence toward the mother and partly it is reinforced by the fact that the mother has later become his rival in his love for the father. The adult man can vent his anger against the degraded sexual object; he can mistreat her, can force her to satisfy all his needs and desires, even perverse ones, and can compel her to attend to his wants as he wished his mother to when he was a little boy.

At this point we are confronted with a specific question. How can we differentiate in analysis between the material pertaining to the oedipal and that pertaining to the pre-oedipal period? This differentiation meets with considerable difficulty under certain circumstances. There are two reasons for this. First, all phases of infantile development overlap; second, a subsequent phase of development is always, to a greater or lesser extent, used to suppress residues of previous phases. And yet, in more detailed and precise examination of the material we discover many differences in the way in which the material is brought forth. In some instances even the bodily posture of the patient may be expressive: he may—as was the case with a patient of Paul Federn[1]—actually imitate the posture of the infant.

A young man who had undergone a successful analysis which to a considerable extent had relieved him of his neurotic work inhibitions, came to me several years later because of a potency disturbance. After some months of treatment, during which he gave me an excellent exposition of his case history and of the results of his former treatment, which had revealed the development of his oedipus complex in all details, the patient's behavior in analysis began to change.

During the first period of analysis he spoke easily and fluently, in a clear and loud voice, even when transference difficulties emerged; as for instance, when he was compelled to reexperience his oedipal desires, and also when his transference resistance took other forms. In the second period of

1. New York. Personal communication.

analysis his personality changed completely. He began to behave like an infant; his voice became high and childish. He no longer spoke as an adult does, but uttered incomplete and childish words and sentences. His emotions and his demands changed from one minute to another. He wept like a small child and clamored for my support and my love; the next moment, he shouted and gave vent to most intense hostility. This acting out in transference was amalgamated with bits of primitive fantasies, as ambivalent as we know the emotional life of the infant to be. These fantasies had an extremely passive content: I should handle him, feed him, nurse him and satisfy immediately all his needs. These passive fantasies were interspersed with reaction-formations: aggressive tendencies appeared and a wealth of suppressed anger and hate crystallized into reproaches and accusations. The slightest change in the tone of my voice, or any movement I might make in my chair, was used in order to produce love fantasies or were taken as occasions for outbursts into invectives. The love fantasies expressed oral and anal tendencies, wishes to be nursed and touched, demands for tenderness and for the satisfaction of exhibitionistic needs.

I succeeded only gradually in persuading him that this change was natural and unavoidable. He became interested in the meaning of the change and succeeded in overcoming his narcissistic pride. He thus surrendered to the material which came from deeper layers of the unconscious.

While in analysis his acting out in transference was discussed, the patient occasionally manifested similar behavior patterns in his relationships with female partners. At the time when I represented to him mainly the mother whom, in identification with his father, he wished to love, but whom he was not permitted to possess, he attempted to partly satisfy his pre-oedipal wishes in a relationship with a young girl of lower social status. During the period in which, in the transference situation, his early ambivalent mother attachment was revived, for a short time he turned adoringly to a much older woman of his acquaintance. Thus, for most of the time his transference relationship to me shifted from one extreme to the other. But gradually some historical events began to enter into his awareness: at the age of two he used to sit on his mother's lap in order to make her tell him stories and show him pictures. He spoke of sensations or feelings of warmth and delight, and expressed this in the childish manner that I have tried to characterize above; but he also remembered outbursts of hostility if and when his mother refused to repeat or to prolong situations which held for him heavenly blessings. Memories from this period were scarce. However, the intensity and clarity of repetition in his acting out in the analysis made a convincing impression on both of us. The adult man who consciously had a strong desire to establish a family life was unconsciously seeking a woman who represented to him the pre-oedipal mother and who could revive all the details of his personal experience. Relationships that satisfied these unconscious perverse and hostile tendencies were to a certain extent disgusting to his adult personality. They disturbed the image of the adored mother of the later oedipal situation. It thus became impossible for him to reconcile love and sexuality. He had to prevent himself from marriage and even from potency with an approved sexual partner.

Another type of man who in spite of a normal sexual potency is constantly compelled to search for new women shows a somewhat similar developmental disturbance. Such men, too, have an urgent desire for a quiet family life as a repetition of the infantile family situation; however, they are always forced to exchange one love object for another. They are mostly infantile personalities, fixated in the pre-oedipal phase of development. What they are in search of is always the mother of the pre-oedipal age, the mother who nursed them and towards whom they can behave as the spoiled child does. Either the adult part of their personality is frustrated in its manly aspirations or the infantile part of their personality is dissatisfied in its hopes and expectations. When in marriage a woman is able to fulfill the wishes of both parts of their personality—and this is possible only with women who have strong bisexual tendencies and a high degree of activity—the marriage can be successful. Otherwise divorces and changes of love objects follow each other. Needless to say, in the desires of these men oral and anal components play a considerable role, both directly in sexual behavior and indirectly in the urge to be fed and to be handled like a little child.

The case of another type of man, whom one might call the mysogynist, is similar. Men of this type similarly show fixation points in the pre-oedipal phase; however, more often they have regressed to this phase because of the intensity of castration fear that they could not overcome. During the oedipal phase, in the eyes of the little boy the father is the castrator. In the analysis of this type of patient one discovers that in an earlier phase the boy was regularly extremely afraid of the mother. When he fails to free himself of his fear, he tends to make the mother responsible for it. Those who cannot overcome castration fear are, as a rule, boys whose fear of their own passive tendencies is related to their *wish* to be castrated. Their hostility remains directed toward the mother. She becomes the really hated object. Moreover, it is the woman who reminds these boys of the possibility of "being castrated"; she is feared and hated also because of this.

I should like to mention here a patient who had a good relationship with his wife, she being able to combine in her personality both mother-images, the oedipal and the pre-oedipal one.

The patient came into analysis because of a work inhibition. After some time we discovered transient periods of disturbance in the relation to his wife. In the transference these disturbances expressed themselves in paranoid ideas; this proved to be a repetition of an experience that had occurred in infancy. As a little boy the patient had had a severe infection disease, and because of it had to be hospitalized for several months. During this period he developed the fantasy of being poisoned, so that he did not dare to eat; he remembered an intense hate of his mother, whom he made responsible for his suffering. The acting out in analysis seemed to show that this event was the second edition of an earlier one that had taken place after the birth of a younger sister. The patient was then one-and-a-half years old, and showed the well known reaction of hostility to the unfaithful mother who had weaned him and given her milk to the other child.

Because of his wife's behavior, which enabled the patient to act out the different tendencies towards her, his marriage had not been spoiled. But the patient developed his work inhibition as a substitute means through which to express his conflict.

The influence of the pre-oedipal phase can also be studied in the formation of the superego. Where the sexual development is disturbed the superego has not been consolidated. Traces of both father and mother images can easily be isolated, as well as traces of the identifications that are forerunners of the true superego formation. I intend to discuss this problem in another context.

However, I should like to mention here a case that shows clearly the fluctuation between father- and mother-identification, in the behavior in life as well as in the superego functions.

The patient was a business man, though he had studied to be an engineer. He was nearly forty years old, very successful in his job, married, and the father of three children. The reason he came for analysis was, as he said, an interest in psychology, which time and again forced him to consider the possibility of changing his career. In these periods he wanted to study psychology in order to become a psychotherapist. He himself was astonished about this fantasy because he enjoyed his work. He wanted to establish a business of his own, and knew he would be able to do so.

In his job he sometimes felt very independent. He then had excellent ideas and invented new plans to increase profit which always or nearly always were successful. Thus he was very much appreciated by his superiors. In other periods, he suddenly became inactive and lost his initiative. He then felt very dependent on the attitude of his chief toward himself. He had to watch carefully each remark, each change in the facial expression or voice of the latter, and was very much afraid of losing the chief's appreciation and sympathy.

The patient's history soon showed that this behavior was a repetition of the oedipal relation to his father. The latter, being a rich and a successful business man also, was the patient's example. The patient rivalled and wanted to surpass him; but the moment he was successful he became guilty and had to punish himself by losing success and activity, perhaps even appreciation. He then had to reconcile his chief—father—and so behaved like a good, dependent child. Thus he turned from the rivalling, active, oedipus attitude, to the passive feminine attitude.

So far analysis went the common, well known way. But how explain this suddenly appearing interest in psychological and intellectual problems?

The family history showed that the patient's mother was a person of a cultural level quite different from the father's. Whereas he was a simple, crude, uncomplicated person, she was a fine, nervous woman, sensitive to science and fine arts. The patient's scientific interest derived from an identification with his mother—but not that which related to his passive love for the father. As a very little boy he had understood that his father had no feeling at all for his wife's interests, and in the passive father attachment the patient's psychological aspirations played no role. His intellectual interests derived from an early mother-identification, a primitive form of love attachment to her.

This mother-identification had various different aspects. The mother had been suffering from a severe mental disease, for which she sometimes had to be hospitalized for several weeks or months. The patient was the only person in the family who had any understanding for this illness. As in early puberty he had heard something about psychology and psychoanalysis, he had become interested in it and produced the fantasy of curing his mother by it. However, in this fantasy the mother became the little child who was handled and treated and loved by him. The psycho-therapeutic fantasy obviously was a later edition of very early mother-baby fantasies in which the patient alternatively played the role of the active (loving and aggressive) mother, and the passive child who wants to be handled and loved. These fantasies were revived in detail in an intense acting out in the transference.

For many reasons I cannot here go into further detail. I hope I have succeeded in showing how the active-passive father relation, demonstrated in the patient's business life, was based on a pre-oedipal active-passive mother-attachment, that found its way out in his intellectual, mainly fantastic, interests. The patient's emotional life fluctuated between these two positions, each of them with a double foundation. His ability to identify with the active mother-image was the underlayer of his later oedipus identification with the father, and it led to the normal, manly part of his personality. The residues and continuation of his early passive mother-attachment were partly transferred to a passive father relation, and produced the split in his adult personality.

The superego formation showed similar discord. Traits of both father- and mother-images could easily be found. In his moral attitudes toward others, for example, the patient fluctuated between crude, rough, ruthless conduct on the one hand, and soft, fine, sensitive conduct on the other. However, as mentioned before, I shall discuss these problems in detail elsewhere.

After the completion of this paper in Holland, I had the opportunity to read the interesting paper of Ruth Mack Brunswick, "The Pre-oedipal Phase of Libido Development" (1), in which many similar problems are discussed. Since my own conclusions have been arrived at independently during the war years, I do not try here to discuss Brunswick's paper.

BIBLIOGRAPHY

1. Brunswick, R. M. "The Pre-Oedipal Phase in Libido Development", *Psa. Quarterly, IX,* 1940.
2. Freud, S. and Breuer, J. *Studies in Hysteria,* Ment. Disease Mon., New York, 1936. (Originally, 1895)
3. Freud, S. "Fragment of an Analysis of a Case of Hysteria", *Coll. Papers,* III. (1905)
4. Freud, S. "Some Psychological Consequences of the Anatomical Distinction Between the Sexes", *Int. J. Psa.,* VIII, 1927.
5. Freud, S. "Concerning the Sexuality of Woman", *Psa. Quarterly,* I. 1932.
6. Lampl de Groot, J. "The Evolution of the Oedipus Complex of the Woman", *Int. J. Psa.* IX, 1928.

THE CHILD'S EGO DEVELOPMENT AND THE TRAINING OF ADULTS IN HIS ENVIRONMENT

By MARGARET E. FRIES, M.D. (New York)*

Planned education of the ego is concerned with the impact of life experience upon the individual as he progresses from birth to maturity. Freud frequently stressed the need for broadening and strengthening the ego (13, 14, 15, 16), and in therapeutic psychoanalysis our attention is focused upon problems of the ego and the need for its development. Balint (2) suggests the need for a sound theory and method of education based on a more precise study of the processes involved in strengthening the ego, while French (9, 10) emphasizes the "learning" and "working through" processes during analysis.

Whether the ego will be strong or weak is determined by the type of life experiences it encounters. Obviously, frequent integrating experiences will help the child to build a strong ego and, conversely, repeated indiscriminate exposure to traumatic experiences will hinder ego development (11).

The problem is how to set the stage during infancy and childhood so that the child can progress from the parasitic to the genital level. A solution proposed here is that we administer "doses of life experiences"[1] in such quantity and quality as are appropriate to the physical, intellectual and emotional status of the child.

Adjustments of conditions to meet the physical and intellectual capacity of the child is a common procedure in physical and educational spheres of life. For example, solid foods are not introduced into the infant's diet until he can digest and assimilate them. Similarly, the

---

*Consultant, New York Infirmary for Women and Children.

1. This concept is borrowed from medicine but widened to form a theoretical foundation for ego development.

three R's are taught when the child is intellectually able to absorb them.

Alpert (1) has indicated such a need in formulating learning situations. Hence, more attention should be directed toward introducing the infant and child to life situations only when they are able to respond to them in an emotionally satisfactory way. It is fundamental to ego development that the child should experience achievement with a maximum of pleasure and a minimum of anxiety, and thinking in terms of adjusting conditions for the child, we adopt this as a premise.

Factors Involved in Dosing

The procedures and findings set forth here resulted from psychoanalysis of neurotic adults and children and from a research study of two groups of children attending the New York Infirmary for Women and Children. The study of one group, now ranging between the ages of five and seven, including their families, was begun during the mothers' pregnancy. Study of the other group, now eleven to fourteen years of age, began in the infants' sixth week. Both groups were followed up in the Well Baby Clinic and Children's Clinic.[2]

Before discussing techniques or procedures in "dosing", let us consider the various factors involved in any such application. The analogy of administering a drug prescribed by the physician is a useful one. Just as medicating a child successfully depends on the general physical state of the child, his age, the potency and preparation of the drug, the effect desired and the attitude of the adult who administers' it, so too, dosing life situations depends on somewhat similar factors. Some of these factors are 1) the "Congenital Activity Type" (17)[3], 2) the physical status of the child, 3) his mental capacity, 4) his age, 5) the type of life experiences he undergoes, 6) the effect desired as a result of the experiences, and 7) the adult's attitude toward the child.

1.   Children differ in their Congenital Activity Type. The difference in responses of the quiet, moderately active and active infant have been described in full by the author elsewhere (18, 19). Infants of these three types approach similar situations in a different manner. The active infant responds more actively than the quiet type to all

2. For a critical survey of research see "Margaret E. Fries' Research in Problems of Infancy and Childhood," by Lillian E. Malcove, M.D. *This Annual*, I.

3. "Congenital activity type" refers to a biological quality of activity and not to activity versus passivity, or masculinity versus femininity.

kinds of stimuli, while the reactions of the moderately active type fall between these two. For example, a restriction of movement that is frustrating to the active child may not be so to the quiet child, whereas situations which are real obstacles to the quiet type are easily overcome by the active type.[4]

2.   Dosing life experiences must also take into account the general physical condition of the child. Ruling out birth injury, the more advanced the infant's myelinization is at birth, the greater is his advantage in overcoming obstacles, as for example in sucking on small, hard nipples. He thereby also experiences success with pleasure on this early level more easily than does the infant with less advanced myelinization. By the same token, the older child who has enjoyed good physical health performs more satisfactorily than the child who has suffered many illnesses or operations.

3.   The different mental capacities[5] of children likewise evoke unlike responses to similar situations. The young child with a high I.Q. is probably the most difficult type of child to "dose" because he is, at the same time, intellectually superior and emotionally immature. The problem of how to handle gifted children has been studied at the New York University Special Clinic (44).

4.   The age of the child is another important factor to be reckoned with in "dosing". We accept without question the fact that behavior which is normal for the infant is not appropriate for the adult—for example, oral gratification through thumb-sucking. Yet this principle in reverse, equally valid, is frequently ignored, for many parents and doctors tend to curtail the period of infancy and expect adult-like performance from the young child. This places too great a strain upon the weak and unformed ego. A long time is required for development from the parasitic existence in utero to the mature adult. The other extreme which also hinders ego development— the tendency among parents to prolong childhood—should not be ignored.

5.   Obviously, every type of experience in life cannot be regulated in quantity, quality and precise time sequence. But some experi-

4. Whether the "Congenital Activity Type" also plays a role in the amount of the individual's libido or in its mode of expression cannot as yet be stated. Certainly it has an indirect influence on libidinal attachment through the nursing situation, the success of which is fundamental to future positive libidinal object relationships.

5. The I.Q. and "activity type" are independent factors, since quiet, moderately active and active types may all have the same I.Q.

ences are far-reaching in their effect on total development and therefore require more attention than others. Such are all new experiences and those requiring abandonment of instinctual pleasures for other culturally-acceptable pleasures. They are doubly important when these experiences center around the erogenous zones.

Although birth is usually considered the first new situation for the infant, actually there are earlier intra-uterine changes to which the fetus must adjust (30, 31, 41, 42). Whatever substantially affects the mother's health affects the fetus indirectly. Since the mother's emotional condition influences her physical health, it is important that she be emotionally adjusted to her feminine role. This is also necessary for the establishment of good rapport between patient and obstetrician; and important for reducing to a minimum the traumatic nature of birth, the infant's first major experience.

All new situations following birth can (but do not have to) become obstacles to the child; e.g., the introduction of solid foods, the first day at nursery school, or a first evening party in adolescence. Therefore, as the individual develops physically and intellectually from a parasitic to an independent state, and psychically from an undifferentiated id and object world to one of the finest differentiation, slow and gradual adjustment to the life situation is necessary. Thus success or failure in the earliest oral phase provides the frame of reference for the next experience, and so on, throughout life.

6. No program can proceed without an aim. This aim is determined by the parents and the society. Hence, in dosing life experiences, the adult must be ever cognizant of the effect he wishes the child to attain from the experience, and of the ultimate goal. Since the object of dosing is adjustment to the group, it must vary with the aim of the given society. In our society, with a democratic goal, the dosing should be of such a nature as to contribute to the gradual strengthening of the ego, so that when the individual reaches physiological maturity he will also have attained genital primacy, will be emotionally secure and will function on an adult level.

7. The conscious or unconscious attitudes of the adult who introduces these new situations into the child's world are the most important determinant of the degree of achievement and affect experienced. The child's success or failure in these experiences — his very adjustment to society — depends on this. Books on child care will be of no benefit to parent or child, however, unless the parent is

emotionally mature. For the adult, in rearing children, will do so according to his own personal needs, neurotic or otherwise. There is no traumatic experience, short of catastrophe, that can have a more destructive effect upon the child than a persistently unhealthy emotional climate in the home. Since it is the parent[6] who will do the "dosing" in the earliest years, the first prerequisite for the infants is emotionally mature parents.

Interaction of Adult Attitudes with Dosing Factors

Let us therefore consider how adult attitudes interact with the previously discussed factors involved in dosing children; namely, the congenital activity type, physical condition, mental capacity, age, type of experience and effect to be obtained. From careful study of the interaction of adult with the total child, it becomes clear how early and how completely the adult's attitudes affect the child (5, 20).

1. Concerning the congenital activity type, it has been found that nurses in hospitals caring for newborns variously affect the amount of activity displayed by the infants. The author has observed that when active, compulsive nurses bathed and weighed infants, these infants reacted with more frequent startle responses than when cared for by a more "quiet" nurse. As early as the lying-in period, the mother's preference—not only in regard to the sex and physiological characteristics of the child, but also in regard to its congenital activity type— plays a role in her emotional attitude toward him. This attitude influences her contact with the child, who experiences varying amounts of gratification or anxiety. For instance, many adults are ambivalent toward the child who has a quiet congenital activity type; they are pleased with him because he is "good", but are irritated by his slow approach to and solving of problems (21).[7]

The quiet child, slow to change from one activity to another in approaching and solving obstacles—neuromuscular, social or mental— evokes a feeling of irritation in many adults. Americans evaluate highly the "go-getter" and feel disappointed when their child fails to measure up to this cultural goal. Often the adult will incorrectly attribute such

6. Although parents are in the strategic position, all other adults who have contact with the child before the latency period need to be emotionally mature. The closer this contact is, the more important is emotional maturity in the adult. In this article, references to the parent also apply to the parent-surrogates.

7. It is thought by the author that probably a serious inadequacy in the emotional environment from birth, if sustained in combination with a pathological hypo- or hyperactive congenital activity type of child, may contribute to future psychoses.

behavior to a low I.Q. instead of to the quiet congenital activity type. Such was the case with the mother of eight-year-old Jean; experiencing frustration and impatience over the child's slow, considered responses, the mother frequently coaxed her to proceed at a faster rate than was possible for the child's biological type, while at other times the mother would simply take over and function for her. This forcing and inconsistency in dosing created a weak ego.

On the other hand, there are parents who respond unfavorably to an active child, but for many different reasons. Mrs. J., eager not to curtail her child's activity, found she became physically exhausted when her baby, at eight months, crawled all over the house; at thirteen months, pushed over the lamps and all sorts of bric-a-brac; and at nineteen months had to be constantly watched and followed to be kept off the highway. Mrs. J. sadly admitted that she would be so exhausted and at such a loss as to how to safeguard her child that she would lash out at him and, at times, unnecessarily curtail him. This active child, as many others, achieved success despite the restraint and disapproval of the environment. A common problem for the active child, however, is the development of guilt with success. The practical implications derived from the study of these congenital activity types are that the needs of each group will vary, that the attitude of the environment must differ toward each group, and that the future character traits and neuroses will vary.

2.   The parent's attitude toward the child's physical condition—both in illness and health—can be either salutary or detrimental. The condition of well-being is frequently overlooked as capable of creating an affect-state, but is nevertheless important, especially in childhood when the goal is to foster optimum health. Through the advances of modern medicine and education, parents are increasingly aware of the importance of the physical well-being of their children, not only at a given period of life, but for the future. Tremendous libidinal cathexis is directed toward the child's health, and guilt with ensuing resentment is experienced by parents when the child deviates from a set standard. Unfortunately, the child's well-being is too often considered by the mother to be a reflection on her care.

The usual childhood infectious diseases often restrict the normal activities of the entire family. Some families take this as part of child-rearing, while others chafe and rebel at such inconveniences. Influenced by the adult's attitude, children frequently experience illness as a punishment for disobedience, while others obtain gratification through their state of dependence and passivity, sometimes desiring to prolong convalescence and its attendant rewards. These affects experienced with illness are the groundwork for future psychosomatic involvements, passive personality traits, and unpreparedness for life situations.

Emotionally mature attitudes are of decisive importance in enabling children to surmount traumatic physical experiences. In the case of John, aged four, who lost a leg in an automobile accident, the parents accepted the tragedy realistically. Recognizing it as a great misfortune, but one to be overcome in every way possible, they obtained professional advice and treatment, both medical and psychiatric. The child's success (as evidenced by his adolescent adjustment in college) in overcoming this experience stands in marked contrast to the prolonged crippling resulting from a fractured leg in the case of Tom, aged five. His family was offered the same opportunities for adjustment as was John's, but the emotional maladjustment of the mother prevented her cooperation. The mother had been lame since childhood, and was decidedly masochistic; and the boy, who had grown masochistic and passive by identification, limped exactly as she did for many months after his fracture had healed.

3. Frequently parents confuse a smart baby with an active one, or a quiet baby with a dull one. It must be borne in mind that the expression of the intellect and the congenital activity type both contribute to the total personality structure. If this does not accord with the parents' own personal ambition for their child they often create unnecessary problems. For instance, most American parents desire their child to excel in the group and feel frustrated when he does not. The narcissistic parent of Elisa, a very clever child, constantly stimulating her further, would say: "You only got a B. Why not an A, as last term?" This ambitious parent exerted greatest pressure in the intellectual realm, but naturally, the same attitude pervaded all phases of the child's activity. In high school Elisa became a complete failure and went into a severe depression. In contrast, however, Anna, a low-average child, succeeded in achieving C—D marks and managed to pass every grade because she was completely accepted by her parents. This realistic acceptance of Anna's limitations by her parents would erroneously be interpreted as "neglect" by many parents.

4. Adults also direct their emotional attitudes or preferences toward different age levels of life. Such predilections stem from a combination of their own particular development with the customs of the time. Culture influences child-rearing patterns. as has been

shown in recent studies (3, 28, 35, 36). Parental attitudes toward the child are dictated by custom and may be consistent from birth or varied with the birth of another sibling, at different age levels, or in new situations (such as going to school, etc.). However, no matter what the cultural direction may be, the individual adult applies this pattern according to his own psychic requirements. The pattern will be satisfactory if the parents are emotionally adjusted, but the expression of neurotic needs displays itself in a desire to prolong or curtail a specific phase of the child's life. Regardless of the neurotic motivation of the parent, the effect is either too much or too little gratification at any given age level.

For example, Mrs. A. responded in typical fashion to each stage of her child's development. She unconsciously tried to' prolong first the infancy and then the childhood of her daughter, as if to delay the maturing of her personality. Unhappy and unpopular in her own adolescence, Mrs. A. became apprehensive when her eleven-year-old daughter began to menstruate, for this reactivated emotions experienced during her own adolescence. This mother, who was governed by neurotic motivation, had not exposed the girl to reality in amounts that would strengthen the child's ego.

The reverse—curtailment of the infantile gratification—is also an expression of the parent's personality. Until recently cultural pressure, transmitted through the medical profession and child guidance literature, has reinforced this trend. Even now a few authorities still urge starting habit training at two weeks of age and discontinuance of the bottle at about eight to ten months.

In order to study the effect of early and late habit training on the development of the total child, a study was conducted (1934) in the Well Baby Clinic at the New York Infirmary for Women and Children (21). One group of mothers was instructed to begin habit training at six months. Despite instructions to the contrary, the compulsive mothers in this group, as well as the other group, insisted upon instituting early habit training. The study showed that any attempt to correlate age at which habit training was started with later personality traits, without consideration of the mother's personality type, would involve a large factor of error.

5. The conscious and unconscious attitude of the adult toward each experience of the child influences the latter's attitudes toward these and other similar experiences along specific lines. The younger

the child, the more does this premise hold, for the infant is entirely dependent upon the environment for his achievement and its associated affect. The infant and child can cry, can call attention to his discomfort; but the amount of tension released depends largely on the wishes of the adult in the environment.

For instance, Mrs. S., who enjoyed nursing, cuddled her child and saw that he grasped the nipple. This child satisfied its hunger easily, completely and with great libidinal pleasure. A very different situation was experienced by Mary, whose mother disliked nursing intensely, terming it "animal-like". Thus Mary achieved satisfaction of hunger despite her mother—but with little or no libidinal gratification. The mother's emotional state in nursing may affect the infant not only directly but also indirectly, since it influences the flow of breast milk.

Clinical investigations prove conclusively that the mother's conscious and unconscious attitude is conveyed to the infant directly through everything she does for him. The Film Studies, a permanent record of Integrated Development Research (22), are invaluable in illustrating the importance of the mother's handling of the child, not only during nursing, but also in undressing, holding, tucking him in, etc. Her fingers, arms and voice produce comfort or discomfort. Anna Freud and Dorothy Burlingham (12) definitely show that kinesthetic sensations play an important role in the infant's development. In the nursery where children have to find substitute mothers, the bodily contact of child with parent-surrogate is an important part of adjustment to the new situation. Furthermore, the mother's attitude to the situation per se helps to mold the child's attitude. Experiments conducted by Escalona (8) on babies under four months further reveal the manner in which the "doser's" preference for foods influences the infant's preference.

As the child grows older and moves about more, many parents, consciously or unconsciously, and for very different reasons, tend to hinder certain activities important to the child's development. For example, Mrs. Y., out of anxiety for her child's safety, and narcissistic Mrs. C., to protect her furniture, checked their four-year-old's repetitious neuromuscular activity, such as climbing up and down furniture and steps, opening and closing doors, and turning on and off electric switches and radios.

In like manner, vocal activity with its accompanying satisfaction is frequently checked by the adult's laughter at the child's repetition and pronunciation of words, the meaning of which he may not fully understand. A later manifestation of this is frequently seen in analyses, wherein the patient expresses anxiety that the analyst will laugh at him. Of course this is not the only reason for such a reaction.

The adult's emotional attitudes toward the erogenous zones influences the manner in which he physically handles the child's organs in washing and dressing, and later on, in answering the child's questions about these parts.

Thus Mrs. Q., who dreaded each act of coitus for fear of impregnation and the pain of childbirth, yet felt that in accordance with modern parent education she must answer her four-year-old child's question about childbirth, explained: "Having a baby doesn't hurt at all. Don't believe when others say it is the worst pain. You see, they give you something to breathe, just like when your tonsils are taken out, and you don't feel anything, for you sleep." It is not surprising that this child expressed her conflict in a sleeping problem.

The recent practice of advising parents to answer their children's questions about sex instead of evading them, is not meeting with uniformly satisfactory results. For here, as in all of life, the parents' own embarrassment or disapproval colors the manner and content of the information given.

6. Although the parents of one community or nation may believe they are striving toward a similar goal for their children, the paths selected for its achievement are highly diverse, and do not always lead to the desired goal. In the United States most parents would state without qualification the wish that their children develop into happy adult citizens, living in independence and freedom under a democratic form of government. Prominent in the American ideal is the concept of rugged individualism which, however, is interpreted by the parents according to their own emotional needs.

Parents who are themselves emotionally mature promote total integrated development in their children. Such children, on reaching adulthood, are able to think objectively without being prejudiced by unconscious infantile conflicts; act in cooperation with a group, instead of acting as isolated individuals; respond to situations appropriately (i.e., if there is real danger, they develop a realistic anxiety which will lead neither to neurotic hypo- nor hyperactivity, but to a constructive solution); abandon wishful thinking and are prepared when danger is imminent.

The other and opposing pattern of individualism, neurotically determined, is unfortunately practised by a great number of adults. They are able only to give lip-service (although they may consciously wish to do otherwise) to the democratic concept, because they have themselves never reached emotional maturity. Their thinking is colored by their emotions, which prevent them from feeling or expressing genuine cooperation.

"The price we pay for rugged individualism is individual neurosis," according to Roy Graham Hoskins.[8] Observation supports this view. Parents who are rugged individualists are often dictators within their homes, while demanding that their children practise true democratic behavior. This double standard—one for the child, another for the adult — creates confusion for the weak growing ego as to the nature of reality. For instance, it is demanded of each child that he cooperate, be honest, be kind to his siblings; while the adult—the rugged individualist—competes aggressively with others in business, tries to avoid paying taxes, and often measures kindness to others solely in terms of direct personal gain. Childhood experiences in such a family do not prepare the child for adult life in a democratic community.

Parents who are limited by the emotional need to be dictators develop anxiety and envy toward their children when the latter show signs of achieving the healthy individualism consciously desired, perhaps, but emotionally rejected by the parents themselves. Such adults then become more rejecting and place ever greater obstacles in the way of the child's achieving emotional maturity. One matriarchal mother who acted and thought for her children expressed the end result of her training most adequately, although she did not see the connection. "All the children are becoming lazier," she said. "They do as little as possible to get by with their parents, teachers, and the world. They have no idea of doing things such as learning for themselves."

As seen above, the parents are the transmitters of the culture. They transmit the institutions in a manner which conforms to their own personality needs. Nevertheless, the culture per se does play a role in the content of what is transmitted.

To summarize: Fostering ego development in the growing infant and child requires emotionally mature adults. One of the greatest

8. From a Salmon Memorial lecture, read at the Academy of Medicine, New York, 1945.

sources of danger to the child is emotionally immature parents, for such parents respond with envy as well as gratification to each step of satisfactory development. This in turn increases their ambivalence toward the child, thereby placing constant obstacles in the way of the achievement of his aim.

Dosing the Child Through the Adult

In view of the foregoing implications, it is important that we reach the parents before the infant can be exposed to such harmful influences. In other words, if we are going to dose life experiences, we must prepare the "doser" to do the job well.[9] Obviously, the most propitious time for this is during the mother's first pregnancy. The mother's total personality affects the fetus. Mothers who are emotionally mature in accepting their feminine role usually feel very well during the pregnancy, may even be happier, more content, and enjoy a greater sense of well-being than previously. But all mothers who feel well need not necessarily be emotionally adjusted. One extreme psychopathic borderline case appeared to the obstetrician to be better adjusted and happier during pregnancy than through her entire life. She followed his orders to take good care of herself, to an exaggerated degree, and thoroughly enjoyed the secondary gains. She refused psychiatric treatment and the obstetrician could not be convinced of the seriousness of the case until she tried to do away with the child at one year of age.

Some pregnant women express their conflict in organic symptoms such as fatigue or in digestive disturbances which may become so severe that they may be mistakenly diagnosed as organic pernicious vomiting (23). In one known case, several abortions had previously been performed, but finally, with psychiatric help, the patient was able to carry through to a full-term pregnancy. Many patients report greater fetal motility when they are emotionally disturbed. What effect this has on the post-natal activity pattern and general development of the infant cannot be stated as yet.

During pregnancy, especially the first, the mother is usually interested in the experience ahead, and has none of the feeling of inadequacy or guilt attached to rearing a child; therefore, she does not have to be on the defensive and is decidedly accessible. Factual information on

9. The procedures to be described have all been tried out by the author with varying degrees of success, both in private practice and clinic practice.

the emotional needs of the child should go hand in hand with education concerning its physical and mental development. This type of prophylactic preparation which gives the parent *insight* into the emotional, as well as the physical and intellectual needs of the child, I have called Preparatory Treatment, in contradistinction to a purely intellectual education concerning the child's needs. Begun during the mother's first pregnancy, this Preparatory Treatment (18) of the parent should continue all through the child's developing years until he reaches maturity.

It is one thing for parents to be intellectually aware of the facts of child development, and another for them to accept these facts emotionally. This is constantly observed in patients during analysis. The problem of how to present the facts becomes one of technique. The author has found that certain psychoanalytic procedures, when modified, can be applied in preparing parents, with satisfactory results. This should in no way be construed as implying brief analysis or an adaptation of analysis, but merely the borrowing of certain analytical concepts to help the parent emotionally to accept and therefore, apply unconsciously the principle of "dosing".

The technique of transference, as in analysis, is the most important tool.[10] It is thus important to establish a positive transference as early as possible, and to sustain the relationship. It is through this positive transference that the parents experience the child-authoritarian relationship in a positive way, in some cases for the first time in their lives.

It is essential that all the relationships of professional workers to parents be as satisfactory as the desired parent-child relationship, in order to enable the carrying out of a constructive program. For through their transference to the obstetrician and pediatrician, the parents experience a relationship to the doctor (the authority of parent-surrogate) which they then mirror in their relationship to the child. There is great need for the physician to realize his role of both medical adviser and parent-surrogate, so that he understands that his own emotional needs should not interfere with the successful execution of this dual role.

Parents also identify with the attitudes expressed in publications. This is being recognized and utilized more frequently. For example, when the New Jersey Department of Health revised its dental pamphlet it also made the phraseology less compulsive. Those in

10. Negative transference would not, however, be productive here, as it is in analysis.

authority indirectly influence the children's lives through the type of relationship they establish with parents or guardians directly handling the child. It is therefore important to help all the adults through a community plan (24). The expert cannot always stand ready to tell the parents exactly what to do in every instance, but he can help them to understand concepts which they can then apply in their own fashion, in their own particular set-up. Here again is a situation parallel to the psychoanalysis of adults. The analyst helps the patient work out his own emotional problems, but it is the patient who handles each reality situation according to his own personality.

Continued help depends upon sustaining the transference relationship. Where this technique has been used in the clinic, one parent expressed herself as follows: "I like to come here, even though there is no quiet room to talk to the doctor and we have to sit on the stairway. She is such a *lady* that it makes a difference." She experienced her pleasure in her identification with the physician—*lady* being her ideal goal.

Another mother who had derived great benefit from psychotherapy identified herself strongly with the Research Study Project. She desired to give birth to her second child in the same hospital even though such a plan involved a three-hour trip for each visit. She felt it would help the research findings as well as herself.

The process of identification not only with the authority (research workers), but also with the experience of other parents of the research group, was utilized to decrease the patients' resistance to the fact of early sexuality. Observations on sexual development related by other mothers whose children had been delivered in the same hospital in which a later group was confined, gained in significance through these parents' identification with their predecessors. Under such conditions they were told that the majority of these children (including those whose study provides the basis of this article) asked their first sex questions between the ages of two and two-and-a-half, that they were either "Where do babies come from?" or "What is the difference between a girl and a boy?" It was further indicated that when these questions were evaded, repression of later ones usually took place, and children never asked further ones; and the parents gained a false idea that the child was uninterested, naive, or "clean-minded". Pointing out the fallacy of such thinking and the past mistakes of earlier parent-patients provided a stimulus for their further thinking along these lines. Through identification with the entire research group, they could accept and report similar questions of their own children as they matured. These mothers found it increasingly possible to work out more of their own anxieties that would otherwise have inhibited them in their relationship with their developing children. Preparatory Treatment of the parents should, as indicated above, continue throughout the child's developing years until he reaches maturity. As in analysis, the elements of time and coincidental life experiences play a role in the patient's accessibility to interpretation.

It was found, moreover, that mothers were more willing and felt freer to discuss sexual matters during the pregnancy and lying-in period than at other times, thus rendering these periods ideal for superficial psychotherapy. The mother could be helped with her own sexual problems, and simultaneously could be given preparatory treatments concerning what she may expect in terms of her child's sexual development. With the New York Infirmary Group, preparatory treatment rather than education was emphasized, for the aim was to reach the parents not only on the intellectual level but on the emotional level as well.

Just as in analysis of parents the child's behavior is analyzed in reference to the parent's emotional life, so too, it is important that the factual data concerning child development be discussed in relation to its significance to the parent. The physician needs to shift his orientation from one of physician for the child to that of physician for the parent. Furthermore, the parent's feelings of frustration and guilt can be somewhat relieved so that they can carry out their parental functions more adequately. Through the conviction that they, too, are recipients of the doctor's attention they will not be as envious of the attention bestowed on the child, will adopt a positive attitude toward the child, and will follow more effectively the doctor's suggestions in regard to dosing.

A child does not grow up in vacuo but within the family, and later in an ever-widening world of adults. The more the emotional needs of all the family members approximate satisfaction, the more successful will be the dosing. For if dosing starts on a satisfactory keel for the child and not for the parents, the latter soon become resentful, hostile and envious, and thus incapable of continued favorable dosing. This is true of many families when rearing their first-born. They make a good start but cannot sustain it.

Encouraging "free association", as in analysis, is another device which with modification can be used successfully. When the parent comes for help in child care, for instance, instead of asking direct questions the interviewer can ask for the child's daily routine. This indirect method avoids placing the mother on the defensive, in attempting to show that she has obeyed the doctor's printed órders. Free of anxiety and guilt, she unconsciously reveals her own way of handling the child, which provides a clue to her inner adjustment. A practical advantage of this method is that it requires relatively little skill, so that in clinics one can utilize workers who are not highly specialized in the field of psychoanalysis.

After the physician has diagnosed the parent's emotional condition, a decision can be made as to which of the parent's problems are important to "work through". Such working through, although very superficial, may frequently provide sufficient emotional release and alleviate enough anxiety-producing misconceptions to permit her to function better as a parent.

Three important misconceptions concerning the "parent ideal" can be introduced to parents, especially during the mother's first pregnancy: (1) that the parent should never feel hostility toward his own child, (2) that the parent should be infallible, as well as omnipotent, and (3) that the parent should "sacrifice until it hurts". None of these are, of course, founded on a realistic understanding of human nature. As long as the parents struggle to achieve this kind of "ideal" parenthood they are in conflict with themselves. They then rationalize that their children are the cause of their failure and project their inner conflict onto their relationship with the children. As one parent expressed it: "As long as we had no children, I was happy and could be a perfect wife. The trouble started when the children were born." If parents can be helped—even on the conscious level alone—to give up these false parent-ideals, they will have more opportunities to experience achievement and gratification, which will improve their relationship with their children.

The problem of hostility, whether in the parent versus the child or the child versus the parent, is repugnant to all parents. Parents put up every defense mechanism available before accepting insight on this point. Many show great antagonism when reading pamphlets on child care. In practice we hear repeatedly, "This new-fangled psychology is all wrong. How could I reject my own baby?"—or, "That my child dislikes me!—he really doesn't mean what he says when he is in a tantrum cursing me."

The idea of ambivalence[11] can be presented more successfully than rejection in a very simple form, such as: "Of course you love your child, but there are times when you are irritated since you are human and all human beings sometimes feel this way." One etiological factor of ambivalence can be simply formulated as follows: "Everyone at times objects to being grown up, with adult responsibilities, and would like to be a child and to be taken care of. Therefore, it is natural at times for parents to feel envious of their own children, who are the recipients of the care and attention that they themselves would like to have." The idea of wanting occasionally to be the child seems to be acceptable to most adults and, with this understanding, they can grasp the implied connotations and become relieved of some guilt and anxieties stemming from their ambivalence. Moreover, it often helps to decrease parental resistance and improve transference, and, lastly, provides a valuable concept that can be referred to later as the child grows older without arousing too much resistance.

There still remains the practical problem of how to help neurotic parents to not vent hostility felt toward their children or at least to divert it. Short of analysis, no satisfactory therapy has been developed, although there are those who feel that application of some of the child-rearing concepts practised in other cultures might help. For instance, the ceremonials in some societies provide outlets for parental aggression, while our society has built a system of defenses that attempt to negate the existence of parental hostility. In the initiation rites of some societies the immediate parents play a protective role, while other adults disguised as "gods" perform the punitive acts of the ceremonial (28). In others the parents themselves act out the hostility. But whether a separation of function exists or not, this aggression stems from the parental need to gratify ambivalent feelings toward the child. In contrast, the ceremonial occasions peculiar to western civilization accord large doses of love to the child periodically (e.g., birthday, Christmas, Easter, during illnesses), while only two—Hallowe'en and April Fools' day—maintain vestiges of their original aggressive character. Considerations of this sort require further inquiry, since they pose the following problems: (1) Can parents release their hostility at certain periods and thus experience less ambivalence at other times? If this is the case, (2) which is less traumatic for the child; that he experience hostility mingled with love

11. The word "ambivalence" is more accurate than "rejection" and is found to be more acceptable since it embraces the positive attitude as well.

persistently, as in our culture, or experience it in large doses, as in the former?

The expression of the concept of omnipotence displays itself not only in attitudes of "Do this because your parents know best," or "Your parents are your best friends," but also in sustaining the myth of goodness, as in the Santa Claus tradition. This places an unnecessary struggle between parent and child. The parents continuously strain to prove their position of infallibility which realistically cannot be done. The children feel deceived by the loved objects and develop a distrust of them and of others.

Many adults feel that to be "good" parents they must sacrifice until it hurts. Mothers like Mrs. B. completely restrict their activities to the realm of the home "so as to be with the children". They give up such emotional gratifications as going out with their husbands, seeing friends and making trips, but afterwards resent it. Mrs. B., emotionally unable but quite able financially to procure adequate care for her children, never left them for an entire day, although it was frequently urgent for her to accompany her husband on business trips. Or, parents frequently try to give their children opportunities which they can financially ill-afford, such as costly extra-curricular activities. In such a situation there is ample possibility for parents to develop increasing resentment and the child to develop greater feelings of guilt. These attitudes then block the child from emotionally absorbing the so-called privileges.

The parents of one adolescent girl sent her to a private school and wanted her to mingle socially with children who had far greater opportunities because of their economic status. Although they wanted her to go to dances, there was tremendous haggling about how they could buy a dress or how they could reciprocate socially in any way. The parents' ambivalence expressed in this monetary way increased the adolescent's hostility and guilt to such an extent that it hampered her seriously in making social contacts.

As important as it is for the child to have the opportunity for new experiences, the idea that the exposure to new situations, per se, is a cure for anxiety or phobia is a fallacy. Many adults think that nursery schools or camps are profitable for all children, regardless of their own motivation in sending them, the manner in which they do it, and the state of the child's emotional development.

Going away to camp entails all the anxieties about new situations, in addition to the relinquishment of gratification in the home environment. While important in the development of most children, it is not equally beneficial for all. Because of the repetition compulsion, the child who is already a behavior problem frequently will convert the situation into one which fulfills his neurotic needs. This unfortunately leads not only to an unhappy experience but also increases the feeling of frustration and inadequacy for both child and family. Similarly, changing of schools for the problem child may only serve to increase his state of anxiety and inadequacy, unless, of course, the new school can modify its program to meet the needs of the child. Many private schools in the past have felt that this should be part of their contribution. However, with the increased demand for private schools, they are rejecting more of the problem children, or accepting them only if they receive psychiatric treatment and show signs of improvement. Planned public programs designed to provide adequate therapeutic assistance to problem children would help immeasurably in ensuring their development into healthy adult citizens.

After clearing up some of these misconceptions by the method described, superficial though it may be,[12] we may hope for an improvement in the emotional adjustment of the parent and an orientation which enables the dosing of the child's life experience to proceed more successfully. Since guidance of the parents is continuous, help should be provided before the problematic situations occur. One cannot, of course, anticipate all the needs of the child, and parents can only be prepared for typical groups of situations rather than for specific ones, or only be given insight into general child-rearing concepts. For instance, parents may be advised in advance that the developing child often cannot tolerate more than one new situation at a time. Therefore, where possible, it is important to regulate the time of dosing to meet both the emotional and physical needs of the child; for example, the timing of a tonsillectomy so that it does not coincide with the birth of a sibling.

It can be explained how the adult's attitude and affect in dosing may modify favorably or unfavorably the child's activity pattern; that the adult need not be disturbed if the child at any one period of life exhibits a modified pattern to a learned situation, but an original pattern to new situations and obstacles—a phenomenon seen constantly in analysis. One mother of a fourteen-month-old, moderately active toddler found that if she left her child in the nursery while she was busy in the kitchen, the infant would crawl and run around the rest

12. Where indicated, deep psychotherapy should be applied.

of the apartment. As this involved physical danger for the uncoordinated toddler, the mother tried closing the nursery door, but this elicited screaming on the child's part. Next, she tried keeping the nursery door open but, without calling attention to it, quietly placed an obstacle in the doorway; at this the child threw itself repeatedly against the obstacle in the doorway and screamed even more violently. Since the mother did not want to follow the grandmother's advice to "Let the child cry it out and be done with the annoyance in a few days," (feeling that the result would be obtained at the expense of violating the infant's personality) she tried placing her in the long-discarded play pen and left the nursery door open. The child was happy and the mother relieved.

The reasons for the toddler's satisfaction at being placed in the play pen were undoubtedly complex; presumably the emotional affect accompanying the mother's actions played a significant part, as did the offerings of a "permissive" environment, in contradistinction to the blocked doorway. Furthermore, the child may have felt more secure in a limited, familiar space, just as newborns often stop crying when they are bound tightly by being tucked in blankets. Significant to our discussion of changes in the displayed activity pattern is the fact that this infant showed in her first months of life a quiet to moderately active pattern but, through environmental stimulation, had been precipitated into activity which superficially made her appear to be an active child. Once given the opportunity to function according to her own biological type, the child quieted down through the removal of an anxiety-producing stimulus. This case further illustrates the need for ingenuity on the part of parents in dosing their children.

Parents should first solve their own anxiety concerning a coming event, either traumatic or normal, so that they may give the child adequate support and help him to overcome his fears. An example of preparation through anticipation may be seen in the case of a mother who through several psychiatric interviews was partially relieved of her apprehension that her child would bleed to death during an operation. After her fears were somewhat allayed she was able to give the child support, rather than increase his anxieties. Additionally she received insight into her need for deeper psychiatric treatment.

Parents can also be informed that initiative and leadership in childhood may be increased or decreased. In fact, as soon as the infant is capable of exerting some voluntary control over his upper extremities, he can be encouraged to cooperate in holding the bottle or the mother's hand that is feeding him, or grasping the spoon for the cereal, rather than be bound down with the bib and blanket so as not to mess. Later, when he is in the crawling or runabout stage, one may hold a ball for the child to take, rather than put it into his hands. Thus one can encourage him either to be active and a participant, or to be passive and a recipient, with very little initiative. Such examples are typical ones for the small child, but the principle is the same, regardless of the child's age or whether the situation pertains to the physical, intellectual or emotional realm.[13]

Work with the New York Infirmary research group proved it definitely possible to prevent development of physiological problems in the child, by utilizing the Preparatory Treatment for the parents. (18). With very little direct help, the children's ego development was good. The frequent secondary rejection, based upon difficulties in feeding and establishing habits of cleanliness was obviated, thereby improving parent-child relationship. Although physiological difficulties can be avoided through this prophylactic approach, it is not possible to prevent the development of undesirable character traits if the parents are very neurotic. This requires deep psychotherapy of the parents. In cases outside the clinic group where one or both parents were analyzed while the child was still in the pre-oedipal situation, results were most favorable and considerably better than when the child was older. In the latter situation child psychotherapy or analysis had to be resorted to in addition to parental treatment.

Dosing the Child Directly

Just as it is necessary to diagnose the parent's emotional condition before treatment, so too, the child's behavior must be diagnosed if he is to be successfully dosed. Naturally, the younger the child, the easier it is to diagnose (18). In addition to the physical, neurological and intellectual examinations, psychiatric interviews and observations of behavior in the clinic, at home and at play are carried out as the child grows older. Other tests based on the principles involved in the Oral Test (17, 20) for the lying-in period have been devised to follow the child's responses to the Presentation, Removal and Restoration of an Object of Gratification (27).

---

13. One mother, to encourage clarity of thought in her child, presented him with problems in abstract thinking. This was accompanied with great encouragement and praise for success. It is too early to report the outcome of this procedure.

Prognostication for the next six months to a year, based on all the diagnostic factors, makes it possible to decide what type of help to give the child, i.e., either indirectly through the parents, or directly to the child.

It is especially helpful for parents who are in analysis to have an occasional educational hour with a child analyst. Nor is their analysis interfered with—rather, it is stimulated. The child derives a double benefit during its critically important formative years, for instead of waiting until the parent's analysis is completed (when much damage to his ego can already have been done) he has the advantage of a planned program of ego development while the parents undergo their analysis.

Just as with the parents, help to the child can be of the intellectual or emotional type and may be given before, during or following a situation. For example, tonsillectomy, as any operation, may be a real traumatic experience to both parent and child. It is an advantage to help both to face it so that the trauma will be minimized as fully as possible.

It was found in this study that enactment of the preparation and procedure for the coming tonsillectomy in play form serves as a splendid medium for the child to become acquainted with the reality that confronts him, and simultaneously permits him to "work through" some of his anxiety. The anxiety of the operation for most children is increased by fear of leaving home and parents for the first time. The enactment of the entire experience with dolls, starting with the trip to the hospital and continuing through each detail (e.g., farewell to parents, enema, omission of breakfast, taking of temperature, anesthetization, operative and post-operative treatment, etc.) minimizes the child's fear of the reality situation and his neurotic anxiety. Through this all-inclusive play approach, initiated anywhere from one to two months prior to the operation, the child is better able to tolerate the operation. This preparation was given to Ruth, aged five, who cooperated thoroughly before the operation, until a towel was put over her eyes, previous to anesthesia. She became panicky until the anesthetist explained that she was protecting Ruth's eyes from ether. Post-operatively, the child commented that in the play preparation this one item had been omitted in her case, an interesting clue to her neurotic problem and what she had repressed.

Anxiety associated with a traumatic event certainly can be partially alleviated, but more difficult to prevent is the anxiety associated

with small daily life situations which accumulates and never is released. In adult analysis, patients frequently report how they were
tricked into going to the hospital for a tonsillectomy and then lost
confidence in their parents. That such recollections are cover screens
is seen in their analysis and substantiated in observations of children
during their growth. For then it becomes evident that these individuals
experience similar affects daily which they repress, only retaining those
memories centered around one big traumatic event. Such was the
case when the parents of Frances tried by deception to get her to do as
they wished. She was constantly tricked into eating certain foods by
the father who pretended he was Uncle Don talking over the radio.
When the child was to go to the dentist, the family said he would not
pull out her loose tooth. When she went to the hospital for a tonsillectomy, she was told instead that she was going to a hotel for a
vacation. By five, this child who experienced deception in practically
all of her activities, tried to handle her distrust and hostility towards
her parents by displacing it onto all physicians and dentists.

The concurrent-play-approach can be used in dosing for example,
when the child becomes a "dental patient" for the first time. The first
visit should be only an orientation visit, getting acquainted with the
dentist, the dental chair, the instruments (25), or perhaps watching the
mother in the role of patient and gaining assurance through identification. At the New York Infirmary the dentist gave the children their first
examination in the playground instead of in her clinic. The value of
such dosing by the clinic was obvious, and subsequent visits found
the child much more willing to cooperate.

The question arises: Is this not "spoiling" children, making them
"soft"? Won't they respond only to situations that are agreeable? This
danger exists if the principle of dosing—bringing the child to cope
with reality—is not used correctly. Any valuable therapy, if misused,
can be harmful. Naturally one cannot be too timid in dosing new situations or the child will have no opportunity to come in contact with the
world he must learn to live in. He should not be unduly shielded from
any kind of life situation, painful or pleasurable, but the exposure
should be commensurate with those factors inherent in the child, as
previously discussed.

Analysis of neurotic adults clarifies this point. Patients slowly
attempt new things, gradually daring to increase their experiences.
In fact, they, and not the analyst, govern their dosing, for it parallels
their emotional maturing. This latter point would also hold true for

children, if adults could permit the growing child more freedom in dosing himself. Davis' experiment (4) showed that children chose a well-balanced diet when offered a choice of foods. In the Well Baby Clinic it was found that infants regulated their own feeding schedule, changing from every three to every four hours and omitting the night feeding (21). Allowing the child to dose himself as far as possible, according to his own needs, offers him the opportunity to achieve with maximum pleasure and minimum anxiety and helps him to meet reality more successfully.

Problems of daily life—emotional, economic, social, etc., must be handled realistically. For instance, a little boy, aged nine, did not understand why his parents were so silent and sad at a particular time. He felt excluded and became hyper-sensitive and restless. When the parents told him that his brother had been killed in the war, he burst into tears, but said, in a tone of great relief: "Now I know what the trouble is; I'm not the cause. I can cry with you." Another nine-year-old was briefly told of the family's limited financial resources, and the sacrifice the situation would entail. He thus derived greater strength from being accepted as a responsible member of the group in meeting the new situation. Exclusion of the boy would have acted as a double trauma to his developing ego; first, through misinterpretation of the actual state of affairs and not being allowed to see reality for what it was, and second, through not being allowed to overcome obstacles in cooperation with the group. Moreover, children need experience in handling their own anxiety.

There are many traumatic situations in life which cannot be anticipated, such as illness or operations. Such was the case with Diana, aged four, who underwent an emergency appendectomy. Repeatedly, the mother had scolded her for eating peanuts with the shells, and now the operation was experienced as a just punishment. She was, on the whole, a well-adjusted child, so that a few hours of play therapy, post-operative while in the hospital, gave her opportunity to release some of her castration anxiety and feeling of guilt. Her need for repression was definitely minimized. She was thus helped over a situation that could have been seriously traumatic, especially since it involved the mother-child relationship in connection with the oral zone.

Some children who are so neurotic that they precipitate accidents require deeper analysis. Such was the case when a four-and-a-half-year-old boy was run over by an automobile, so that the amputation of his entire left arm was necessary. As the parents were in analysis, they consented—although with considerable resistance—to have analytic help starting ten days post-operatively for the child. Play therapy for over one month revealed that this accident was of his own making. By starting treatment on the tenth day post-operatively, he was allowed little time for repression, so the material was accessible. However, care had to be taken not to increase his anxiety, guilt and masochism so soon after the operation, for fear of completely destroying this child's already very weak ego. These few therapeutic hours gave the child an opportunity to abreact some of his anxiety, to check repression, accept reality better, and, it has been hoped, to possibly break through his repetition compulsion.[14]

Dosing the Child Through Community Planning

Since the child and the parent in most cases never come in direct contact with the psychiatrist, if dosing is to succeed it is important to orient as far as possible all adults who influence the child. These include all medical personnel—obstetricians, obstetrical nurses, pediatricians, family physicians, public health officers, public health nurses, social workers, educators, religious leaders, radio and film directors, as well as household employees.

Many of these adults are being reached through the spread of psychiatric and psychoanalytic concepts. Again, the problem is how to help these adults to accept intellectual information emotionally and thereby apply it. Contributions from the files of Psychosomatic Medicine (7, 34, 43) have been a real influence for those oriented in organic medicine, as well as curricular changes in medical schools. There is even a tendency now to swing too far over and to overlook some difficult organic diagnoses by calling them psychosomatic symptoms.

So, too, the seminars for social workers, nurses and educators are leading their members to greater insight into their own individual character traits, improving their professional productivity. Many of these professional workers are receiving psychiatric treatment or psychoanalyses. A program of orientation was conducted by the director of the Social Service Department and this author for the medical social workers of the New York Infirmary for Women and Children. Psychiatric concepts and approaches thus infiltrated into all the contacts the social workers had with doctors, nurses and patients.

The project carried on at the New York Infirmary in dosing chil-

14. After an interim period of one year, he is now undergoing complete psychoanalysis.

dren to life situations could profitably be expanded into a community-wide project where all adults who handle children could cooperate to produce maximum integrated development. Techniques popularly used by the medical and teaching professions could be employed to induce social awareness of such a program. For instance, a deep awareness on the part of the public has been created for such procedures as are used in the elimination of diphtheria and smallpox, in persuading parents to attend well-baby clinics, etc. Such a national campaign to arouse interest in an integrated community program could be undertaken, but the job is a difficult and challenging one, for here in psychiatry we are dealing with emotional attitudes which are not always easily accessible (24).

Effect of Cultural Institutions

It must be remembered, finally, that all child-rearing concepts are affected not only by the individual parents and the community, but also by the particular culture in which the child develops. Anthropological investigations have revealed how dosing in cultures other than our own has molded the children into patterns of those cultures (22, 24, 26, 29, 32, 33, 36-40).

Our own civilization, with democratic culture as an aim, does not have an easy task. For a democratic society, in order to functior completely, must have adults of emotional maturity (24). It is far more difficult to achieve emotional maturity (on the genital level) for the masses than it is to fixate them on a pregenital level of anal sado-masochism, as is accomplished in some other cultures.

BIBLIOGRAPHY

1. Alpert, A. "The Solving of Problem Situations by Pre-School Children", *Bureau of Publications,* Teachers College, 1928.
2. Balint, M. "Ego Strength and Education of the Ego", *Psa. Quarterly,* XI, 1942.
3. Bateson, G. "Cultural Determinants of Personality", in Hunt, J. McV., *Personality and the Behavior Disorders,* Ronald Press, 1944.
4. Davis, C. M. "Self-Selection Diet by Newly-Weaned Infants", *Amer. J. Diseases of Children,* 36, 1928.
5. Dennis, W. "Does Culture Appreciably Affect Patterns of Infant Behavior?", *J. Soc. Psych.,* 12, 1940.
6. Dennis, W. and Dennis, M. G. "Cradling Practices of Pueblo Indians", *Amer. Anthrop.,* 42, 1940.
7. Dunbar, F. *Psychosomatic Diagnosis,* Hoeber, 1943.

8. Escalona, S. K. "Feeding Disturbances in Very Young Children", *Amer. J. Orthopsychiatry*, XV, 1945.
9. French, T. "A Clinical Study of Learning in the Course of a Psychoanalytic Treatment", *Psa. Quarterly*, V, 1936.
10. French T. "Ego Analysis as a Guide to Therapy", *ibid.*, XIV, 1945.
11. Freud, A. *The Ego and the Mechanisms of Defence*, Hogarth, 1937.
12. Freud, A. and Burlingham, D. T. *Infants Without Families*, Int. Univ. Press, 1944.
13. Freud, S. *The Ego and the Id*, Int. Psa. Lib., 1923.
14. Freud, S. *Group Psychology and the Analysis of the Ego*, ibid., 1921.
15. Freud, S. *Beyond the Pleasure Principle*, ibid., 1922.
16. Freud, S. *New Introductory Lectures*, Norton, 1933, Chap. III.
17. Fries, M. E. "Factors in Character Development, Neuroses, Psychoses and Delinquency", *Amer. J. Orthopsychiatry*, VII, 1937.
18. Fries, M. E. and Lewi, B. "Interrelated Factors in Development: A Study of Pregnancy, Labor, Delivery, Lying-in Period and Childhood", *ibid.*, VIII, 1938.
19. Fries, M. E. "Psychosomatic Relationships Between Mother and Infant", *Psychosom. Med.*, VI, 1944.
20. Fries, M. E. "Mental Hygiene in Pregnancy, Delivery and the Puerperium", *Ment. Hyg.*, 25, 1941.
21. Fries, M. E. "The Formation of Character as Observed in the Well-Baby Clinic", *Amer. J. Diseases of Children*, 48, 1935.
22. Fries, M. E. "Guide to Film I: Some Basic Differences in the Newborn" "Guide to Film III: Psychological Implications of Behavior During the Clinic Visit" "Guide to Film IV: Family Life of the Navaho Indians" *Film Rental Library of New York University, New York.*
23. Fries, M. E. "The Study of the Emotional Development of Children", *Med. Woman's J.*, August 1936.
24. Fries, M. E. "Importance of Continuous Collaboration of all Agencies in Dynamically Handling Each Child", *Nervous Child*, 3, 1944.
25. Fries, M. E. "Psychiatry in Dentistry for Children", *J. New Jersey State Dental Soc.*, April 1941.
26. Fries, M. E. "National and International Difficulties", *Amer. J. Orthopsychiatry*, XI, 1941.
27. Fries, M. E. "Diagnosing the Child's Adjustment Through Age Level Tests", *Psa. Rev.* (in print).
28. Goldfrank, E. "Socialization, Personality, and the Structure of Pueblo Society", *Amer. Anthrop.*, 47, 1945.
29. Gorer, G. *Japanese Character Structure and Propaganda*, Institute of Human Relations, Yale Univ., 1942 (mimeo).
30. Greenacre, P. "The Predisposition to Anxiety", *Psa. Quarterly*, X, 1941.
31. Greenacre, P. "The Biological Economy of Birth", *this Annual*, I.
32. Kluckhohn, C. "Patterning as Exemplified in Navaho Culture", *Language, Culture and Personality*, Sapir Mem. Pub., 1941.
33. Kluckhohn, C. and Mowrer, O. H. "Culture and Personality: A Conceptual Scheme", *Amer. Anthrop.*, 46, 1944.
34. Liddell, H. S. "Alterations of Instinctual Processes Through the Influence of Conditioned Reflexes", *Psychosom. Med.*, IV, 1942.

35. Lippitt, R. and White, R. K. "An Experimental Study of the Effect of Democratic and Authoritarian Group Atmospheres", *Univ. Iowa Stud. Child Welfare,* 16, no. 3, 1940.
36. Mead, M. and Bateson, G. *Balinese Character,* N. Y. Acad. Sci., 1942.
37. Mead, M. *From the South Seas,* Morrow, 1939.
38. Mead, M. *And Keep Your Powder Dry,* Morrow, 1942.
39. Roheim, G. "Freud and Cultural Anthropology", *Psa. Quarterly,* IX, 1940.
40. Roheim, G. "The Psychoanalytic Interpretation of Culture", *Int. J. Psa.,* XX, 1941.
41. Sontag, L. W. "Differences in Modifiability of Fetal Behavior and Physiology", *Psychosom. Med.,* VI, 1944.
42. Sontag, L. W. "The Significance of Fetal Environmental Differences", *Amer. J. Obst. & Gynec.,* 42, 1941.
43. Weiss, E. and English, O. S. *Psychosomatic Medicine,* Saunders, 1943.
44. Zorbaugh, G. "How May the Community Utilize Its Gifted Children", *Ment. Hyg.,* 24, 1940.

HOSPITALISM

A Follow-up Report on Investigation Described in Volume I, 1945

By RENÉ A. SPITZ, M.D. (New York)

I.

The striking picture of the infants studied in Foundling Home encouraged us to make every effort to get whatever information we could on the further development of the individual children. Distance made it impossible for the author to attend to this personally. The investigator who assisted in the original study was therefore directed to ascertain, at regular intervals, certain objectively observable facts on all those infants who were still available. He visited Foundling Home during the two years following our own study, at four-monthly intervals. On these occasions, equipped with a questionnaire prepared by the author, he asked the nursing personnel a series of questions. He observed each child's general behavior, and tried to make contact with each. He took some motion pictures of them, and a set of stills at the end of the two years, Finally, some bodily measurements, namely, weight, height, and occipital circumference, were taken.

The questions referred to three principal sectors of personality:

1) Bodily performance: the gross indicator used was whether the child could sit, stand, or walk.

2) Intellectual capacity to handle materials: the gross indicator used was whether the child was capable of eating food alone with the help of a spoon, and whether he could dress alone.

3) Social relations: these were explored by ascertaining the number of words spoken by each child, and by finding out whether he was toilet trained.

We are only too well aware that the resulting information is inadequate for a thorough study. As will be seen, however, even this inadequate follow-up yields a number of instructive data.

As is usually the case in follow-up investigations, only a relatively small number of the children originally seen could be checked on. Two years ago, when we first visited the ward reserved for the children from birth to one-and-a-half years, and the ward for children from one-and-a-half to three years, a total of 91 children were present. In the course of the first year, 27 of these died of various causes, among which were an epidemic of measles, intercurrent sickness, and cachexia; by the end of the second year, another 7 of those originally seen had died; this represents a total mortality of over 37 per cent in a period of two years.

Thirty-six children could not be learned about because: 23 had been taken back to their families; 7 had been adopted (mostly by their own illegitimate parents); 2 had been placed in children's institutions; and 4 could not be accounted for.

At the time of this writing[1] 21 children of those originally seen are still at the institution. Of these the youngest is two years of age, the oldest four years and one month. The data on their development are as follows:

1) Bodily development:
   Incapable of any locomotion: 5
   Sit up unassisted (without walking):   3
   Walk assisted: 8
   Walk unassisted: 5

   Total   21

2) Handling materials:
   Cannot eat alone with spoon: 12
   Eat alone with spoon: 9

   Total   21

   Cannot dress alone: 20
   Dresses alone: 1

   Total   21

3) Adaptation to demands of environment:
   Not toilet trained in any way: 6
   Toilet trained, partially:[2]   15

   Total   21

1. June 12, 1946.

2. These children are trained "to a certain extent". According to my observer many of the so-called "toilet trained" children were found to soil in their beds; their training appears to be limited to their making use of the toilet when put on it.

4) Speech development:
       Cannot talk at all: 6
       Vocabulary: 2 words: 5
       Vocabulary: 3 to 5 words: 8
       Vocabulary: a dozen words: 1
       Uses sentences: 1

                                      Total   21

As seen from these data, the mental development of these 21 children is extraordinarily retarded, compared to that of normal children between the ages of two and four, who move, climb, and babble all day long, and who conform to or struggle against the educational demands of the environment. This retardation, which amounts to a deterioration, is borne out by the weights and heights of these children, as well as by their pictures.

Normal children, by the end of the second year weigh, on the average, 26½ pounds, and the length is 33½ inches. At the time of this writing, 12 of the children in Foundling Home range in age between 2.4 and 2.8; 4, between 2.8 and 3.2; and 5, between 3.2 and 4.1. But of all of these children, only 3 fall into the weight range of a normal *two-year-old* child, and only 2 have attained the length of a normal child of that age. All others fall below the normal two-year-level—in one case, as much as 45 per cent in weight and 5 inches in length. In other words, the physical picture of these children impresses the casual observer as that of children half their age.

In our previous article on the subject (in Volume I) we expressed the suspicion that the damage inflicted on the infants in Foundling Home by their being deprived of maternal care, maternal stimulation, and maternal love, as well as by their being completely isolated, is irreparable. Our follow-up confirms this assumption. After their fifteenth month, these children were put into more favorable environmental conditions than before, i.e., in the ward for the older children. This is a large room, sunny, without the partitions which in the ward for the younger children isolated the infants from each other and from every environmental stimulus. Three to five nurses are constantly in the room, and they chat with each other and with the children. The children are also taken out of their cots and placed on the floor. Thus they have infinitely more active stimulation than they previously experienced in the ward for younger children. Notwithstanding this improvement in environmental conditions, the process of deterioration has proved to be progressive. It would seem

that the developmental imbalance caused by the unfavorable environmental conditions during the children's first year produces a psychosomatic damage that cannot be repaired by normal measures. Whether
it can be repaired by therapeutic measures remains to be investigated.

We have advisedly spoken of psychosomatic damage. From the
figures given above it can be seen that quite apart from the inadequate psychic and physical development, all these children showed a
seriously decreased resistance to disease, and an appalling mortality.
Those who survived were all far below the age-adequate weight
reached by normal children of comparable age.

II.

In view of these findings we once again examined the data on
Nursery, the institution compared to Foundling Home in our previous
article. The organization of Nursery did not permit a follow-up
extended to the fifth year, as did that of Foundling Home. As a rule
children leave Nursery when they are a full year old. However, a
certain number of exceptions are made in this rule, and in the course
of our study of Nursery, which now covers a period of three-and-a-
half years, 29 children were found who stayed longer than a year.
The age at which these left varied from the thirteenth to the eighteenth
month (1.1 to 1.6). This means that the *oldest* of them was *half-a-year
younger* than the youngest child in our follow-up in Foundling Home,
and *two-and-a-half years younger than the oldest*. In spite of this
enormous difference in age, the Nursery children all ran lustily around
on the floor; some of them dressed and undressed themselves; they
fed themselves with a spoon; nearly all spoke a few words; they
understood commands and obeyed them; and the older ones showed
a certain consciousness of toilet requirements. All of them played
lively social games with each other and with the observers. The
more advanced ones imitated the activities of the nurses, sweeping
the floor, carrying and distributing diapers, etc. In all these children,
tests showed that the developmental quotients which in the eleventh
and twelfth months had receded somewhat,[3] not only came up to
the normal age level, but in most cases surpassed it by far.

But the gross physical picture alone, as expressed by the figures
on morbidity and mortality of the children in Nursery, is sufficiently

3. See this Annual, I, p. 69. The average retardation in the developmental quotient
was approximately 12 points during the eleventh and twelfth month; to be discussed
in a later publication.

striking. During the three-and-a-half years of our study of Nursery we had occasion to follow 122 infants, each for approximately a full year.[4] During this time *not a single child died*. The institution was visited by no epidemic. Intercurrent sickness was limited, on the whole, to seasonal colds, which in a moderate number developed into mild respiratory involvement; there was comparatively little intestinal disturbance; the most disturbing illness was eczema. The unusually high level of health maintained in Nursery impelled us to look into its past record. We investigated the files of Nursery for ten years prior to the beginning of our work there. We found that during the whole of the last fourteen years a total of three children have died: one of pneumonia at the age of three months; and two of pyloric stenosis, the first at the age of one month, the second after several operations at the age of nine months.

It is in the light of these findings, which show what can be achieved in an institution under favorable circumstances and adequate organization, that the consequences of the methods used in Foundling Home should be evaluated.

4. Exceptions to this are 6 children who because of circumstances in their families left before their tenth month. This is more than counterbalanced by the group of 29 children who stayed longer than one year.

THE PSYCHOANALYTIC STUDY OF
INFANTILE FEEDING DISTURBANCES

By ANNA FREUD (London)

In the psychonalytic study of children interest frequently has been concentrated on one or the other of the feeding problems of infancy and childhood. The first disorders of this kind to attract the attention of analytic authors were the upsets of feeding after weaning (Freud, Abraham (1), Bernfeld (3)). These were investigated in the beginning indirectly, through the after-effects for the individual's emotional life as they showed up under analytic treatment in adulthood; later on directly, during the observation and treatment of young children. Other feeding problems gradually came into the field of analytic vision. Endre Petö (14) devoted a paper to the emotional attitude of the mother, as an important factor for the success of breast-feeding. Merrel P. Middlemore (12) made a systematic study of the "suckling situation" between mother and newborn infant, and interpreted some of her findings in the light of Melanie Klein's theories of the conflicts of the oral phase. Edith Jackson (10) and G. J. Mohr (13) stressed the importance of emotional factors in nutrition work with infants and children. Editha Sterba (16) drew attention to the interrelations between habit training and feeding disorders; Otto Fenichel (7), James Strachey (17), Melitta Schmideberg (15) and others, to the connection between feeding inhibitions and inhibitions of intellectual activities. Emmy Sylvester (18) in a recently published case of psychogenic anorexia traced the influence of the mother-child relationship on the origin and course of the disturbance. Refusal of food owing to the repression of oral sadism and oral introjection has played a large part in the psychoanalytic theory of depressive states and melancholia (see Freud (8), Abraham (2), Melanie Klein (11)).

Psychoanalytic studies of this kind have been instrumental in shedding light on the origin and meaning of specific feeding disorders, especially of the graver types and those which occur as single symptoms within the framework of a neurotic illness. Less notice was taken of the common feeding difficulties which occur in the everyday life of otherwise normal children. Nor have the findings of the various authors been correlated and systematically applied to the wide field of feeding problems which ranges from manifestations like simple fluctuations of appetite, and transitory food fads, to severe disorders which endanger the child's health, and sometimes its life.

The function of eating serves primarily the biological bodily need for nourishment and operates in agreement with the id forces and ego forces which are jointly directed towards the self-preservation of the individual. The function of eating, as such, lies therefore outside the sphere of psychological conflict (see Hartmann's "konfliktfreie Sphäre"). Eating may, on the other hand, become invested with sexual and aggressive meaning and thereby, secondarily, become the symbolic representative of id forces which are opposed by the ego.

The need for nourishment announces itself to the child's awareness by the sensations of hunger. The painful tension which is created by the sensations of hunger urges the child to take appropriate action (announcing its hunger to the environment by crying, later on asking for food, or helping itself to food). The appeasement of hunger through the intake of nourishment is felt as satisfactory and is accompanied by pleasure. Since the infant's behavior is dominated by the urge to avoid pain and discomfort and to gain pleasure, the urge for self-preservation through feeding is reinforced by the urge to gain pleasure through feeding.

There are, according to these conditions, three main ways in which the function of eating is open to disturbance:

(i)   through changes in the organism which directly or indirectly affect the organism's drive to survive, or the need for nourishment. (*Organic feeding disturbances.*)

(ii)   through changes in the pleasurable character of the function. (*Non-organic disturbance of the instinctive process itself.*)

(iii)   through sexualisation or aggressive use of the function, which involves the activity of feeding in conflicts with the ego forces and leads to states of neurotic anxiety, inhibition and symptom formation. (*Neurotic feeding disturbances.*)

(*i*)   *Organic Feeding Disturbances.*

The organic feeding disorders lie outside the field of analytic interest except in those cases where they become the basis of, or otherwise combine with, non-organic disorders. In states of severe physical illness, weakness, exhaustion, strain, and in certain states of convalescence, the organism is forced to a lower level of adjustment (9, Gesell and Ilg, p. 112), and the need for food, with the accompanying sensations of hunger, is decreased. Some children show a steady sustained appetite even during illness or malaise (Gesell and Ilg, l. c.); but with the majority the appetite falls to a low level with a consequent reduction of intake. Such children are at these times "bad eaters" for physiological reasons.

Where it is necessary, on medical grounds, to urge the child to eat beyond the limits of its appetite, or where mothers, for their own reassurance, force the child to eat against its will, emotional factors may enter into an otherwise simple feeding situation. Eating then becomes symbolic of a struggle between mother and child, in which the child can find an outlet for its passive or active, sadistic or masochistic tendencies towards the mother. To win a victory in this battle may, for the child, become more important than to satisfy its returning appetite. In such cases the phase of "bad eating" outlasts by far the phases of illness and convalescence, or may become the starting point for permanent non-organic feeding troubles. Where the child can be permitted in illness to adjust its feeding to the level of its appetite, it will return to its former normal feeding standards as soon as the need for food returns to normal level.

(ii) Disturbances of the Instinctive Process.

The satisfaction of hunger constitutes the first experience of instinctual gratification in the child's life. An infant who feeds successfully is a contented and "happy" infant. So far as the mother, by providing nourishment, guarantees this satisfaction and thereby provides for a pleasurable experience, the child, its instinctive need, and the environment, are all in perfect harmony.

On the other hand no mother gives food to the child without imposing on it at the same time a feeding regime which constitutes on the part of the environment the first serious interference with an instinctive desire of the child.

The current feeding schedules for the first year of life are based on detailed physiological knowledge of the infant's bodily functioning. The number of mothers who do not follow the advice either of their own pediatricians or of the Medical Officers and nurses of the Welfare Clinics diminishes in England and America from year to year. The mixed diet of the toddlers is, in the middle classes, chosen according to similar advice; in the poorer parts of the population it is left almost entirely in the hands of the mothers, and determined by the food habits and circumstances of the other members of the family. With older children scientific planning of a balanced diet may be introduced again where the child shares in nursery- or school-meals.

Some feeding regimes are, thus, based on medical-hygienic knowledge; others are the result of preconceived ideas, sometimes sensible, sometimes outdated and often superstitious, handed down to mothers by the former generation. In each case they are the embodiment of what a specific environment believes to be wholesome, advantageous and suitable for the various ages. It is a common feature of all the current feeding regimes in our civilization that they take maximum account of the bodily requirements for physiological health, growth and development, and little or no account of the pleasure which should be an invariable accompaniment and inducement to the feeding process.

The amount of pleasure which an individual child gains from eating depends only partly on the adequate fulfilment of bodily requirements; for an equally large part it is dependent on the manner in which the food is given. The child finds feeding most pleasurable when it can eat what it likes, how much or how little it likes and in whatever way it likes. The average feeding regime which regulates the child's meals according to quality, quantity, frequency and procedure, therefore inevitably interferes with the element of pleasure in all these respects.

In the last decades the feeding schedules for infants have inclined towards strict and fixed hygienic regulation and have left little room for individual fluctuations. Recently many authors show a growing tendency to stress the importance of individualization in the supervision of infant feeding (see Gesell and Ilg, l. c.), and to allow for a certain amount of adjustment of the schedule to the individual child. But even with a more flexible feeding regime of this nature the interference with the natural process will remain considerable. It is inevitable under conventional feeding conditions that infants and toddlers are made to cease feeding while they still feel unsatisfied; or that they are urged to continue when they feel that they have had enough; or that they are given foods which are considered necessary for the diet but which they dislike; or that they are offered sweets at moments when they prefer savouries, or savouries when they prefer sweets; that the temperature of liquids or the consistency of solids is not according to preference; that they are passively fed at an age when they desire to handle the food actively; or forced to use implements when they prefer using their fingers, etc. On all these occasions the child will feel displeased, frustrated, uncomfortable, and will connect these painful sensations with the feeding process.

Further discrepancies between an imposed schedule and the child's wishes arise about the incidence of feedings. The former provides for meals at set times, while the wishes turn to food, or the satisfaction connected with it, for ulterior motives too, to allay anxiety, loneliness, longing, boredom, tiredness or any other emotional upset. This means that for the child food acts as an important general comforter, a function which is disregarded in most feeding schemes. Where the child's wish for food remains unfulfilled at such moments, it feels deeply dissatisfied.

A similar discrepancy exists between child and environment about the question of timing meals. The adult's conception of the length of waiting times after sensations of hunger have appeared is different from the infant's. In infantile life instinctive needs are of overwhelming urgency. There is no organized ego, able to postpone wish-fulfilment with the help of the thought processes or other inhibitory functions. Nothing therefore will diminish the painful and distressing tension of the need except immediate satisfaction. Where hungry infants or toddlers are made to wait for their meals, even for minutes, they suffer acute distress to a degree which may prevent them from enjoying the meal when it finally arrives.

On all the occasions enumerated the child experiences sensations of a disagreeable and painful nature instead of pleasure. Where the disappointments, dissatisfactions and frustrations connected with the feeding experiences become too frequent they may, in time, outweigh the pleasures and ultimately spoil the child's attitude to the whole feeding process.

Urged by the physiological need of the body and by pressure from the environment, children will continue to eat even when the process of feeding has become dissociated from the powerful urge for pleasure which originally characterizes every instinctive drive. But meal times will then have lost their former attraction and instead be tiresome tasks; forced labor rather than an occasion for wish-fulfilments. The children will then eat slowly instead of greedily; be easily distracted from their meals, or demand to be entertained while eating; object to more types of food and be more distrustful of new foods than they otherwise would; need considerable urging to take in sufficient nourishment; and cannot, as their mothers express it, "be bothered to eat", or will be "too deep in play" to come for their meals. They have become "bad eaters" owing to loss of pleasure in the function.[1]

If doctors, mothers and nurses are right in taking the child's desire for food as a blind instinctive force, without the discrimination and self-regulation which are essential factors in the parallel feeding situations of young animals, then the imposing- of feeding schedules from without, with the loss of pleasure and the eating disturbances consequent on it, are inevitable. On the other hand recent studies on these lines, made under completely changed feeding conditions, do not confirm this distrust in the self-regulating powers of the child's appetite. Clara M. Davis (4, 5, 6) has shown in her experiments with nursing infants, infants of weaning age, and older children in a hospital setting that infants and children can, under carefully regulated conditions, be trusted to make their own choice according to quantity and quality among selected foods rich in the nutritional elements essential to growth, and that under these conditions they will have better appetites, eat more and have happier mealtimes than children fed in the usual manner. The pleasure which they obtain from the gratification of their appetite will be fully maintained and form an essential element in the smooth functioning of the feeding process.[2]

(iii) Neurotic Feeding Disturbances.

Eating, more than any other bodily function, is drawn into the circle of the child's emotional life and used as an outlet for libidinal and aggressive tendencies.

a) *The relationship between eating and the stages of object love:* The newborn infant is self-centered and self-sufficient as a being when it is not in a state of tension. When it is under the pressure of urgent bodily needs, as for instance hunger, it periodically establishes connections with the environment which are withdrawn again after the needs have been satisfied and the tension is relieved. These occasions are the child's first introduction to experiences of wish-fulfilment and pleasure. They establish centres of interest to which libidinal energy becomes attached. An infant who feeds successfully "loves" the experience of feeding. (Narcissistic love.)

When the child's awareness develops sufficiently to discern other qualities besides those of pain and pleasure, the libido cathexis

1. In a discussion of these problems in 1933 Dr. Grete Bibring suggested that the very widespread reduction in the pleasure of eating in the European children of the twentieth century might well be a consequence of the growing rigidity of the then current schedules of infant feeding.

2. The author can confirm these findings from experience with toddlers in the Jackson Nursery in Vienna 1937-38 and the Hampstead Nurseries in London 1940-45.

progresses from the pleasurable experience of feeding to the food which is the source of pleasure. The infant in this second stage "loves" the milk, breast, or bottle. (Since, on this level of development, no certain distinctions are made between the child's self and the environment, this libido attachment forms a transitional stage between narcissism and object love.) When its powers of perception permit the child to form a conception of the person through whose agency it is fed, its "love" is transferred to the provider of food, that is to the mother or mother-substitute. (Object love.)

It is not difficult to pursue the line of development which leads from these crude beginnings of object attachment to the later forms of love. The infant's first love for the mother is directed towards material satisfaction. (Stomach love, cupboard love, egoistic love; "to be fed".) In a next stage object love is still egoistic but directed toward non-material satisfactions, i.e. to receive love, affection, approval from the mother; "to be loved". As the child progresses from the oral and anal to the phallic level, object attachment loses its egoistic character; the qualities of the object increase in libidinal importance while the immediate benefit from the relationship becomes less important. The next and highest stage of development is the ability to love the object regardless of benefit (altruistic love).

Where infants are breast-fed, and the milk and breast are in fact part of the mother and not merely, as with bottle-fed babies, symbolic of her, the transition from narcissism to object love is easier and smoother. The image of food and the mother-image remain merged into one until the child is weaned from the breast.

Psychoanalytic authors have been repeatedly accused of exaggerating the upsets to the feeding situation caused by weaning (see for instance Gesell and Ilg, l. c.). Pediatricians and psychologists stress the fact that where weaning takes place in slow stages with the gradual introduction of other foods and other means of feeding (spoon, cup), no shock is felt by the child. In the author's opinion this is only reliably so where weaning takes place in the first period of narcissistic enjoyment of feeding, when the child's unfavorable reactions are to alterations of the feeding condition which has proved satisfactory and where upsets can be avoided by the avoidance of sudden changes. At the latter stages of developing object-relationship weaning signifies, besides the changes in food and the means of feeding, an entry into a new phase of the mother-relationship to which certain children are unable to adjust themselves smoothly. The difficulties on the emotional side may find their outlet as difficulties of adjusting to the new food.

Though food and the mother become separated for the conscious mind of all children from the second year onwards, the identity between the two images remains so far as the child's unconscious is concerned. Much of the child's conflicting behavior towards food does not originate from loss of appetite or a lessened need to eat, etc., but from conflicting emotions towards the mother which are transferred on to the food which is a symbol for her. Ambivalence towards the mother may express itself as fluctuations between over-eating and refusal of food; guilty feelings towards the mother and a consequent inability to enjoy her affection as an inability to enjoy food; obstinacy and hostility towards the mother as a struggle against being fed. Jealousy of the mother's love for the other children of the family may find its outlet in greediness and insatiableness. At the stage of repression of the oedipus complex refusal of food may accompany, or be substituted for, the inner rejection of the phallic sexual strivings towards the mother.

Eating disturbances of this type normally disappear in adolescence when repressions of the infantile relationship to the parents are revised and solutions for them have to be found on a different level. Where the feeding disorders arising from the child-mother relationship have been especially severe, they may return in adult life in the form of psychosomatic disorders of the stomach or digestive tract.

Mothers, though they do not produce these feeding difficulties in their children, nevertheless may behave in a manner which aggravates the pathogenic elements in the situation. Under the influence of their own unconscious phantasies they often continue much longer than necessary to act as the connecting link between the child and the food, and on their side to treat the food which they offer as if it were a part of themselves; they are pleased and affectionate when the child accepts the food, and as offended when food is rejected as if their love for the child had suffered a rebuff; they beg a badly eating child to eat "for their sake", etc. This attitude of the mother coincides with the unconscious attitude of the child and thereby strengthens the unconscious emotional tendencies which are a threat to feeding. Mothers cannot alter the unconscious phantasies of their children. But they can, by their actions, strengthen the healthy, conscious moves towards the next stage of development. That is, they can give the child direct access to food as early as possible, trust the self-regulating powers of its appetite within sensible limits and thereby increasingly withdraw from the feeding situation, in the measure in which the child learns to handle food independently.

With children in the pre-oedipal phase the feeding disorders of this origin normally disappear when mother and child are separated (away from home, in nursery-school, in hospital). In all later phases, the conflicts arising from the mother-relationship persist as inner conflicts regardless of the mother's presence or behavior. The feeding disorders which are dependent on them then transfer themselves automatically to every available mother-substitute.

b) *The relationship between feeding and the oral pleasures:* The connection between feeding and the oral component of infantile sexuality is so close and its pathogenic influence so obvious, that analysts often make the mistake of diagnosing all infantile feeding disturbances automatically as "oral disturbances".

From the beginning of suckling the infant derives from the milk flow two different kinds of satisfaction: one from the appeasement of hunger, the other from the stimulation of the mucous membranes of the mouth. The latter, oral, satisfaction remains from then onwards through life a constant accompaniment of every feeding situation. When a mixed diet begins, oral satisfaction is gained from the taste and consistency of the various food substances and plays an important part in the formation of the various individual likes and dislikes for food. (Preference for sweets or salty foods, for hot or cold liquids, etc.) This winning of libidinal pleasure from an otherwise non-libidinal body function is an added stimulus for the child's feeding, the significance of which cannot be too strongly emphasized. An infant's or toddler's diet in which this element is disregarded (i.e., a drab, dull diet, or one in which too many items are "distasteful" to the child) defeats its own ends by lowering the total gain in satisfaction from the intake of food with a consequent decrease of the child's appetite.

In the oral phase of libido development, oral pleasure, though originally discovered in conjunction with feeding, is sought and reproduced independently of the feeding situation in the numerous forms of thumb-sucking, as an auto-erotic oral activity. As such it may be pursued by the infant as a substitute for feeding (while waiting for food or when feeding has to be interrupted before the child is fully satisfied). It may enter into competition with feeding (when infants are unwilling to remove the thumb from the mouth to take the teat of the bottle or the spoon filled with food). It further plays an important part, completely independent of feeding, as a general comforter (like food) before sleep, when the child is lonely, dull, etc.

Through the intimate connection between feeding pleasure, oral pleasure, and the roots of object-relationship, oral tendencies become

the first carriers of the libidinal attachment to the mother. Oral attitudes are consequently as decisive for shaping the child-mother relationship as the latter is decisive in determining the child's attitude to food.

The oral pleasures are an asset to feeding while the child can
enjoy them without interference from the environment or from its own
ego forces. When they are repressed, or otherwise rejected by the ego,
serious upsets for feeding result. It is impossible for the child to give
up or ward off the element of oral enjoyment without losing simultaneously its enjoyment of food and its wish to eat.

c) *The relationship between eating and the aggressive instinct:*
Since Abraham's study of the oral-sadistic phase of libido development,
the aggressive significance of eating has received constant attention
in psychoanalytic literature. According to Abraham oral sadism is at
its height after teething, when eating symbolizes an aggressive action
against the food which is in this way attacked and consumed, or
against the love object that is represented by the food. Melanie Klein
and her followers emphasize the significance of oral aggressive phantasies for early childhood and their after-effects for later normal and
abnormal development. (According to Melanie Klein aggressive meaning is attached even to the child's first feeding experiences, independent
of the possession of teeth.)

Oral-sadistic (cannibalistic) phantasies are under no circumstances
tolerated in consciousness, not even when the ego is immature. They are
rejected with the help of all the defence mechanisms available to the
child in this early period of life.

The consequences for feeding are inhibitions of eating, refusal
to bite, to chew, or to swallow the food. These feeding disorders may
reach their height at the toddler stage, though at that time the child
still freely uses its teeth for aggressive biting, as a weapon in fights
with other children, or to express anger and resentment against the
mother.

Where the repression or other defence mechanisms used against
cannibalistic wishes are not completely successful the child remains
anxious about its oral sadism, not only in the oral phase but all through
childhood, with serious consequences for the pleasure felt in eating.
Children of this type feel guilty when they enjoy food and eat only
under pressure of need or under compulsion from the environment, and
with no freedom or abandon. They eat slowly and sometimes keep
unchewed food in their mouths for long times. They show certain well

known dislikes and minor or greater food fads which originate in the fear of hurting or destroying a living creature. They anxiously watch their eggs for possible signs of a partly hatched chicken; they are simultaneously attracted and revolted by the idea of eating sweets, biscuits, cakes, etc., which in their shape imitate a human body, or an animal, or any recognizable part of it; they are not able to eat chickens, rabbits, pigs, etc., which they have known alive. Sometimes a compulsive vegetarianism becomes the last safeguard before a far-reaching eating inhibition is established.

In extreme instances, the defence against oral sadism leads to neurotic self-starvation. In this case the mechanism used is that of turning the aggression away from objects to the individual's own body which is thereby seriously threatened or even destroyed.

d) *The relationship between eating and the anal pleasures:* While infants are still passively fed they accompany the process with certain movements of their hands or fingers which indicate an impulse towards action. When they are encouraged to help themselves to food or to handle the spoon, it becomes evident that their intention is not directed towards feeding themselves but towards handling the food, playing with it, smearing it over the table or over themselves, etc. It is an error to ascribe this messing of the young child to lack of skill. The child's actions in this respect are deliberate and intentional. They are motivated by the pleasure of smearing, an anal-erotic activity transferred from the excrements to the foodstuffs which are similar to the former in consistency, color, temperature, etc. Behavior of this kind begins approximately at the age of eleven months and reaches its peak at the height of the anal phase of libido development. Where it is tolerated by the environment the anal pleasure gained from the actions contributes appreciably to the pleasure of feeding. The handling of food which is in the beginning stages merely messy and possessive merges gradually into purposeful actions of self-feeding. Food which is at first only held tightly or squeezed in the fist, finds its way into the child's mouth, etc. Children who are permitted to develop their self-feeding methods on the basis of this pleasurable anal attitude towards food become skillful in feeding themselves with their hands and fingers earlier than others and shortly afterwards make an easy transition to the use of the spoon.

Where messing with food is interfered with too strictly by the environment and the child is prevented from adding anal pleasure to the other feeding pleasures, appetite suffers. To keep a child in the anal phase from smearing food necessitates its being kept passively fed for a longer time which has, secondarily, an adverse influence on eventual self-selection of food, on the child's relationship to the mother, etc.

At the period when anal tendencies become repressed and relegated to the unconscious, a whole series of feeding difficulties make their appearance, especially in those cases where habit training has been too sudden or too severe. The reaction-formation of disgust which is set up in consciousness to prevent the return from the unconscious of former wishes to play with excrement, take it into the mouth, etc., is transferred to all those foodstuffs which by their look, touch or smell remind the child of the now forbidden dirty matter. As a result, many children form violent dislikes of squashy and smeary foods, of green or brown substances, of sausages, occasionally of all sauces and creams, regardless of taste. Where children are forced to eat the foods which disgust them, they react according to the strength of the anal repressions, with being sick, with loss of appetite, with a widening refusal of foods, etc. Where their disgust is understood as an inevitable outcome of the defence against anal urges, and where the resultant food fads are tolerated, the disturbances remain limited to certain substances, and transitory in character. When the anal repressions are firmly established, anxiety with regard to the underlying unconscious tendencies diminishes, and the majority of temporarily "disgusting" foods are readmitted by the child into its diet.

In the interest of the child's appetite, anal pleasure should be permitted to enter into the combination of feeding pleasures, and, for the same and other similar reasons, habit training should be carried out gradually and leniently. This is in contrast to the conventional but psychologically unsound attitude that children should as early as possible be in control of their excretory functions and acquire good table manners.

The intimate connection between the child's behaviour in these two respects can be proved experimentally. Where children in the latency period are urged to make a sudden advance in their table manners, they almost invariably react by regression to smearing and messiness in the lavatory, or vice versa.

Other anal admixtures to the feeding situation arise from a connection, made during the transition from orality to anality, between the ideas of intake of food and output of excrement, and between the body openings which serve the two functions. The feeding disorders which originate from them are of the type described in Editha Sterba's paper quoted above. (Retention of food in the mouth as equivalent of retention of stool in the rectum.)

e) The relationship between eating and certain typical fantasies of the phallic phase:

Certain fantasies of the pre-oedipal and oedipal phase have a specific bearing on the neurotic eating disturbances.

During the conflicts and struggles of the oedipus complex, many children escape anxiety by regressing from the phallic level to the earlier pregenital levels of libido development. This leads to the conception of parental intercourse by mouth, a phantasy which is frequently reinforced by actual observation of fellatio acts. The consequent sexualization of the mouth (by means of genital as well as oral libido) with the repressions following on it, endangers the function of eating by producing hysterical symptoms, as for instance globus hystericus and hysterical vomiting.

In one of the typical infantile theories of sex it is asserted that babies are conceived through the mouth (oral conception) and born through the rectum (anal birth), the intestines being substituted for the womb. Anxiety and guilt which become attached to these birth phantasies lead to refusal of food (warding off the wish to be impregnated), to a horror of getting fat (in defence against the phantasy of being with child).

Where fixations to the oral level and the regression to them are especially powerful, the wish to be impregnated takes the form of a fear of being poisoned which leads to severe eating inhibitions.

Guilt feelings arising from sexual competition with the parents and from death wishes against them lead to the masochistic desire not to grow up, which may express itself by means of refusal of food.

The penis envy of the little girl which may lead to the fantasy of biting off the male genital combines oral-sadistic with phallic elements. It frequently causes symptoms of hysterical vomiting without reference to specific foods.

Conclusions

The various types of eating disturbances, which have been separated off from each other in this paper for the purpose of theoretical evaluation, are invariably intermixed and interrelated when observed clinically. Organic feeding disorders become the basis for the non-organic types. Neurotic disturbances arise more easily where loss of pleasure in the function of eating has prepared the ground for them.

Considerate handling of the child's feeding, with a reasonable amount of self-determination, to safeguard the child's appetite, makes the function of eating less vulnerable and less favorable ground for neurotic superstructures.

BIBLIOGRAPHY

1. Abraham, K. "Pregenital Stage of the Libido", *Selected Papers.* (1916).
2. Abraham, K. "A Short Study of the Development of the Libido Viewed in the Light of Mental Disorders", *ibid.* (1924).
3. Bernfeld, S. *The Psychology of the Infant,* New York, 1929.
4. Davis, C. M. "Self-selection of Diet by Newly-Weaned Infants", *Amer. J. Diseases of Children,* 36, 1928.
5. Davis, C. M. "Self-selection of Food by Children", *Amer. J. Nursing,* 35, 1935.
6. Davis, C. M. "Choice of Formulas made by Three Infants Throughout the Nursing Period", *Amer. J. Diseases of Children,* 50, 1935.
7. Fenichel, O. *The Psychoanalytic Theory of Neurosis,* Norton, New York, 1945.
8. Freud, S. "Mourning and Melancholia", *Coll. Papers,* IV. (1925)
9. Gesell, A. and Ilg, G. *Feeding Behavior of Infants,* Lippincott, Philadelphia, 1937.
10. Jackson, E. "Prophylactic Considerations for the Neonatal Period", *Amer. J. Orthopsychiatry,* XV, 1945.
11. Klein, M. *The Psycho-Analysis of Children,* London, 1932.
12. Middlemore, M. P. *The Nursing Couple,* Hamish Hamilton Medical Books, London, 1941.
13. Mohr, G. J. "Emotional Factors in Nutrition Work with Children", *Ment. Hyg.* XII, 1928.
14. Petö, E. "Säugling und Mutter", *Zeit. f. psa. Päd.,* XI, 1937, 3/4.
15. Schmideberg, M. "Intellektuelle Hemmung und Esstörung", *Zeit. J. psa. Päd.,* 3/4, 1934.
16. Sterba, E. "An Important Factor in Eating Disturbances of Childhood", *Psa. Quarterly,* X, 1941.
17. Strachey, J. "Some Unconscious Factors in Reading", *Int. J. Psa.,* XI, 1930.
18. Sylvester, E. "Analysis of Psychogenic Anorexia in a Four-year-old", *this Annual,* I.

THE PSYCHOGENIC TIC IN
EGO DEVELOPMENT

By MARGARET W. GERARD, M.D., Ph.D. (Chicago)*

Although there is a considerable volume of literature upon the subject of tics, only a few papers attempt to explain the production of the symptom from a psychodynamic viewpoint. Many authors describe the varieties of forms of the symptom or discuss its statistical frequency or the like.[1] For present purposes, I shall attempt to review only those papers of import to a study of the psychodynamic factors involved in the production of the symptom and of the character formations found in tiqueurs.

Ferenczi (3) in 1921 suggested that the tic represents an equivalent of onanism, in which the libido connected with genital sensation was transformed into "muscle erotism" and displaced to other parts of the body. This displacement, he stated, resulted in decreased genital potency and an increased pleasure in muscular movement. Beyond the onanistic significance, Ferenczi believed that many tics represented a method of warding off suffering, similar to reflex withdrawal from a stimulus. However, he claimed also that some tics inflicted injury upon the self and compared this condition to the extreme self-mutilation of schizophrenics. In the same paper, he described several cases of compulsive neurosis in which the patients carried out rituals with a variety of manneristic movements. The individual elements in the ritual were compared with tic movements, and he offered this comparison as evidence that tics were often hard to differentiate from compulsive acts. In attempting to explain the dynamic cause of the symptom, he stated that it was a "narcissistic disorder of a person who is hypersensitive and unable to endure a physical stimulus without a defensive reaction". The narcissism of such a person was described as a constitutional narcissism

*From the Institute of Psychoanalysis, Chicago, Illinois.

1. Since the writing of this paper a series of articles on tics has appeared in *The Nervous Child* (13). They are interesting and rich in information concerning treatment, parent-child relationships, art expressions, and Rorschach responses of tiqueurs, and they follow the theoretical concepts of Mahler (9, 10, 11) concerning the neurodynamics and psychodynamics of the tic.

in which the smallest injury to a part of the body strikes the whole ego, and which he believed to have resulted from an organic condition. He offered two reasons for the latter conclusion. The first consisted of the fact that in analyzing patients who presented a tic as part of a group of symptoms, he was able to cure the patient of other symptoms but the tic remained unaltered. The second reason grew out of his belief that paranoia and schizophrenia, psychoses which often exhibited stereotyped movements, were of organic origin.

In a paper discussing Ferenczi's analysis, Abraham (1), drawing conclusions from one of his own cases, stated that tics could not be differentiated from compulsive obsessive acts except in two respects. In one respect, the tiqueur does not attribute any significance to the symptom in his mental life as does the obsessional patient. In the other respect the obsessional patient fears disaster from the omission of the compulsive act and experiences anxiety from its suppression, whereas the tiqueur fears no disaster and experiences only discomfort with symptom suppression. Abraham also believed that the tic, like the compulsive act, possesses a hostile component, even though he yielded the possibility of an erotic element as well.

In three papers on the subject, Mahler (9, 10, 11) discussed the tic as a problem related to body motility in general. She defined it as an involuntary, lightning-like, repetitious jerk of a physiological group or groups of muscles; a purposeless motility without logical or rational goal, but the patterns of which in the beginning may have represented purposive and intentional movements. For the one case which she described in detail as well as for those examined in a statistical study of 33 cases, she formulated the psychodynamics of the tic system as "a resultant of the interaction of instinctual, ego and socio-environmental factors" She claimed evidence for both erotic and aggressive components in the instinctual forces involved, such that the tic represented provocative erotic aggression toward a mother or father, as well as the defense against the aggressive parent. She hypothesized that in the process of development of a tic, "cathexis in the motor sphere" was involved, and this cathexis was caused by a conflict occurring between an increased need for motor activity on the part of the patient and interference in that activity by an environmental agent. She attributed the patient's increased need for motor activity to a secondary environmental factor of excessive restriction and over-stimulation, and a possible primary constitutional motor factor, as Ferenczi had suggested earlier. In the detailed case, she believed the constitutional factor consisted of "an underlying substratum or organic disease of the central nervous system . . . probably a neuro-physiological inferiority", and because of this inferiority she stated that "the prognosis is unfavorable for this disease". However, in the later paper (11) she claimed she had achieved symptom cures through psychotherapeutic approaches.

In the statistical studies Mahler (11) described several interesting similarities both in character and behavior of the patients and in attitudes and behavior of the parents. Of 33 child tiqueurs studied 79 per cent were boys and only 21 per cent were girls. Many of these children exhibited awkwardness in large body movements and facility in small muscle coordination as exhibited in mechanical aptitude. Many of them had great ambitions for athletic skill but their athletic achievements were poor. In school, the greater number were restless and inattentive and their achievements were below that expected for their intellectual capacity. All showed evidences of increased body narcissism and a tendency to hypochondriacal self-observation. Parents in many instances held perfectionistic goals for their children's intellectual achievement and in many cases were over-indulgent to the children in the oral stage of emotional relationship; anal and urinary over-solicitude was far less common.

Levy (8) defined the psychogenic tic as a "superfluous, involuntary, brisk, repeated rhythmical movement set off by a mental process", the origin of which is emotional and represents an inhibition of an impulse which is regarded by the individual as dangerous or shameful. In a study of the psychic content of the tic he found every variety of sexual and aggressive impulse inhibited by the fear of consequences. He claimed that the tic was either a partial representation of the original impulsive act or a protective gesture to avert danger. He equated tics with compulsive movements but also differentiated them from each other by suggesting that a tic represented the motor expression of an act in its initial phase and a compulsive movement in its end phase. Certain repetitive movements found among animals when restrained, such as the head weaving of stalled horses, or the rocking movements of caged bears, he considered as tics, and compared them to the stereotyped movements of infants restrained in an orphanage who indulged in head rolling, banging, or body swaying. He found that these movements decreased or disappeared when the physical restraint was removed. In this article, however, Levy does not attempt to differentiate dynamically between "tics" which cease with freedom from restraint and those true tics which continue to occur in a great variety of situations in which no physical restraint occurs. Two factors he found to be associated with the symptom were general restlessness of the tiqueurs and compulsive and meticulous behavior in their parents.

A summary analysis of the papers by these authors discloses certain similarities in their conclusions and certain dissimilarities. Both Mahler and Levy noted similarities in the attitudes of the parents of the patients. Levy mentioned that the parents were compulsive and meticulous while Mahler describes the parents of her cases as ambitious for intellectual achievement. Abraham, Mahler and Levy found both erotic and hostile aggressive components in the tic, although Ferenczi mentioned only the erotic component. All of them noted the narcissistic orientation of the patient while Mahler emphasized the muscular cathexis in this narcissism, and described for some of her patients hyperactivity, excessive body interest, poor large-muscle coordination and fine-muscle skill.

Both Ferenczi and Levy suggested that the tic served to ward off suffering as well as to express, partially, an impulsive wish.

Ferenczi and Mahler claimed that a constitutional inferiority played a role in the production of the symptom, and consequently suggested a poor prognosis. Mahler offered no evidence for a constitutional factor, but suggested it as a hypothesis. Ferenczi based his claim for a constitutional factor and poor prognosis on his comparison of tics with schizophrenic mannerisms as well as upon his inability to cure the symptom by analysis. If one defines the term "tic" more specifically, and excludes schizophrenic mannerisms from the definition, his argument for a constitutional basis and a poor prognosis is not tenable. Mahler based the poor prognosis on a case described in detail, but claimed cures from psychotherapy in a later paper. It is possible that the discrepancy in her claims may have been the result of an error similar to that of Ferenczi, since the description of the behavior of the analyzed case — with multiple mannerisms, hyperactivity, silly erotic aggressive behavior and only slight superego repression— approximates some forms of childhood psychoses more closely than it does forms of behavior found in the other tiqueurs described by her, by other authors, or by this author. If this one case were that of a psychosis, and the others described in her statistical studies were true tics, one can readily understand the reason for the unfavorable prognosis in the former instance and the therapeutic successes in the latter cases.

Comparisons with compulsive ritualistic acts were made by both Abraham and Levy. Abraham stated that they differed only in the emotion associated with inhibition of the movement; that is, discomfort with inhibition of the tics, and anxiety with inhibition of the compulsive act. Levy differentiated between the two in his statement that the tic represented the initial phase of an act whereas the compulsive movement was its end phase. And finally he equated tics with rhythmic movements resulting from artificial restriction of activity, but did not explain why the former continued and the latter ceased upon removal of restriction.

For the present study, cases were chosen which presented, as part of the symptom picture, a simple tic which consisted of a rapid contraction of a group or groups of muscles occurring at irregular intervals without evidence of an appropriate purpose.[2] The muscles involved, however, consisted in all instances of voluntary physiological units, such as are found in eye-blinking, lip-pursing, pants-hitching, etc. Although most frequently the movements were not produced voluntarily, the patients were often aware of their occurrence. Although the theoretic conclusions are based upon the analysis of 13 such cases, 3 of which were adults, only those in which the circumstances at the time of the onset of the tic were known accurately are discussed in this study. All of the cases were analyzed for a year or longer, and during treatment the character patterns of the patients were well revealed and the dynamic factors involved in the symptom production were exposed. A thorough historical study of the children's cases included, also, an evaluation through interviews of the attitudes and the behavior of the parents toward the patient in order to define the role of daily experiences in the symptom choice and in the character development.

The ages of the children ranged from three to ten at the time treatment was undertaken. Except in the case of one four-year-old girl, the tic had been present for several years and had not been considered as a problem by the parents who brought the child for the treatment of other symptoms. Of the 13 cases the number of males was higher than that of females, as in Mahler's studies, i.e., 10 to 3, but there were

2. This definition is closer to Mahler (11) than to Levy (8) who includes "rhythmical" in his definition of the movement. Since a rhythmical sequence is not mentioned in other papers as characteristic of tics and since my own experience contraindicates any rhythm in tic occurrence, such qualification appears unjustified. The slow movements of schizophrenic mannerisms or other habit reactions such as ear-pulling, masturbation, etc., and compulsive ritualistic acts which some authors correlate with tics, are excluded from this definition since the psychodynamic purpose of the tic is different from these.

revealed no marked differences between the males and females in the ego mechanisms concerned in the tic production, in the role of the tic in the total character constellation, nor in the attitudes and behavior of their parents toward them.

Although there were variations in the secondary symptoms presented by the children, different events acting as precipitating causes of the tic, and considerable variations in motor skill, intellectual ability, and interests, all of them presented important and interesting similarities. In all of the cases the mothers, and in some cases both parents, were ambitious for the child in realm of intellectual achievement and of conformance to non-aggressive behavior. As mentioned, this parental characteristic was noted also by Mahler and Levy. The mothers were affectionate, but firm and controlling in their behavior toward the child; friendly and even-tempered in their personal relationships, and efficient and ambitious in work. All the children before treatment were somewhat shy but had winning manners toward adults and were conforming to adult authority. Fears in one form or another such as night terrors, fear of separation from a parent, fear of the dark, fear of being injured, etc., were symptoms possessed by all of them. They were more narcissistic than the average child of similar age, as suggested by Mahler (11) and Ferenczi (3). This orientation was exhibited in bragging, selfishness with siblings and playmates, etc.; but they also had concomitant fear of failure in a variety of areas and fear of competition with other children.

Of particular importance were the similarities disclosed in relation to the precipitating causes at the time of the onset of the tic and its incorporation into the ego structure as a defense mechanism against anxiety. It is interesting that tics are described in the literature as inappropriate muscular contractions. In the following cases, however, it will be seen that, at its onset, the tic was an appropriate response for the particular child to an overwhelming traumatic experience. Only later the tic continued to occur in other situations fraught with anxiety for the child, but in which the movement was no longer an appropriate reaction.

The traumas which preceded the first tic noticed by the parents were all sudden frightening occurrences which would cause, in the majority of children at the same age, violent muscular responses such as crying, running away, temper outbursts or physical attack. These natural responses were inhibited in these children by a fear of punishment, or of loss of love, should they react to the trauma with the use of the natural muscular response. In the majority of instances, the factors responsible for the inhibition of crying, running away, attack, etc., were the restrictive training and attitude of the parent or parents. In one instance, added to this general parental attitude was a specific threat to the child at the time of the traumatic experience by the individual responsible for inflicting the trauma. Several factors operated in achieving such marked conformity to parental inhibition of aggressive behavior. The child's wish to conform came from the desire to maintain the love of the mother. As is well known, this wish is present in all young children but operates successfully only when the child actually experiences the pleasures of his mother's love, and when he is aware of those activities which the mother will reward with affection versus those which will provoke rejection. Since the mothers of these children were affectionate when the child was "good", i.e., not aggressive, but were firm and consistent in their demands for conformity and disapproving when not obeyed, the child learned early that he could maintain his mother's love by certain restrictions upon his own activity. The conflict which the child must solve in this situation is a typical instinctual conflict described by Alexander (2); in this instance, a conflict between the aggressive impulses and the drive for love and dependence.

The ego mechanisms used in the solution of the conflict were inhibitions, substitution of a part of the act, and denial, which are the simplest and earliest learned defense mechanisms (7). A more elaborate mechanism such as adequate substitution, sublimation, conversion, undoing, projection, etc., was not possible because of two circumstances; one was the immaturity of the pre-latency ego, and the meager development at this early age of the cognitive process, or intellectual capacity;[3] the other circumstance was the mother's ambitious attitude toward the child, which made unacceptable to her the unskilled attempts at more complete substitution or sublimation of which the child might have been capable in the pre-latency years.

As will be demonstrated in the case discussions, the tic at its onset served the same purposes that many neurotic symptoms serve—inhibition of the direct expression of the instinctual wish, and partial satisfaction of that wish. In some instances, also, it served to shut out or deny the awareness of the traumatic experience (8). As an example, in case 1, a four-year-old boy, following a first view of his father's amputated leg, developed a bi-lateral blinking tic preceded by a sudden rapid widening of the palpebral fissure. During the treatment of this

3. See French's discussion of the role of cognition in ego development (5, 6).

boy, analysis of the symptom disclosed the widening of the palpebral fissure to be a partial substitute for the wish to see more; the blinking to be a visual denial of the traumatic sight and its implications, and a partial substitute in muscular action of his repressed castrative wishes toward his father. These latter wishes were precipitously aroused from his unconscious, to which they had been previously relegated, when he was presented so suddenly with the actuality of his father's injured condition; a symbolic or displaced castration.

Also, common to all the tic cases, as for many varieties of neurotic cases, the symptom followed the "repetition compulsion" phenomenon. The tic was repeated not only to serve as a defense against the specific traumatic experience, if and when it occurred again, but also became generalized and was used as a reaction to every anxiety-producing situation. This phenomenon was the result of isolation, in which the awareness of the traumatic experience was repressed and isolated from the fear and the reaction to the fear (the tic). Fear and tic thus became correlated so that consequently the reaction (the tic) occurred when any kind of fear was felt. This subsequent fate of the symptom accounts for the so-called "inappropriateness" which various authors emphasize as typical of tics.

Of interest also, perhaps, in view of assumptions in the literature of a probable constitutional factor in the use of the neuromuscular system for the production of the neurotic symptom (3, 8, 11), none of my cases presented actual hyperactivity. Parents of most of them did complain of their child's activity. This, when described and observed in detail, was found to be normal for the child's age. The mother's preference for quiet, restrained, conforming children, made this normal childish activity unacceptable to them. This is in direct contrast to Mahler's finding of "a progressive general muscular restlessness and hypermotility" (11). However, since her diagnoses were mostly gleaned from histories taken from the parents, it is possible that their evaluation of restlessness was influenced as in the case of my patients by their own neurotic attitude toward childish aggressiveness and activity, or that the restlessness was a secondary symptom not always equated with the tic.

Ferenczi (3), as well as Mahler (11), claimed a constitutional factor in tic formation, but Ferenczi based his belief in part on his inability to cure the tic by psychoanalysis by which he relieved concurrent symptoms. This tenacity of the symptom was not exhibited by the cases presented here nor by the other children with tics who were analyzed but are not discussed in detail in this paper. When the dynamic factors producing the tic were well analyzed, the symptom was discarded and no other abnormal neuro-muscular activity ensued, during the three or more post-analytic years in which the cases were followed. However, in defense of Ferenczi's conclusions, I have found that in the treatment of adults who possess tic-like movements as one of their symptoms, analysis has decreased the frequency of the tic but has never cured it completely. Also, in a few child cases, the tic returned from time to time, when the parent relapsed to the previous repressive perfectionistic attitude.

This difference between the results in the treatment of children and adults accords with our experiences in the treatment of children in general. If one analyzes a child in the pre-latency or latency period and, at the same time, can effect changes in the environment such that the child is no longer exposed to the experiences which produced the symptoms and the distorted character patterns, a much more extensive and permanent cure is effected than in adults who, even after analysis, maintain noticeable remnants of old ego mechanisms within the frame work of the modified character pattern which has been achieved through analysis. This difference can be explained by the fact that the young child is still in a developmental stage and his methods of reaction are much less fixed than are those of the adult. One might compare the child to a sapling which may be bent at an angle by the application of pressure. If this pressure is continued, it produces a bent tree which can be straightened only partially by reverse pressures. Corrective pressure, however, exerted during the growing period can straighten the sapling so that it becomes a normally straight tree.

Summary of Cases

Case 1. John, (age 7½, I.Q. 122), was referred for a learning inhibition which was so severe that he had been unable to learn to read and was repeating the first grade. His difficulty did not include inability to recognize or write letters or numbers but in putting letters together into words and numbers into combinations. He also exhibited an eye tic which had been present for three years, consisting of a sudden widening of both palpebral fissures immediately followed by a rapid blinking of both eyelids. John was a bright boy with shy but winning manners and a ready smile. He was conforming at home and with other adults, and tended to be a follower with other children of his age; but if the play became rough he would withdraw to play by himself. He was over-solicitous and affectionate with his four-year-old sister and, although he tended to dominate her in their play, he yielded to her easily if she cried. He disliked rough sports but possessed some mechanical skill both in the execution and the planning of a project. He had a fear of dogs and of the dark as well as frequent nightmares from which he awoke screaming and in some confusion.

Both parents were ambitious for their children's school achievement. The mother was meticulous as to manners and repressive of any aggressive or hostile behavior. She was a tense, active but friendly woman, proud of her domestic perfectionism and of her husband's success. The father was an ambitious and hard worker, successful in his profession but with a tendency to depressive moods. He was frequently irritable at home, particularly when he was suffering from pain in one leg which had been amputated below the knee, following an automobile accident in his youth. He wore an artificial leg which fairly successfully masked the injury of which he was very ashamed. Although he was often affectionate with both children he frankly favored John's sister and insisted that the boy protect and love her.

Birth was normal and breast-feeding for five months was followed by easy weaning to a bottle. There had never been any food difficulties. Excretory training begun at four months for bowel control was complete at six months and urinary control was complete at fourteen months both for night and day. He walked alone at about twelve months and was talking in short sentences by about eighteen or twenty months. When he was one-and-a-half his mother had pneumonia and during her months of hospitalization he was irritable and fearful of the strange nurse who cared for him. A traumatic event occuring during this time was of significance relative to his fears which started then. The nurse had left him alone in a play pen in the yard; she heard him crying but finished a task before going to him. She found a Great Dane had jumped into the pen and was licking and pawing the baby who screamed in terror. The onset of his night terrors and fear of dogs followed this experience and upon the return of the mother he was aggressive and hostile when directed. The mother controlled these outbursts by spanking and by irritation and by praise of any docile acceptance or friendly gestures on his part. Within a few months he became quite conforming but more dependent, clinging tightly to the mother when out of the house and following her around at home. He played less freely, often asking permission of his mother before he started with a toy and begging her to play with him.

When he was three-and-a-half his sister was born. For this he had been prepared enthusiastically by the parents who talked often about the new baby he was going to love and care for. He responded to her arrival with an increase in the frequency of his nightmares but this gradually decreased as he was allowed to fondle and hold the baby. He was awkward with her, however, and was often scolded if she cried when he was playing with her and once when he dropped her. When he cried himself, he was scolded for being a baby but was consistently praised for gentleness and quietness. At about this time the father spent more time with John and urged him to help with tools and woodwork. He developed considerable mechanical skill about which he bragged to his mother and others. She discouraged this bragging, always pointing out his goal of skill equal to the father. His response to this was usually withdrawal to his own room or an exaggerated over-solicitude for the sister and, occasionally, refusal to work with his father but insistence upon making something by himself, with which he was never satisfied.

At about four a second important trauma occurred. Awakening from a fearful dream he ran trembling into his parents' room when they were preparing for bed. Suddenly he stopped moving with his eyes glued to his father's amputated leg which he had never seen before because of the father's exaggerated care in hiding what he considered a shameful inadequacy. His father, embarrassed, exploded in a temper and ordered him back to his room; the child went very docilely but was restless and cried out often during the remainder of the night. The next day the eye tic was noticed whenever the father was present. The parents were unable to remember how soon the tic began to occur in situations other than the presence of the father, but within several months the mother had noted its fairly frequent occurrence: when he was scolded, was with strangers, was frustrated and so on. It was still present when he was referred for treatment.

At about four-and-a-half he was severely scolded by the mother of a neighbor child when she caught him viewing the little girl's genitals in the bathroom. John's mother was embarrassed by the news of this event and forbade him to play with the girl. His tic became worse after this event. During the next three years the child attended nursery school, kindergarten and first grade. During these years he continued to be a conforming, fairly passive child, at first playing fairly well in directed groups with other children but withdrawing noticeably during first grade from group activities, preferring to stay in school at recess with the teacher. His nightmares continued but less frequently than at four. Although he could not learn to read he liked school and disliked to be absent when ill with colds.

At seven-and-a-half he was referred for therapy by the teacher who recognized the neurotic factor in his learning difficulty. He was in treatment for a year with bi-weekly interviews and was seen occasionally the following year. Interviews with the mother were maintained in the beginning at monthly intervals in an attempt to help her to understand the correlation of John's difficulties with her restrictive, perfectionistic demand upon him. Insight into her own character difficulties led her to seek treatment for herself with another psychiatrist within about six months. After this time discussions with her concerning John changed from office interviews to occasional telephone conversations.

With the analyst, John at first was friendly but withdrawn in his play. For some time his main interest was lining up small cars and pushing them forward to see how far they would run. His only conversation at this time was, "See how good I am," "I make them go farther than the other children," "I'm smart," "I read best in my room" and so on. One day one of the cars hit a chair leg and broke a fender. His tic was very noticeable at this time and he said he would fix the fender. With Duco he mended it very well and commented, "I'm the best fixer in my home—even better than Daddy." This followed a period in which he mended various broken toys in the toy box, bragging as he proceeded. He found one doll with a broken leg which he insisted upon mending, saying, "Mary (his sister) is broken, no, Daddy is broken, no, I am broken." His tic was marked and at the end of his speech he threw down the doll and said, "Everyone is broken. I can't fix it. The wood won't work." Tears came to his eyes and the analyst said, "Maybe you wonder why Daddy's leg is broken." He jumped up and said, "No, No!" more vehemently than he had ever spoken before. He put his right hand over his genitals and said, "I know. It is because a car ran over him and it hurts him but he's fixed. He wears a wooden leg. I know it is, he said so. I'm sure it is." After some discussion by the analyst as to how frightened he must have been when he first saw his father's leg, he said, "I can't look at it, it's awful." During this period he became quiet, leaned close to the analyst and showed no signs of the eye-blinking. Following a series of further interviews in which he was very friendly and played dominoes with the analyst at his own request, he began to peep at the analyst's dominoes before he would play one of his own. Upon the analyst's jokingly saying "It's fun to peep, it's fun to really know things," he answered with a smile, "I look all over, I look at everything, I know everything." Then, "I used to say I could read but I can't. I'm dumb like Mary." It was suggested to him that maybe he was afraid to look at things for fear he'd learn something frightening like seeing his father's leg. He blinked and answered excitedly, "I want to break everything up and run and run and run only I can't do it. Gee would they kill me if I did!" When it was suggested that perhaps he thought his mother wouldn't love him and would punish him if he was aggressive he quieted down with "Dad too; he always takes mother's side and he always sticks up for Mary—Gee they are mean. No, they aren't. Mother's o.k. but I get sore at Dad, he's always butting in. He thinks he's perfect. Someday I'll be better and bigger; that will show them!" He smiled very warmly at this and took a deep breath and relaxed with "Let's play dominoes again."

In the middle of a play he suddenly said very quietly, "I try to look at the girls in the bathroom;" to the analyst's, "Maybe you want to see how they are made," he answered, "I want to look at their penis." He discussed at some length his belief that girls really had penises and if he could really look clearly he could see them. Following interviews were concerned with sex instructions during which he was avidly interested in pictures of male and female genitals. At one time he drew a woman, then crossed out the breasts and added a penis, then crossed out the penis, and redrew the breasts then scribbled over it saying, "It is all mixed up now."

As his confusion concerning anatomy and sexual functions were gradually being cleared up, he admitted his own castrative fears, his jealousy of his father, his fears of his own destructive wishes toward his father and his fears of being injured in retaliation. Within the framework of this discussion, hostile wishes toward the sister who displaced him, and toward his mother who controlled and deprived him, were also uncovered gradually as he became able to discuss his fears of retaliation from his mother as well as from his father. During this period also he was able to recall and tell the content of various dreams. These repeated like a theme song, situations in which he was about to be attacked by a variety of fearful figures both male and female, such as witches, robbers, devils, ghosts, and in which he was terrified but "frozen" as he called it, and was unable to move either to attack or to flee. During the whole period the parents noticed a decrease and finally a cessation of the tic. In the treatment hours he became gradually much more friendly and merry. He was active building with blocks and making airplanes. Painting them, he took great pleasure in smearing the paint and camouflaging the planes by painting over and over with various colors. He entered gradually into competitive play at school and became one of the best "batters" in baseball. At first his relationship to his sister changed from over-solicitude to hostile teasing which gradually gave way to tolerance and neglect of her with only occasional verbal criticism. His interest in reading became quite marked: he began to read and write words and often in the hour he would ask to read a simple book. Arrangements were made for tutoring as he evidenced decrease in blocking and he then progressed rapidly so that he was almost up to grade by the end of the school year. His fear of dogs showed some decrease after he had worked out his own fears of injury as retaliation for his hostile destructive wishes, to both parents and his sister. He differentiated often between dangerous dogs, meaning strange ones, and nice dogs in which class he placed the analyst's cocker spaniel. At the beginning of the visits he would not enter the analyst's house until he had been assured that the dog was locked up. As he became more aggressive and less fearful he asked to see the dog, which he approached tentatively at first and at each visit more fearlessly until toward the end he would insist on the dog's staying with him during the hour; one day while petting her he said, "I love her; someday I'm going to have one too." At the present time he still shows restraint with strange dogs but no longer evidences any panic upon meeting them.

In this case, an analysis of the historical events plus the material uncovered in therapy lead to certain theoretical conclusions which offer the most valid explanation for the production and maintenance of the symptoms until therapy resolved the conflicts and made available constructive outlets for his impulse energy. The mother's prohibition and punishment of aggressive activity taken in conjunction with her rewarding by love and praise of his repression of hostility and competitive strivings offered a fairly rigid framework within which he could work out his conflicts. By inhibiting his aggressive protests, repressing his rivalrous hostility and compensating with over-solicitude he was able to gain a maximum of pleasure from his mother's love, but at the expense of his aggressive impulses. These, at first, were offered sublimated channels of expression in his handiwork but the mother's depreciation of his accomplishments and her emphasis on a too ambitious goal of achievement robbed these sublimations of their satisfactions and inhibited further attempts at thus transforming the repressed aggressive energy into constructive activity.

At the time of the traumatic incident when he saw his father's injury, his aggressive impulses had already been repressed so that fear of the expression of his rivalrous hostile impulses toward his father, arising out of the oedipus phase and the consequent fear of retaliation from the father,

produced an unconscious conflict expressed only in his nightmares in which
he was impotent in the face of danger. The view of his father's leg
represented a confirmation of the dangerousness of his hostile wishes toward
his father; the rage of his father at this time confirmed the retaliative danger
from the father. Since repressive training had made an aggressive solution of
the conflict impossible, his reaction became denial, a technique he had used
previously to solve hostile feelings toward his mother and sister. Denial by
word (4) was clearly expressed during the therapeutic hours as he first
talked of his father's leg. Denial in act (4) took the form of the eye tic in
which he closed his eyes to shut out the view. Such a small-muscle activity
was probably preferable to one more grossly aggressive, since the mother
had early prohibited gross muscular movement in preference for quiet in-
offense muscular activity. It is interesting, in view of the theory that an
impulse can never be completely repressed and that it continues to seek
devious symptomatic outlets, that the "wish to see" claimed part of the
symptom expression. This was expressed in the palpebral fissure widening
which momentarily preceded the eye closing. The vigorousness of the muscular
contraction of the lid muscles suggests that the tic condensed, also, into its
action a substitute muscular expression for the aggressive hostile wishes.

The use of the symptom to protect himself, at first, from further visual
traumas as in viewing the sex organs of the little girl, and then later as a
defense against any anxiety-producing experiences was clear in the subsequent
history of its occurrence. This development is in line with our knowledge of
the usual course of most neurotic symptoms. The other problem which was
noted only when he went to school, the learning inhibition, correlated directly
with the fixation of the mechanism of denial and its elaboration to protect him
from learning anything through visual experience. The widening of the field
in which denial was used probably grew out of the fallacious reasoning from
the specific to the general such as "I looked and I learned something
dangerous, therefore I must not look and learn."[4]

Case 2. Robert (aged 10, I.Q. 136) was referred to the analyst because of
a generalized anxious behavior. He was a tall sturdily-built boy, shyly friendly,
with meticulous manners and a quiet but anxious mien. He exhibited a
marked mouth tic in which he pursed his lips tightly together and grunted.
According to the mother, his fears reached panic proportions whenever he
was expected to be on his own, either at home or in unfamiliar situations.
He refused to ride alone on the bus or streetcar or to go to friends' houses
to play. The final straw which influenced the parents to seek treatment was
his reaction to their leaving him alone in the house for about an hour one
afternoon. When they returned, he cried hysterically, was trembling and was
quieted only after he was given a sedative at the doctor's advice.

Although Robert had been for four or five years an anxious child, his
fears had increased noticeably in the last five or six months after plans had
been made for him to go to camp the ensuing summer. He had been ambiva-

---

4. See Sylvester and Kunst (12) for an excellent analysis of the psychodynamic
factors in some reading inhibitions.

lent about going; afraid that he would be homesick but he wished to go with his friends who discussed enthusiastically their own camp plans.

Robert's mother was an attractive, excellently-groomed woman of thirty-nine who was friendly but aloof. She talked proudly of her well-run routinized home and of her activities in various civic organizations in which she held executive positions. She emphasized the importance of rules and routine in living and in the bringing up of children. She believed that she had been able to cope well with all the problems of child development until Robert's fears had become so severe. Although his tic embarrassed her, she considered it an idiosyncrasy which would gradually disappear with time, since he had learned to control himself so well in other realms. She was ambitious for her children's achievement, already tentatively planning professions for both boys.

The father was a jovial man who worked sporadically in his father's business but, because of an independent income, was able to lead a fairly irresponsible life. Although the mother disapproved, he kept irregular hours and was frequently out of the home. He spent very little time with the children and demanded immediate obedience and conformity to his wishes when he was with them.

Robert's older brother, Richard, fourteen years old, was a conforming boy who was successful in school, independent, with a few close friends. His interests were normal for his age except in that he had not been allowed to enter athletic activities because of his health. He had developed asthma at about four and attacks occurred at irregular intervals during the winter months. He frankly rejected Robert, calling him a sissy and a dummy. He had been cruel to him when he was younger but with the mother's consistent control he gave up his open antagonism and merely ignored and depreciated him. Although the mother claimed that she loved both boys equally, she spoke with pride of Richard's success in school, of his good manners, and his confidential relationship to her, and she exhibited shame when talking of Robert and his symptoms.

Robert's development had progressed normally in the early years. He was bottle-fed and took solids easily when they were introduced to his diet. Although the mother did not remember the age of excretory training, it was achieved without difficulty by the nurse who cared for him for seven years, after which she left to be married. She was a rigid perfectionistic person who pleased the mother with her insistence upon routine and strict discipline. The mother was proud of the fact that the nurse had prevented the development of any aggressive problems and that Robert preferred to play quietly instead of roughly and actively. From an early age, he had withdrawn from children when they were rough or demanding and gave in rather than fight for his rights. The mother knew of no incidents of masturbation but was sure that the nurse would have punished him if she had noted any masturbatory activity. To her knowledge, Robert had never asked any sex questions nor had he been given any sex information.

At four he had entered nursery school; for the first few months, each morning as they entered the school he clung to his nurse, begging her not to leave him. She was firm, insisting that he be a big boy and scolding him if he cried. As he became familiar with the school he accepted attendance although he never became enthusiastic about it. At five-and-a-half the tic was first noticed consequent to the following experience. Robert had been watching Richard play with his electric train in the basement play room when an older boy joined them. Although all the details of the occurrences were not known, it was later learned that the friend had attempted fellatio with Robert, threatening to kill him if he cried or told. That evening Robert had refused to eat, kept whimpering and when asked what was the trouble all he did was to look apprehensively at his brother. When pressed, Richard finally admitted the fellatio attempt but insisted that Robert had kept his lips clamped tightly and the boy's penis had not entered his mouth. Both brothers were scolded by the mother for the event and Robert was told that if he would leave the older boys alone, he would not get into such difficulties. Not only did this experience usher in the tic which persisted but it also increased Robert's fear of being left alone. Night terrors with incoherent talking in his sleep gradually developed and occurred, according to the mother, whenever the boy was overly tired, or had an exciting day or had been anxious. In the following year, the only new difficulty which was noted was a slowness in learning, despite his superior ability, which difficulty the teacher explained by his inattentiveness and his tendency to daydream. He was conforming in school and kept up with his grade but at the bottom of the class instead of at the top where his I.Q. of 136 would place him.

In spite of his shyness, Robert entered into the therapeutic interviews with enthusiasm and frankly admitted his wish to overcome his fears. Occasionally he would ask to play a game of checkers at which he was adept, but in general the sessions, twice a week for a year, were conducted entirely on the verbal level. He revealed a rich fantasy life of which he told shyly, admonishing the analyst not to let his family know. In his fantasies he identified with superman, and his exploits included magical control of his enemies, devil-like creatures who wished to destroy him. By his merely looking at them they became frozen to the spot and could move only as he commanded. In one fantasy, which he produced in the hour after discussing his fear and hatred of his brother, he tore off long tails from the devils. When one was gone another grew in its place, each longer than the other. Finally they were so long that the devils were tangled in the coils of the tails. During this recital he became quite excited, ticking repeatedly, and laughing uproariously. He tore off a rope from a pull toy in the room, jumped on the sofa and said, "See, this is the way it goes." He wrapped the tail around himself and squirmed as if he were trying to free himself. He had tucked one end in the front instead of the back of his trousers and the analyst commented that, starting in front, it looked more like a penis than a tail. For a moment he looked frightened, then said, "Why are penises different? Sometimes they are enormous and stiff. Sometimes like mine." After an explanation that differences of size correlated with differences in age, the analyst said, "I wonder when you have seen large ones?" He sat very stiffly, kept ticking so badly that he could hardly talk, but finally got out, "Lots of times. I've seen Daddy's and Richard's." To the analyst's, "And who else's?" he said, "You know, didn't mother tell you? That time in the basement." To a sympathetic reassurance he asked, "Why does it get so stiff? I know! Richard told me—to make babies; but why doesn't it get bitten?" When asked if he thought intercourse took place through the mouth, he looked surprised and said, "Of course, how else? Richard told me that is the way they make babies." After some sexual information during which he revealed ignorance of the female genitalia, he was able to tell of the fellatio trauma, of his terror, of nightmares in which he was attacked by enormous men trying to push a penis or a club, sometimes a sword, down his throat. He was always alone in the dream and would try to scream for help but no sound ever came out. His tic ceased during the recital and he returned to his quiet and confidential mood. At the next interview, he said, "I've been thinking about that silly idea I had that babies were made in the mouth; you know, once I looked at Daddy on purpose to see if he really had a penis still." He giggled at this and laughingly said, "Daddy licked me for breaking into the bathroom. I pretended it was an accident." He was quiet for awhile, then, looking up with his old shy manner, he said, "You know, accidents can't happen in our family." The analyst took this opening to suggest that perhaps his parents were very strict. And with this lead, he complained at great length about the things at home that must or must not be done. It was interesting that with each complaint of his mother he countered with praise of her and with a description of the comfort he felt in her presence, definitely exposing the ambivalence in his feelings toward her. The analyst interpreted this ambivalence, emphasizing the fact that because he really loved her he wished to obey her, and it was hard for him to be critical of her. He admitted this but said he would not dare to disobey her. Interestingly enough, however, soon after this discussion the mother complained of his defiance at home, which irritated her particularly because he refused to wash properly and was irritable when she asked him to do things for her at home which he had previously done automatically. He admitted, however, that the tic had markedly decreased and that he was now independently going to other children's homes to play, although he had not attempted any excursion alone on buses or streetcars. In the interview, he bragged of his increasing courage, and his fantasies took on a picture of independence in which he stayed out all night seeking adventure while his parents suffered at home from their loss of him. These fantasies were told with a twinkle and with the reassurance that he would never really do it; and in the end of the fantasy, he finally returned home to be welcomed like the prodigal son and to relegate the brother to the background. A final dream which seemed to put an end to the tic was frightening to him. He was alone in a large empty room and a frightening figure began to approach him. As the figure put out his arm to grab him, Robert sunk his teeth in the figure's hand and then saw that it was his brother. He was trembling when he awakened but he remembered saying to himself, "I'd kill him, I'd chew him all up." In retelling the dream, he was able to talk quite calmly of his anger at his brother and of how often he had been terrified of him, but of his fear of tattling because "they always took his part". He said, "I can't do anything right. Richard is an expert. I'm a fumbler." He was reminded by the analyst of his fear at the time of the fellatio experience, and it was suggested that perhaps his tic represented a defense against the attack but also a defense against his own hostility which might be expressed in biting. His relaxation after this interpretation and the consequent cessation of the tic indicated the verity of the reconstruction.

In the treatment of this case, the mother was seen at infrequent intervals in an attempt to help her relax in her perfectionistic attitude toward Robert. She was able to change only when specific details of handling situations were discussed with her, but on the whole she remained much the same, with only slightly more tolerance for aggressive behavior than previously. However, since Robert became less anxious, he was able to enter into competitive sports with his friends and thus sublimate his aggressive energy with little active hostility or disobedience at home. With a decrease in his fear, he was also able to give up much of his distraction during school hours, in compensatory superman fantasies, which made possible a marked improvement in school achievement. It was not until he was twelve that he finally went to camp; his adjustment during the two months was a happy one.

In this case, as in the previous one, we find a tic developing in a child inhibited in aggressive outlets by a repressive nurse and a mother who was ambitious for mannerly behavior and too superior achievement. The tic developed following a trauma in which he was unable to protect himself adequately both because of his own fear of his aggression and because of the threat of death. The tic thus represented a substitute for a protective movement, the lip closure, and the grunt, a cry for help. The tic then later became a reaction in other anxiety situations in which it was no longer appropriate. His fear of leaving the family was a protection against the expression of his own aggression and the fear of retaliation in injury, since the traumatic experience had shown him his own inability to defend himself adequately.

Case 3. Mary (age 4, I.Q. 117[5]) was brought to the analyst because of two main difficulties. She performed repeatedly a "sniffing" tic which had been of about a year's duration, consisting of nose-wrinkling accompanied by a rapid inspiration, followed immediately by a noisy expiration. She also had a tenacious constipation with moments of voluntary holding back of her feces. At these times she would squat on the floor with her knees drawn up, her arms tightly circling her bent legs, and would hold her self rigid with an anxious look on her face. Then she would suddenly relax and continue her interrupted activity. After about five to seven days of constipation, occasional hard balls of feces would appear in her panties. The mother had noticed that she became increasingly anxious at these times and that the tic became more frequent. During the constipation period, she would never defecate in the toilet although she was placed there at least twice a day, but after the feces began to appear in her panties, she would finally have a large hard stool in her panties. After this she became much more relaxed and ticked less frequently until a new cycle of constipation began, and the whole performance was repeated. Other symptoms which were

5. This I.Q. was obtained at the time of a referral, but the precocity both of her development and of her intellectual behavior indicated that she was a superior child, whose performance in the test situation was below her actual capacity probably as a result of neurotic blocking.

revealed in the first interview with the mother were 1), infrequent night terrors from which she would awake crying and could relax only if she were taken into the mother's bed; and 2), a fear of separation from the mother which made it impossible for the mother to leave the house without her during the day, or for her to play outside the house it tne mother was not present.

Mary's mother was an attractive, vivacious woman of thirty-five years with a ready smile and an efficient, intelligent manner. She had been a successful primary grade school teacher before her marriage, with a reputation among other teachers for keeping perfect order in the class room, and of exacting quick obedience. At the same time, her pupils seemed very attached to her. She had been eager for children and Mary was born a year after her marriage. She entered into the care of the child with enthusiasm and an ambition to have a perfect child. She was a meticulous housekeeper and prided herself on the fact that her tasks did not interfere with a rich social life.

The father, ten years older than the mother, was a successful lawyer, devoted to his wife and children, but ambitious for them. He was very disturbed by Mary's symptoms and was so punitive and irritable at each excretory lapse that she had gradually withdrawn from him and appeared fearful in his presence. At these periods he obviously favored a sister of fifteen months who was an attractive, friendly baby.

Mary's birth was normal and she was breast-fed on a four-hour schedule. Weaning was accomplished without difficulty at about six months and she accepted solid foods as they were added gradually to her diet. Bowel training was begun about the fifth month and urinary training about the ninth month. By a year she was completely trained, even for night wetting. The mother was meticulous in maintaining a routine for eating, sleeping, toilet and play time. She was firm in discipline and consistently rigid in punishing aggressive behavior such as hitting, breaking, tempers, etc. She usually isolated Mary but occasionally spanked her for these acts. In general, the mother was affectionate and warm, but allowed Mary little free play. During play periods, she taught her how to build with blocks, arrange doll furniture in the doll house, and suggested the direction of doll play. By two, Mary was a very well-behaved obedient child, but already showed hesitancy and anxiety in learning new skills such as tricycle riding, climbing, and the like. After her sister was born, when Mary was two-and-a-half, she was eager to play with the baby but when she tried to poke at the baby's eyes was punished for touching her. The mother took full care of the sister, and Mary was cared for by the baby nurse who stayed on with the family. Mary began to be somewhat stubborn with the nurse and developed some incontinence of urine and feces, for which she was punished by the nurse, as well as by her mother.

When she was three, the mother one day went to waken her from her nap on the nurse's day off, and found her smearing feces all over her face. Deeply shocked, the mother slapped her and scrubbed her face vigorously while Mary spluttered and gasped. To further punish her, the mother refused to talk to her the rest of the afternoon, while she cared for the baby. The next day the tic was noticed, and the voluntary constipation started. Her next bowel movement did not occur for six or seven days and then only after an enema which was prescribed by the doctor. During the following year, it was noticed that the tic became worse whenever Mary was anxious, was presented with a task to do, was with strangers, and so on. The nightmares developed during this year, and she clung more and more persistently to her mother, often following her around the house instead of playing. She refused to play with the sister, and when they were left alone, Mary made her cry. She became very neat and orderly, arranging her toys in specific order on the toy shelves and looking anxious and protesting when the toys were placed in a different arrangement by the nurse.

In the first interview Mary appeared as a shy, anxious and unsmiling child who ignored the analyst completely and refused to let the mother leave the room. For play, she chose doll furniture and the small dolls. She arranged the furniture meticulously into rooms, looking to the mother for approval at the placing of each piece of furniture. She put the dolls to bed, each in a separate room, and after waking them, washed them thoroughly, dressed them, and placed them in separate chairs in the living room. Then she repeated the undressing, going to bed, getting up and so on, until the hour was over, when she went away holding tightly to the mother's hand. At the next interview, after two days, she allowed the mother to leave the room but frequently looked into the waiting room to see if the mother was still present. In following interviews, once assured that her mother was waiting for her, she played without interruption, but for several of the interviews she looked frequently at the analyst, saying, "Is that all right?" Gradually, she played more freely and then began to bring the analyst as a collaborator into the play, asking her to dress the dolls, wash them and so on. It was remarkable how carefully she handled the toys, and how skillfully she could walk among the pieces of furniture without displacing or knocking over any of them. If, as rarely happened, a piece was knocked over, she looked at the analyst anxiously and ticked repeatedly. To the analyst's, "Never mind, here, we can knock them over and put them back easily," she responded by relaxing and continuing with her activities. The play became more detailed and covered most the events of daily living. One day she made small balls of clay which she called "grunt", her name for feces, and placed them in the panties of the little girl doll. She always spanked and scolded the doll when she found the balls in the panties, pretending to discover them unexpectedly. One day, she smeared clay all over the girl doll's bed, became quite excited, ticked as she rubbed it off and scolded loudly. The analyst said, "Poor Mary, she just wanted to play with the grunt and it was fun. If we pretend it is clay instead of grunt, she can rub it all over everything and no one cares." To this she smiled, for the first time, and began tentatively to rub the clay over the bed, the bed clothes and finally over the doll. This play continued with increasing abandon and without a noticeable tic for several interviews, then one day she said, "The baby won't grunt in the toilet. Now sit there until it comes out!" She placed the doll on the toilet seat, made clay balls which she surreptitiously placed in the toilet, then said, "O.K., there it is. You can get off." She wiped the doll vigorously, and then repeated the play many times, before putting the dolls to bed. For several interviews, she repeated this toilet play and the fourth day changed the routine with, "She's going to grunt by herself now." She put the doll on the toilet, and instead of waiting excitedly, began to get out the other furniture and arrange it into rooms. She put the nurse in the kitchen, the baby in bed, commenting, "She's having a nap," and finally put the mother and father at the dining room table. Then she took the girl doll off the toilet saying, "She can eat now," and without looking for feces in the toilet, or wiping her buttocks, she placed her at the table with the parents saying, "Baby is too young to eat, now. She has to finish her nap." It was following this hour that the mother reported that Mary had defecated for the first time in the toilet without telling her mother first, but afterwards she had run to her mother excitedly and had pulled her to the toilet, and pointing to the feces, said, "Look mummy! Look at all the grunt."

In the following hours, she gradually gave up the toilet play and entered into a routine in which the nurse took the baby out for a walk, and the big doll remained with the mother and played and talked with her. To the analyst's, "It is fun to have the baby out of the way," Mary said very solemnly, "She's always in the way. I always have to give her my candy. She's a stinky. I wish mother never borned her." The analyst reassured her that all big sisters were angry when babies got in their way and took mother's time. Following this period, Mary entered into much more active play, choosing blocks to build with, and laughing uproariously when she knocked them down.

The treatment interviews of this case were held at tri-weekly periods for three months and weekly for another four months. The tic decreased after the first period in which she smeared the clay over the bed, and ceased entirely after the block play had begun. Her constipation continued for about a year but decreased gradually from the seven- to ten-day periods through three- to four-day periods until the stools occurred daily. However, following the first voluntary movement in the toilet at home, she never again soiled her panties. Gradually, during this period her play at home became freer, she clung less to the mother and nightmares ceased. Coincident to interviews with the child, weekly visits with the mother were instituted, in which she was offered insight into the causative factors producing the symptoms, and was given specific advice as to methods of handling the children to give them greater freedom of expression in activities of their own choice. This mother was able to relax, remarkably well, her perfectionistic attitude and her ambitious pushing of Mary toward achievement beyond her age level. She also learned to handle the sibling rivalry in such a way that she could keep the children from injuring each other, but was able to accept without too great distress their verbal antagonism.

An analysis of the events involved in the production of the tic in this case seems clearly to indicate that psychodynamic factors were involved similar to those of the other cases. The nose-wrinkling expressed denial of the smelling pleasure and probably hostility toward the punishing parent. Such a grimace is used often by children to represent rejection of a person. The short inspiration was a substitute for the pleasurable smelling sensation which is normally achieved through a deep, long inspiration. The expiration expressed a denial and an inhibition of that pleasure. The precipitating trauma was, in this case, punishment by the mother at the moment of the child's indulgence, which was followed by a prolonged rejection by the mother. Inability to protest against the mother's behavior was due to the repression of this child's aggressive and hostile impulses, accomplished through the developmental years by the mother's restrictive training in which she had punished aggressive activity and had rewarded docile conforming behavior by her love. The development of adequate sublimations for aggressive impulses was hampered by the mother's dissatisfaction with the child's performance and her consequent direction of the child's play. This, at the moment of panic, when the child was probably overwhelmed by several conflicting impulses—a hostile retaliation, a wish to continue indulgence in pleasure and a need to conform—an integration was achieved through a neurotic symptom which partially expressed all wishes and yet did not permit activity which might lead to further danger. The second symptom, constipation, undoubtedly developed as a further protection against dangerous activity. Fear of defecation led to avoidance of the toilet, and occasional involuntary defecation into her panties probably occurred when the physiological need overpowered the protective device. Previous to the traumatic event, the child's conforming behavior had partially broken down. Her regression as exhibited in the incontinence which began after the birth of her sister probably resulted from the disillusion she felt at the mother's relegating her to the nurse while she cared for the baby. Incentive for conformity was thereby weakened, and hostile retaliative impulses intensified. This disbalance allowed repressed impulses to partially reappear. It is interesting that there was evidence that this child had begun to defend herself against the uncontrollable act of defecation by a compulsive undoing, as seen in her meticulous orderliness. This is the only case, in my series, in which a compulsive sequela was exhibited. As has been mentioned above, Levy (8) suggested that the tic was the forerunner of a compulsion ritual. This case suggests the circumstances in which such a phenomenon may occur, although there is no evidence that it is an inevitable end result of a tic in all cases.

Case 4. Charles (age 9, I.Q. 124) was referred for treatment because of fear of and withdrawal from any aggressive activity. Sports, which were compulsory at his school, he evaded whenever possible. If forced to play, he fumbled balls, ran very poorly and trembled noticeably. He preferred to play with girls and would dress often in his sister's clothes and parade before a mirror. He was afraid of injury, and nursed minor cuts and bruises by bandaging them with an antiseptic dressing. In the last two or three years he had developed a phobia of riding in trains and, when in one, insisted on standing up, in the middle of a car in order, he said, "to be more protected in case of accidents". He also had a complicated tic consisting of three rapid movements which occurred simultaneously. He would suddenly ball his right hand into a fist over his genitals and quickly run the fist up the fly of his pants as if hitching them up. At the same time, he jerked his head backward and to the left. His school achievement was average but below his capacity and his writing and composition were poor.

Charles' mother, of thirty-seven years, was a plain, small woman, with a friendly but aggressive manner. She was a portrait painter who had gained a small reputation because of her accuracy in reproduction and the meticulousness of her painting. Like the mothers in the other cases she was an efficient, methodical woman who maintained an active life. Although she had several maids, she oversaw all the housekeeping and planned the work. As well, she painted and entered into a rich social program. The children had been trained in a rigid routine and, except for the younger daughter, were early inhibited in aggressive or hostile activity. The mother stated that she preferred them to play quietly and disliked rowdy children. She admitted, smiling, that she had been unable to accomplish the same conformity in her younger daughter that she had produced in the two older children. She had set a high goal of achievement for all of them, and believed that firm consistent training would teach them habits of work and good manners. She admitted that she pushed them to learn, since she thought that satisfaction with less than the best would lead to carelessness and to lack of ambition. Although she punished carelessness and aggressiveness severely, she was a warm, affectionate mother when the children were "good", to use her own word. This mother revealed a prudishness concerning sex, and when asked about sex instruction, she admitted that she would be too embarrassed to offer it. She did not believe that any of the children but Charles had ever masturbated and he had been severely punished when he had been caught at it when he was about five years of age. This incident will be discussed later in detail.

The father, of forty years, was a short stocky man who was, like his wife, an efficient and ambitious person. He was a moderately successful business man but admitted dissatisfaction with the position he had been able to achieve and hoped that his children, particularly his son, would go farther than he. He was proud of his wife and devoted to her. Although presenting a friendly, even-tempered manner outside the home, he was domineering and critical with the children and, like the mother, urging them always to better achievement. He was particularly critical of Charles for his "sissy" ways and gave him footballs, trapezes, etc., to encourage "manly" sports. He felt very frustrated when Charles, forced into sports, was awkward and fearful.

Ann, a sister of twelve, was an attractive, shy child, very well-mannered, with a few close girl friends. She was the father's favorite. Jane, six years of age, was an attractive, tomboyish girl who preferred to play with boys and used her brother's sports equipment in her play with them. She was enuretic, was afraid of the dark, and had occasional nightmares.

Charles' early development was uneventful. Breast-fed until about five months he was easily weaned and easily took solids as offered. Excretory training was instituted in the third month for bowel control and, about the sixth month, urinary control by day was begun. Night wetting continued until a year of age when a routine of picking him up at eleven o'clock was instituted. After this, he became dry at night. However, by the age of four he began to go voluntarily to the toilet during the night.

Any kind of destructive activity was inhibited from the beginning and, by three, he was already a well-behaved, obedient child who would sit for long periods looking at picture books, quietly scribbling or playing with his teddy bear. This latter play consisted mostly of rocking in a small rocker with the animal in his arms. When he was four, the mother was pleased with his quiet behavior with adults and his excellent social manner. She remembered that with guests he always said "How do you do" and "Good bye" voluntarily and often repeated the mother's, "It was nice to have you" as the guests left.

When he was three, and the sister was born, the mother noticed no particular reaction to the baby's coming, other than curiosity which he expressed when watching the baby being bathed. Once, the nurse reported, he touched the sister's genitals and said, "All gone?" with a questioning inflection. She spanked his hand, scolded him for touching the baby and told him to go away, which he did obediently. The mother reported this event to show how easily his sexual curiosity had been curbed. The baby slept in his room until he was about seven, when he was given a room of his own in order to have space for the gym equipment which the father had purchased "to make a man of Charles". His shy, withdrawn behavior was obvious at five when he went to kindergarten. In the group, he showed a marked preference for the girls and became fearful and clung to the teacher when the children were rough or aggressive. This teacher also noted that he showed little independence in activities, often asking for permission or for direction. The teacher had told the mother that he was "too good and too polite". This incensed the mother, but she admitted to the analyst when she brought the child at nine, that it was possible that the teacher had been right, since he had developed into such a "sissy" and such a fearful child. The teacher had also noticed that he peeped surreptitiously at the little girls when they were in the toilet together.

At six a traumatic event occurred. The father, going into his bathroom one afternoon, caught Charles naked in front of a long mirror masturbating. In a rage, he slapped Charles so hard that a red mark remained on his cheek. He ordered him to get into his pajamas and to go to bed without his dinner. Charles obeyed without a comment. In the morning, the father admonished him again and told him if he ever masturbated again, that the doctor would have to cut the foreskin. While the father was talking, Charles put his hand over his pants fly and the father raised his hand to slap him. Charles jerked his head back and looked so frightened that the father restrained himself from hitting him. It was that evening, that the mother noticed the tic when the family was eating dinner. It occurred so frequently that Charles had difficulty eating. She sent him to the kitchen to finish the meal. Eating in the kitchen was her usual punishment for carelessness in table manners. There-after, the tic continued but in various situations whether or not the father was present. The mother believed that it became worse when he was tense or anxious. The fear of riding in trains was noticed sometime during the ensuing year and became sufficiently severe to avoid taking him any place on a train unless absolutely necessary. During the following years, he became increasingly passive and anxious.

At the first interview, Charles appeared as a well-built, slender boy with a noticeable stoop. He was shy and fearful but very polite. Treatment had been explained to him by the mother, at the analyst's suggestion, as help for him in overcoming his fear of trains. When the analyst explained that they would talk and play together so that they could become better acquainted and that by learning more of his interest she could help him, he said "Daddy wants me to be strong, too," and he ticked repeatedly. When asked what he might like to play he answered, "You tell me, I don't know," but he looked at the boxes of airplane parts. With the suggestion from the analyst that they might make one, he said "If you don't mind." In the next few interviews, airplanes and boats were constructed. At first, he asked for direction at each move but, by the fourth hour, he went along on his own, and asked for help in holding glued pieces together, while he worked on other parts. He responded to praise with, "I'm not really good." When it was suggested that he feared failure if he did things on his own, he answered "I can't do anything. Daddy wants me to play football; I can't kick the ball; the boys don't want me to play; they call me 'Butterfingers'." He ticked repeatedly at this time, and stopped working on the plane. The analyst pointed out that he was really a smart boy and had a well-built body, but probably some fear inside him made him anxious and awkward and interfered with his using his strength. Maybe he was afraid of being injured in play as he was afraid of trains. To this he said, "Don't tell anybody, but I wish I were a girl! They get it much better!" When the analyst said, "I know just how you feel! Then you wouldn't have to play football, and get into all those dangerous situations." He relaxed and smiled, as if it was the first time anyone had understood him. Then the analyst said, "But, you know, girls have troubles, too. Sometimes they want to be boys." At this he began to giggle so hard that he choked and tears rolled down his cheeks. Finally he said, "That's what Jane wants." He told then, very confidentially, of his love of his sister Ann's clothes, and how he dressed up in them when he dared. At these times, he fantasied himself as a beautiful movie actress whom everyone adored.

At the next hour, he smiled in a very friendly way, and began immediately to bring articles out of his pocket. Among these things, was a chocolate bar which he gave to the analyst saying, "We can eat that together. You break it in two." When this was done and the chocolate eaten, he picked up a comb and a mirror with, "I fluff up my hair like a girl's." Then he took a ribbon and tied it around his hair saying, "Now, I am a girl!" The analyst complimented his looks and said, "Outside a girl, but underneath, what are you?" With a conspiratorial whisper he said, "There too," hesitated, then blurted out, "I stick my 'pea' between my legs." To the analyst's, "And then you're exactly like a girl?" he looked embarrassed and said, as if disappointed, "No, not really, I just pretend." Then the analyst said, "I think you would really like to know what is the difference between girls and boys." He answered, "I saw Jane, she hasn't any 'pea'." At this, he ticked repeatedly. When the analyst offered to give him information, he said, "Oh, please do!" With drawings, the anatomical differences were explained while Charles sat very quietly and asked no questions.

At the next few hours, he asked for repetitions of the explanations, made drawings himself, and compared them with the analyst's drawings asking, often, "Is, that right?" At one interview during this period, he related the following dream from which he awoke frightened and trembling. In the dream he was riding in an automobile with the family. Suddenly, there was a terrible crash. Then he was standing at the side of the road looking at the automobile which was broken in many pieces. In the middle of the pieces, his father was lying all bloody. He thought, "He's dead," and started to walk toward the father's body. Suddenly, the father stood up; and he was enormous. He came toward Charles with his hand raised menacingly. Trying to run, Charles could only move the top of his body backward. He awoke, just as the father reached him. In associating to this dream, he said that his father had "terrible tempers", that he was always frightened if he was alone with his father who admonished him constantly because he was a sissy. He hated sports; sometimes he dreamed he was trying to play football and he was smashed all to pieces and could see the blood all over. Thinking of the wrecked automobile, he remembered his fear of trains. He said that he felt sure every time he rode on a train, it was going to be wrecked and he would be all maimed. He remembered seeing a man with an arm cut off, and after that he always thought of losing his arm in a wreck. When asked about his father's menacing arm, he ticked repeatedly, and couldn't answer. The analyst told him that she remembered the time his father had hit him in the bathroom, and sympathized with the terror he might have felt. He relaxed and said, "Daddy said he'd cut off my 'pea'." The analyst then explained that boys often heard that but assured him that really it never happened. Charles answered, "But he said so!" To an explanation of circumcision which the father had meant, he asked for pictures to explain it, and became quite absorbed in the subject. Later he said, "Sometimes, I want to touch my penis, but I don't dare it. I put it between my legs and I feel safe." The analyst reminded him of his saying that he pretended to be a girl by this measure and she suggested that perhaps his wish to be a girl was a wish to be safe; that is, if he had no penis, no injury could occur. To this, he confided a fantasy, in which he had frequently indulged. He fantasied that his father went away on a trip, and never came back. He alternated between the thought that his father was killed in an accident, and the thought that he just got lost and didn't know how to get back. The analyst suggested that this fantasy was a good way to get rid of the punishing father, but also it would successfully punish the father for his cruelty to Charles. She interpreted the indecision between the two ways of eliminating the father as due to, first, the fantasied consummation of the death wishes toward him, and then, second, from guilt and fear, the softening of the destructive wish by allowing the father to live but to be lost from the family. Charles seemed relaxed and relieved during this interpretation, but smiled as if he were happy, only after the analyst had explained how common such death wishes were in children, and that really he would not kill his father, nor his father kill him, nor cut off his penis. At this point, the analyst told him that the way he ran his hand up his trouser fly made her think that he might be protecting his penis unconsciously. He agreed that it could be so, and then said, "I always feel better after I do it. But why do I double up my fist?" It was suggested that the fist could be a wish to protect himself by fighting back, too. He laughed and said "Gee, would I punch in his face if I hit!" And he began striking out in the air with his fist as if he were boxing.

The next hour, he voluntarily commented "I don't have to jerk around any more. When I think of it, I think of beating up John and am I strong!" John, it was revealed, was the popular football player in his class. When asked if he thought he could play games, now, he said shyly, "Maybe sometime. But I'm no good at it. I'm no good at anything." Encouraged to elaborate on this, he complained about his mother who always wanted him to do things better than he could. He said, "If I try to do anything, I think of hearing mother say, 'You should do it this way, that isn't good enough,' and then I stop." Further interviews included much repetition of his complaints against his mother, with the accompanying retelling of incidents in which his mother was nice when she kissed him goodnight, brought him candy and so on. His love for his mother was interpreted to him, as well as his despair of pleasing her. He was encouraged to make models in the hours, for which he was praised by the analyst, and by the mother at the analyst's suggestion. One day, he made an elaborate valentine for his mother, which he took home with, "I bet she'll like this."

Weekly interviews with the mother to give her insight into the dilemma into which her conforming, ambitious training had led Charles emotional growth allowed her to relax enough to accept, partially, more aggressive behavior and to give at least verbal praise for his productions and achievements. For greater security in activities with boys, the parents accepted a plan for recreational excursions with a kindly and sympathetic college student, who taught him to play ball, skate, etc. This teaching was casual and began with very simple skills, increasing in difficulty and activity by slow steps.

Symptomatic improvement included cessation of the tic, following Charles' avowal of its uselessness; progressive decrease of his fear of trains during the treatment period with an increasing lack of interest in feminine dress and activities. Within a year after treatment had ceased, he was a fairly normal boy, entering into school sports, but not as enthusiastically as in constructive play and reading.

Reviewing the causative factors of the tic in this case, we note, as in the other cases, that aggressive outlets were denied by Charles' mother who offered him the satisfaction of her love only for conforming behavior and who discouraged the transformation of energy into sublimated activity by her depreciation of his performance. Thus inhibited, the child's defense against the terrors of his father in the traumatic event involved the use of specific protective muscular movements appropriate for warding off the danger and for partial impulse indulgence. The head movement attempted to avoid the blow; the balled fist expressed an aggressive wish to attack the father who attacked him; the hand moving up the pants fly covered the endangered penis and at the same time, allowed partial masturbatory sensation. Repetition of these movements in other anxious situations in which the tic was no longer an appropriate protection followed, as in other cases, the dynamic rule of symptom repetition. Feminine identification proved to be a further protection against his destructive fantasies toward his father and the consequent fear of destruction at the hands of his father. Since riding in a train often symbolizes sexual activity, the choice of the train as the dangerous situation may have had sexual significance for Charles, although this was not clarified in the analysis.

Discussion

In these cases summarized above, certain common factors are in evidence, as was indicated in the introduction. The tic, in each instance, followed a traumatic experience which aroused the fear of being injured. The tic became a defensive response of the small muscles which was appropriate at the moment of the trauma but became inappropriate as it was further used in response to different fears. The small muscle contractions were substituted for more normal large muscle aggression because of previous parental prohibition of such activity and the fear of loss of love or fear of punishment which had become equated in the child's mind with such aggressive motion. In other words, previous to the precipitating trauma, the children already were aggression-inhibited youngsters. In the cases of many children brought up with equally strict parents, aggressive energy is transformed gradually into constructive sublimated activity of competitive games, building and carpentry, cooking, sewing, etc. Two factors inhibited adequate sublimations in these children. One which seemed to operate effectively was the ambitious attitude of the parents which led them to depreciate the child's achievement. Withdrawal from such activity, therefore, protected the child from the further pain of the parent's disapproval. The other factor which made successful sublimation impossible was that the child was too young, both in physical and intellectual growth, to be able to turn to a sufficient variety of activities with success.

French (5, 6, 7) has given us clues to the circumstances in which an ego defense mechanism develops instead of an adequate and acceptable expression of the impulse seeking an outlet. According to his theory, the defense mechanism develops when the normal synthetic function of the ego breaks down, interrupting the successful striving toward an integrated goal. This may occur when instinctual tension becomes too great or when there is too great a gap between instinctual need and opportunity for fulfillment. As a result of these circumstances, the ego becomes fixated upon the obstacle which is blocking successful achievement of the goal. Adequacy in overcoming the obstacle is then interfered with by a variety of factors: 1) the intensity of the emotion which confuses the cognitive or thinking process; 2) a poor or inadequate development of the cognitive process; and 3) the struggle for dominance between different goals. Under these circumstances, an inadequate substitute solution is achieved which we term a defense mechanism and which is expressed in the individual by his neurotic symptoms.

If we scrutinize the circumstances present at the time of production of the tics, it is evident that the events satisfy the criteria suggested by French for the development of a neurotic solution with the use of an ego defense mechanism. In these cases the goal toward which the child was striving, that of maintenance of the parents' love by acceptable constrained activity, was interrupted by the sudden traumatic event which stimulated strong hostile defensive impulses. The ego, at this point, was confronted with the task of integrating these two opposing impulses striving toward opposing goals. It was unable to synthesize the two impulses satisfactorily because both were charged with such intense emotion that neither could yield its goal to the other, and also because intellectual development (cognitive process) was not sufficiently advanced to aid in a rational compromise satisfactory to both impulses. The ego was also constricted in choosing a satisfactory solution by the previous inhibitory influence of the parental training which made dangerous many normal childish activities.[6] The ego then became fixated on the obstacle, the traumatic event, and a compromise solution was achieved which satisfied partially the conflicting impulses and expressed partially the associated emotions. The tic warded off danger, was a partial substitution for impulse expression, and maintained parental love by a non-taboo action. Omitted from this solution was the criterium for an adaptive act; that is, the use of the energy for striving toward a constructive goal. As French claims, a neurotic rather than an adaptive solution leads to constriction of the ego. This condition is clearly shown in the tic case, when as the child develops the ego reacts to all anxiety-producing experiences with the tic rather than with a reaction fitting to the particular event. Thus, learning to react differently to new situations is restricted by the repetition compulsion and the character development is retarded. Character development can progress normally again in the child only after a reversal of the process which led to the development of the tic is achieved. This is accomplished through the corrective experience of psychotherapy and of modified parental behavior toward the patient. Within this new environmental framework, the ego, no longer pressed by fear, is able to discard the old method of solution, the tic, to experiment with new and more constructive solutions, and thus to widen the ego span.

6. The narrowed "integrative field" which French discusses.

BIBLIOGRAPHY

1. Abraham, K. "Contribution to a Discussion on the Tic", *Selected Papers,* Hogarth, 1921, p. 323.
2. Alexander, F. "The Relation of Structural and Instinctual Conflicts", *Psa. Quarterly,* II, 1933. p. 181.
3. Ferenzci, S. "Psychoanalytic Observations on Tics", *Further Contributions to the Theory and Technique of Psychoanalysis,* Hogarth, 1921, p. 141.
4. French, T. "Defense and Synthesis in the Function of the Ego", *Psa. Quarterly,* VII, 1938, p. 38.
5. French, T. "Analysis of the Goal Concept", *Psa. Rev.* XXVIII, 1941, p. 61.
6. French, T. "Goal, Mechanism and Integrative Field", *Psychosom. Med.* III, 1941, p. 226.
7. Freud, A. *The Ego and the Mechanisms of Defence,* Hogarth, 1937.
8. Levy, D. M. "On the Problem of Movement Restraint", *Amer. J. Orthopsychiatry,* XLV, 1944, p. 644.
9. Mahler, M. S. "Psychosomatic Studies of 'Maladie des Tic' ", *Psychiatric Quarterly,* XVII, 1943, p. 579.
10. Mahler, M. S. "Tics and Impulsions in Children: A Study of Motility", *Psa. Quarterly* XIII, 1944, p. 430.
11. Mahler, M. S. et al. "Clinical Follow-up Studies of the Tic Syndrome in Children", *Amer. J. Orthopsychiatry,* XV, 1945, p. 631.
12. Sylvester, E. and Kunst, M. S. "Psychodynamic Aspects of the Reading Problem", *Amer. J. Orthopsychiatry,* XIII, 1943, p. 69.
13. Symposium, "Tics in Children", *Nervous Child,* IV, 1944-1945.

PSYCHOANALYTIC CONTRIBUTIONS TO THE PROBLEMS OF READING DISABILITIES

By PHYLLIS BLANCHARD, Ph.D. (Philadelphia)*

Introduction

The child with a reading disability typically is of average or superior intelligence, able to achieve an I. Q. of 90 to 150 (or more) on oral intelligence tests such as the Stanford-Binet, although rating considerably lower on group tests of intelligence which require reading the questions or instructions. Such a child's failures in school are due not to lack of intelligence but to inability to read well; for example, competency in arithmetic computation is rarely affected, since learning to add, subtract, multiply, divide, etc., is not dependent upon ability to read to the same extent that learning many other subjects is dependent on it. Difficulties in writing and spelling words often are associated with reading disabilities, but disabilities for reading and spelling may appear independently of one another.

Reading disabilities are far more common among boys than girls: statistical studies indicate that eighty per cent or more of children with disabilities in reading are boys. We do not yet have an adequate explanation for this.[1]

*From the Philadelphia Child Guidance Clinic.

1. Monroe has suggested that possibly reading defects, like certain biological variations, may occur more frequently in boys because constitutional factors that impede learning to read are largely characteristic of the male sex (26, p. 98). In the light of psychoanalytic contributions, Blanchard has advanced another hypothesis. She notes that Nunberg stated in regard to the early psychosexual development of girls, that their active, aggressive strivings tend to be held in check by passive, feminine tendencies, seldom reaching the same strength as in boys (29). This may mean that boys more frequently than girls encounter difficulties in the normal repressive and sublimative processes in connection with the aggressive drives for which reading, according to psychoanalytic theories, is one means of sublimation (3). For the statistics on sex and reading disabilities, see (2, 26), and other psychological studies of reading disabilities.

For the purposes of the present discussion, it will be convenient to divide reading disabilities into two categories—those of neurotic origin, and those arising from non-neurotic ·sources. Emotional disturbances may of course be present in both neurotic and non-neurotic cases. The distinction between the two types depends upon the fact that in the non-neurotic group, emotional conflicts have developed largely out of the situation of failure in learning to read, which is in itself a cause of chagrin to the child, and as reactions to the attitudes of parents and teachers to the failure. In the neurotic kind of disability, on the other hand, emotional conflicts and difficulties in personality development have preceded the reading disability, which is a neurotic symptom growing from these earlier maladjustments. Gates, who has probably done research over a longer period of time and on larger numbers of cases than anyone else, estimates that in about seventy-five per cent of children with severe reading disabilities, emotional disturbances and personality problems will be present. He states that in about one-fourth of these cases, the emotional and personality difficulties are the cause of the reading disability, while in the other three-fourths they result from the disability for reading (15).

It is well to emphasize the above statistical data, for while a psychoanalytic orientation enables us to understand the etiology of neurotic reading disabilities and to offer proper therapy for those cases, it is not the approach to be preferred for all. If the figures quoted from Gates are fairly accurate, we may expect that about 20 per cent of reading disabilities will be of the neurotic type, amenable to psychotherapy followed by remedial teaching, but about 80 per cent will be non-neurotic and able to respond to remedial teaching immediately, without its being preceded by psychotherapy. Occasionally, however, even the non-neurotic child suffers from such severe emotional disturbances as a reaction to the failure in reading and the family attitudes toward it that psychotherapy may be required prior to instituting a program of special methods of instruction.

In the present discussion, we shall be concerned chiefly with the smaller group of reading disabilities (the probable 20 per cent mentioned above) in which the trouble in learning to read is an outgrowth of personality maladjustments and is one of the child's neurotic symptoms. Careful differential diagnosis is necessary in order to determine whether we are dealing with this type of case or whether the reading disability is of non-neurotic etiology.[2] Diagnostic reading

2. The etiology may be quite as complicated in the non-neurotic cases as in the neurotic ones, since the disability for reading may arise from a variety of sources. For example, certain neurological conditions may be a primary factor. Nielson (28) mentions that injury to the angular gyrus of the parietal lobe impairs its function of recognition of symbols, including letters and words; or lesion of Wernicke's area, causing loss of the function of recognition and recall of sounds of words, may result in reading disability since ordinarily in learning to read the sounds of words must be associated with the visual symbol of the written word. Nielson states, however, that individuals who have suffered destruction of the cortex of the angular gyrus can be taught to read by the Fernald-Keller method, which utilizes kinaesthetic factors in learning (9). Orton's neurological theory of reading disabilities, stressing faulty unilateral cerebral dominance, which causes images formed in one side of the brain to conflict with those formed in the other side, is too widely known to need more than passing reference (30). This hypothesis has been questioned by other investigators because the errors in reading ascribed to a defect in cerebral dominance often are susceptible to alternative explanations not considered by Orton. See, for instance, Schilder (36). Defects of vision or hearing are probably more frequent etiological factors in reading disabilities than neurological conditions. Gates has summarized a number of controlled statistical studies which show that vision defects have been found in 44 per cent of reading disability cases as compared to 38 per cent of good readers, while a hearing loss of 15 per cent or more occurred in 30 per cent of reading disability cases but in only 11 per cent of good readers. Left-handedness, left eye and hand dominance or mixed eye and hand dominance, once thought prominent in association with failures in learning to read, appear only 10 per cent more frequently among children having trouble with reading than among those who learn to read satisfactorily (17, 26).

When children have difficulty in learning to read, attitudes of parents and teachers often are such as to exaggerate the problem until it grows into a real disability. Preston described the reactions of parents to their children in 100 reading disability cases (34). Some of the parents were deeply worried and anxious; others thought the children lazy or stubborn; still others were bewildered by the child's not learning to read. Some of the parents were irritable or reproachful while others scolded or beat the children. Preston also reported on the attitudes of 32 school principals toward reading disabilities of 40 pupils (35). Only four of the principals had any insight into the poor reading as cause of poor school work; the other 28 principals ascribed the trouble to low mentality, poor physical condition, psychopathic or delinquent tendencies; none of these opinions proved correct when the children were examined by physicians and psychologists.

In learning to read or spell words, psychologically speaking, we know that visual, auditory and kinaesthetic sensations, perceptions and memories are associated in a complex mental activity, involving both analytical and synthetic processes (7). To put it more simply, in learning to read words, there must be visual perception and recognition of letters and combinations of letters in association with the sounds of these combinations, while the meaning of the word also must be associated with the letter combinations that form it. Perhaps children who learn to read easily employ this complex mental process early in reading. Certainly, in many reading disability cases, the chief cause of trouble has been failure to acquire this approach. One such case is described in detail in the literature, showing how a seven-year-old boy, who chanced to be highly gifted in visual perception and memory, was depending upon these gifts for learning words, never associating the spoken word with the written one. Thus he could reproduce words that he had seen in writing but was unable to pronounce them and did not know how to say them when he encountered them in reading lessons. (This case appears as Case I, Tommy Nolan, by Blanchard, in *Psychiatric Interviews with Children* (41).

Besides such possible factors as those indicated above, poor educational training may result in inability to read. Once, in a school survey, tests were given to a whole third grade in which none of the pupils could read due to incompetent teaching in the first and second grades.

tests alone do not differentiate the neurotic from the non-neurotic child with a reading disability, for the same types of errors ordinarily are made by both. Emotional reactions to reading tests may be significant, however, in distinguishing between neurotic responses and attitudes toward the failure in reading resulting from it. Careful medical examinations (including tests of vision and hearing), a developmental history, and a study of the child's personality are important. Only on the basis of data so obtained, as well as the findings from psychological tests, can we formulate an adequate diagnostic opinion as to whether a reading disability in any given case is a neurotic symptom or stems from other sources. If we fail to detect the presence of emotional factors in this kind of diagnostic approach, we shall be made aware of them by the child's inability to respond to remedial teaching, for one characteristic of the neurotic reading disability is the child's failure to learn to read by any method of instruction, given either individually or in a group, until there has been a recovery from his neurosis.

Historical background (Review of the literature)

Most of our current knowledge about reading disabilities has been acquired since 1920. Previous to that time, there were some reports in medical literature on cases of "word-blindness" or "word-deafness" but appreciation of the full extent of trouble with reading among school children did not come until the application of psychological tests revealed that many children who would formerly have been considered mentally deficient were in reality failing school work because of lack of reading skill and were of normal or superior intelligence. Contemporaneously with the development of psychological testing methods, techniques for psychoanalytic work with children were being devised under the leadership of Anna Freud. New light on special educational disabilities, including those for reading, came from both clinical psychology and child analysis. Although psychologists had to devote considerable time from 1920 to 1930 to perfecting diagnostic reading tests and conducting statistical studies comparing groups of children with reading disabilities to control groups of good readers (7, 8, 16, 18, 19, 21, 27), they became aware fairly soon of an association between emotional or personality disturbances and reading disabilities. Simultaneously, psychoanalysis was revealing that there sometimes seemed to be a causal relationship between unconscious emotional conflicts and attitudes and scholastic failures in special subjects.

Psychology and psychoanalysis have been in considerable agreement in including emotional factors in the etiology of some reading disability cases. Thus, Jones stated that disabilities for a particular school subject were often due to an inhibition of interest because that subject was unconsciously associated with some personally disagreeable idea or topic and that after the unconscious associations were brought into consciousness through psychoanalysis, the individual was able to master the subject which had been failed previously (23). At about the same time, Lois Meek had observed that young children showed wide individual differences in their emotional attitudes toward reading even in their first lessons (25) and Elizabeth Hincks published a series of case studies in which she emphasized the relationship between reading disabilities and personality maladjustments, stating her belief that in a few of her cases the child's emotional conflicts were significant in the etiology of the disability for reading (20). Although advancing a neurological explanation for reading disabilities, Orton noted emotional disturbances often coincident with them, but for the most part considered that the emotional maladjustments grew out of the experience of failure in reading rather than that they preceded it (31, 32). Gates, in his earlier writings, mentioned the possibility that emotional problems and personality maladjustments might be contributing factors in some cases of reading disability, and has since given increasing attention to these factors (15, 16, 17). Blanchard reported several cases of reading disability or arithmetical disability where emotional disturbances also were evident, indicating that these disabilities might develop from a child's emotional attitudes toward the subject (3a, 4).

After these beginnings in the nineteen-twenties, the early thirties saw still more study devoted to the role of emotional factors in the production of reading failures. Strachey's article on unconscious factors influencing the reading process appeared in 1930 (37). In 1935 and 1936, papers by Tulchin and by Blanchard reported clinical case summaries showing that some children's difficulty in learning to read was a symptom of emotional conflict or neurotic illness (3, 5, 6, 39).

In his general theoretical paper, Strachey reviewed the evidence that reading represents a sublimation of oral tendencies, especially those of sadistic and destructive nature. Hence skill in reading breaks down when these oral drives are unstably or incompletely repressed and sublimated: reading threatens to bring about release of too many unsublimated sadistic and destructive oral impulses instead of providing a sublimated outlet for them. Tulchin, in his series of cases, described such emotional factors as emotional instability, resistance to authority, feelings of inadequacy, infantile personality, anxieties and conflicts arising from family relationships, such as sibling rivalry or marital disharmony of parents as contributing to reading disability. From her case material, Blanchard arrived at the conclusion that a common etiological factor was difficulty in handling aggression, with excessive guilt and anxiety over hostile, destructive or sadistic impulses and fantasies, which frequently were oral in form, as suggested by Strachey. Blanchard also described certain similarities between reading disabilities and neurotic symptoms as the latter are seen in psychoanalysis. The neurotic symptom, from this viewpoint, in one sense originates from an effort to solve ambivalent guilt conflicts; it affords a disguised expression for repressed instinctive drives but at the same time relieves anxiety and guilt about those drives through the self-punishment of illness or securing punishment from others. In like manner, a reading disability often disguises hidden motives; also it satisfies the guilty need for punishment by exposing the child to a situation of failure at school and criticism both there and at home.

In their book "Common Neuroses of Children and Adults" (33) English and Pearson enumerated four emotional situations that might be a basis for reading disability: (1) Some unpleasant and painful experience may have occurred during the early efforts to learn to read so that the child becomes conditioned against reading or has a negative attitude toward it. (2) If there is great antagonism of a child to a parent, and the parent constantly stresses success in reading, the child may express rebellion through refusing to learn to read, when he dare not openly resist the parent. (3) If a child has been severely inhibited in peeping, his superego may place a ban upon acquiring knowledge by visual means. Reading implies learning things by use of vision and the inhibition may readily become attached to that subject. (4) Letters and words may come to represent curious anal-sadistic fantasies and in attempting to keep these repressed, the child may avoid reading or introduce into it word distortions that afford disguised expressions of the fantasies.

Sylvester and Kunst, after studying thirteen reading disability cases, concluded (1943) that trouble in learning to read is one aspect

of disturbances of the exploratory function of the instinctual tendencies, the manifestation of curiosity as an aggressive, self-assertive
activity becoming a source of anxiety to the child, with reading disability serving as a defense against this anxiety (38).

Psychoanalytic theories as applied to reading disabilities

From the preliminary orientation of the preceding introductory
comments and sketchy history of the literature, we come to our chief
purpose—a brief review of certain psychoanalytic theories that help
to explain how difficulties in reading may sometimes develop out of
emotional conflicts and neurotic tendencies. Anna Freud has described how a young child's training (education) is facilitated by his
love of adults and his wish to retain their affection and approval (10).
The child accepts instruction from his parents, in his preschool years,
motivated by his love of them and his desire to please them. If the
parent-child relationship is a less affectionate one and engenders
considerably more than an ordinary amount of friction, the child may
express hostility to the parents in negativistic behavior toward their
training. We often see this in young children who refuse to be toilet
trained or who will not talk although quite capable of doing so.

When the child enters school, the attitudes he has previously had
toward parents may be transferred into his relationship with his
teachers. If he has liked his parents and been willing to learn what
they taught, he will often adopt the same positive attitude toward
learning from teachers. On the other hand, when a child has had
more than the usual amount of hostility toward parents and reacted negativistically toward their instruction, he may carry over
these patterns to his teachers, regardless of whether they are pleasant
or unpleasant people in their own right. Sometimes this situation results in the child's becoming a disciplinary problem in school but
sometimes he yields to the classroom discipline and centers his negative responses upon learning, either in general or in particular upon
learning to read.

A well-known psychoanalytic contribution to education is the
concept that learning offers an opportunity for the sublimation of
instinctive drives. In the first years of life, the child tends towards
fairly free and open expression of sexual curiosity and interests, and
of aggression, with the latter often directed against animals or
people. During the latter part of his preschool life, if development
has been normal, the child begins to control and modify such in-

stinctive behavior. Anna Freud has spoken particularly of the importance of aggressive drives being sublimated by turning their energy into constructive rather than destructive activities and into the accomplishment of all sorts of tasks (12). By the time a child enters school, he should at least be started on this road of sublimation of sexual interest and aggression and his school work offers a chance for further sublimation. If the child has acquired very little capacity for sublimation, he may not be able to take advantage of the opportunity for it afforded by school tasks. He is apt then to develop into a poor student and a behavior problem as well, but will be more likely to fail in all subjects than to have a disability for some one, such as reading.

In the reading disability cases, more frequently the child will be suffering from severe unconscious conflicts, with repression of impulses and imperfect capacity to sublimate them, so that much of his energy is used up in maintaining repression and not enough is left over for such a complex mental process as learning to read. Moreover, this type of child often tends to resort to restriction of ego activities in order to escape painful situations and now may utilize this defense mechanism to avoid the painful experience of seeing classmates excel his achievement, giving up all effort to learn to read as a way of evading competition where he knows he will appear inferior to others (11). This soon results in the child's being so far behind in the subject that he has a real disability for it.

Either traumatic experiences or chronic subjection to excessive emotional strain in the relationship with parents may result in unconscious conflicts that interfere with a child's learning. A good example of a traumatic emotional experience is that of a child who has been separated from one or both parents. In working with the English children during war time, Anna Freud found that loss of parents or separation from them was a severe trauma for the child (12, 13); we have known this for some time, too, in our clinical work with children placed in foster homes or institutions and temporarily or permanently separated from their own parents. Such a traumatic experience may be an immediate cause of trouble with learning if the child is emotionally disturbed by it at the time of school entrance or during early school years. Again, the emotions surrounding an earlier traumatic occurrence may be reactivated by some later event of similar nature that revives the memories and feelings associated with the original traumatic situation.

A child suffers from chronic emotional stress when exposed constantly to unfavorable family relationships over a long period of time. One illustration would be the kind of family life in which parents are antagonistic to each other, are constantly quarrelling, and use the child's behavior or disciplinary questions as a means of provoking each other into arguments or criticizing each other. Under these circumstances, a child often feels that he is to blame for the disharmony between the parents and is caught in conflict between guilt over the trouble that he occasions and resentment and hostility toward the parents for the way they are using him. Another familiar illustration is continuous unfavorable comparison of a child with a brother or sister, which results in jealousy and hostility toward the parent and the favored sibling coming into conflict with love for those members of the family.

In these chronically unfavorable family relationships, reading sometimes becomes a focus of the parents' dissatisfactions with the child, especially if the child should chance to have some trouble with it. When the parents' complaints center upon reading, there is all the more likelihood of any mild difficulty growing into a severe disability and becoming one of the neurotic reactions to parental pressures. In these parent-child relationships where there are chronic situations affecting the child's emotional development, psychotherapy for the child is unlikely to be of much benefit unless there is also work with the parent.

It is logical to inquire why children with hostile attitudes towards parents and teachers, or children suffering from emotional conflicts and neurotic repressions, should have trouble in learning to read more frequently than in learning other subjects. Sometimes, of course, a child's emotional problems do interfere with learning some other subject or prevent mastery of any school work at all. But as Gates stated, the majority of failures in the first years of school life are due to reading, and this subject does seem to be a source of far more trouble to children than any other single one.[3] Thus we need to seek for an explanation of these facts.

In the primary grades, learning the fundamentals of reading is a more complicated mental process, probably requiring greater expenditure of energy and better sustained attention, than learning the first steps of arithmetic. Hence a child may have enough energy left

3. For statistics, see Gates (17).

over from maintaining repressions and may be able to sustain attention sufficiently well to learn his number work but not his first reading lessons. Furthermore, reading is symbolically, for the unconscious, a sublimated aggressive, sadistic activity, according to the psychoanalytic viewpoint (24, 37). Therefore, while reading offers an excellent opportunity for the sublimation of aggressive tendencies for a child whose development has been normal so that he is free to sublimate them, for a child whose neurotic conflicts are largely concerned with trying to keep aggressive drives repressed, even a sublimated expression and satisfaction through reading may not be permissible to the ego and superego. We shall come to some clinical case material illustrative of this statement a little later.

In his *Psychopathology of Everyday Life,* Freud explained certain likenesses between errors in speaking or writing and the mechanisms of neurotic symptom formation. The psychoanalytic concept of the neurotic symptom regards it as a compromise between wishes to gratify an impulse and the need to refuse gratification or even to deny that such an impulse exists. In a symbolic manner, the symptom gratifies a repressed instinctive impulse but at the same time disguises both the gratification and the existence of the impulse itself. Freud described many errors of speech or writing that served the same purpose; when we come to case reports, we shall see that errors in reading sometimes afford symbolic gratification or expression of a repressed impulse while concealing it and not admitting its existence.[4]

Undoubtedly still another reason why neurotic or emotionally disturbed children are likely to develop disabilities for reading rather than for another subject is the fact that reading content can so easily become associated with emotional conflicts. In the psychoanalytic literature, there are many illustrations of the ways in which single words or certain combinations of words become surrounded with a whole constellation of emotionally colored associations, so that a person may seek to evade using those words or forget them. The content of reading, either as it consists of separate words, or contains certain letters, or tells about certain things, may become associated with emotional conflicts already present in the child's life. If this happens, the child may dislike reading because he has

4. This statement is not intended to imply that errors in reading must always resemble a neurotic symptom, however, for defective vision or some other condition may cause errors in reading that superficially are very similar to the errors resulting from emotional conflicts.

found it emotionally disturbing, or refuse to read in order to avoid the danger of recurrence of the emotional disturbance, or when he does read, may be so upset and apprehensive that he will make many mistakes.

For example, if a child pictures the letter C and certain other letters as animals with mouths open ready to bite him, he may want to have nothing to do with reading matter because many words have these letters and recall his fears of being bitten, as actually happened in two cases seen at the clinic. Both children who thus spoke of letters biting them were struggling to repress hostile wishes toward baby sisters whom they wished to bite or eat up; their reactions to the letters were expressions of their feelings of guilt and need to be punished, in one sense; in another sense, we might say that as usual there was a wish disguised by the fear.[5]

An experimental investigation conducted by two psychologists supports the psychoanalytically derived theory that reading content which is emotionally disturbing leads to difficulties in reading. A study was made of the responses of four students without fear of high places and of six students who did have this fear, when given reading matter that might activate it. Their comprehension and memory for reading material was first tested by a paragraph selected because it seemed to contain nothing that could be associated with high places or falling from them. They were then given a paragraph of similar length and difficulty but describing a person hanging from the top of a tall building by an overall strap caught on a projecting plank, in imminent danger of falling to his death. The four students who were not fearful of high places comprehended and recalled about the same amount from both reading paragraphs. The six students who suffered from a phobia for high places, on the other hand, made mistakes in reading, read more slowly and could recall much less of what they read in the second paragraph describing the man in danger of falling from the top of the tall building (40).

Many children's books have been carefully edited with the idea of excluding material that might be emotionally disturbing. Obviously, however, since unconscious attitudes of the child are involved, it is impossible to choose reading content free of all emotional coloring, even if it were considered advisable. We cannot protect a

5. More detailed account of these two cases appears in the paper previously referred to (3).

child from encountering letters or words that for some reason he has endowed with symbolic significance. Furthermore, story content that activates painful emotions for some individuals will not do so for others (as indicated by the experimental study just mentioned). Thus the same reading content may have an emotional value of one sort for some children but may arouse no emotional response or a quite different emotion for other children. More extensive censorship and editing of children's reading actually could abate neither reading disabilities nor emotional conflicts, for the former are the outgrowth from many possible sources and the latter exist before the child reads disturbing content, indeed determine whether he will be disturbed by it. Moreover, if we could succeed in robbing books of emotional stimulus, we should lose one of the greatest incentives to reading, for both children and adults alike read as a means of obtaining emotional excitation and not merely to secure information. This incentive to learning to read has already been partially lost, in our modern times, because radio and movies compete with reading as sources of emotional excitement and satisfaction.

Cases illustrating neurotic reading disabilities

For purposes of brevity, the following illustrations will not be complete case summaries but will consist of material selected chiefly to clarify points made in the preceding general discussion. Since the selection has been made for research purposes and to illustrate theoretical concepts, no implications as to therapeutic methods and techniques are intended.[6] In some instances, longer case reports have been published previously (in papers referred to in reviewing the literature on reading disabilities). Perhaps it should be stated that the children were seen at the clinics, appointments being once or twice weekly for varied periods of time. When the children were living in their own homes, case work with the parents was quite as important as psychotherapy for the children.

The first case illustrates a chronically unfavorable parent-child relationship in which the child was under constant emotional strain. For some three years prior to his referral to clinic, the boy had been the object of his father's anxiety and criticism, focused upon the subject of reading. Why the boy developed difficulty in reading and

6. Viewpoints on psychotherapy may be found in the author's contributions to the symposium on *Psychiatric Interviews with Children* (41).

other neurotic symptoms should be self-evident from the case material presented below.

Case. 1.   Matthew was a twelve-year-old boy who was repeating fifth grade and still failing the work. He was considered mentally deficient by parents, teachers and classmates but psychological examination showed that he actually was of superior intelligence, with an I. Q. of 133.

The boy's father had had considerable difficulty in his vocational adjustments and had often been unemployed. He displaced anxiety from himself onto worry about the boy's future, stressing success in school as a preparation for later vocational success. When the boy was in third grade, the father began to supervise his school work. Although Matthew's teachers gave him good marks in reading, his father decided that he was poor in this subject. The father came to this conclusion after asking Matthew to read matter that was far too advanced for a third grade pupil. From that time, however, the father centered his anxiety upon the boy's reading and began to tutor him in it. Invariably, he scolded and criticized the boy during these home lessons, so that they always ended with Matthew in tears and his father in a temper. It is not strange, therefore, that the boy made no further progress in reading between the third and fifth grades or that by the time he was in fifth grade, he had a serious reading disability. By then, also, he was so sensitive to criticism that he would burst into tears at the slightest reprimand from a teacher and would fight with any child who said a teasing word to him.

Neither remedial teaching nor psychotherapy helped in this case so long as the boy remained at home, for the father was unable to change in his relationship to the boy, continued to displace anxiety onto him, and could not be induced to forego tutoring him. When the boy went to a boarding school and was thus freed from his father's anxiety and criticisms, he was able to learn to read with the help of individual remedial teaching.

Unfavorable comparisons with a brother or sister have been mentioned in the literature as another type of chronic family situation leading to neurotic conflicts and trouble with reading, in some instances. In the next case, comparisons between a living child and a brother who had died were intimately associated with the reading disability.

Case 2. Patrick was a nine-year-old boy, of normal intelligence (I. Q. 105) but was unable to read. Remedial teaching provided at school was unsuccessful in helping him to learn reading. There had been three children in the family—a first son who had died, Patrick, and a younger sister.

In his interviews with the therapist, Patrick soon spoke of the death of his older brother as having occurred shortly before he himself started first grade. A little more than a year later, Patrick said, he received a book as a birthday gift but he had not liked it, for when the stories were read to him, they proved to be about people who were killed. He had hated the stories and cried whenever he saw the book. After hearing those stories, he felt that he never wanted to hear a book read again nor did he ever want to read one himself.

At first, during his interviews, he stressed his love for his mother and his dead brother and dwelt upon wishes always to be good and kind to people. However, he soon became jealous of other patients, was angry with them for coming and with the therapist for seeing them. He complained that the therapist was just like his teachers, preferring other boys to him. After awhile, he began to accuse his mother of never having loved him as much as his dead brother. He told how she often talked about the dead child, saying that he had learned to read very quickly and criticizing Patrick for not being as apt at reading. "I wouldn't want to be like my brother," Patrick asserted contemptuously, "maybe he could read but he couldn't stand up for himself with the other kids. I'm a good fighter. They don't dare pick on me."

Patrick also told of his mother's weekly visits to his brother's grave and the tears that she shed each time she went there. Discarding his desire to be good and kind, he went on to express his wishes to dig up the brother's body and bury it somewhere so far away that his mother would never be able to find the grave and visit it. Or better yet, he would burn the body, destroying it completely. He then told how he hated his mother when he believed that she was behaving as if she wished his brother had lived and he had died. Similarly, he hated his teachers and his therapist when he thought that they might prefer other boys to him.

The mother, in the above case, had brought the boy to the clinic at the insistence of the school; she rarely kept her appointments with the social worker but sent the boy alone for his interviews with the therapist; finally, she withdrew him from therapy before it was completed. The material is therefore of interest only in connection with the etiology of the boy's reading disability. Obviously, when he first came to therapy, his conflicts about his mother and brother had been unconscious and he had repressed his resentment and hostility. His wishes to be good and kind were defenses by which he maintained the repression. The book with stories about people being killed naturally stirred up the repressed aggressive drives and threatened to bring them into his conscious experience. In turn, this aroused feelings of guilt and anxiety (shown in his weeping whenever he saw the book) as he came closer to awareness of his hostility toward his mother and his dead brother. Thus another defense and way of maintaining the repressions was refusal to learn to read, for he feared that reading content might release aggressive impulses. Self-assertion through being different from his brother was indicated by his stating his preference for being a good fighter rather than a good reader and his desire not to be like his brother. This was another motive influencing his negative attitude toward reading. Again, not learning to read was a disguised expression of hostility toward the mother who wanted him to be clever in this respect.[7] He identified the teachers who wanted him to read with the mother and also rebelled against learning to read to please them. Indeed he transferred his jealousy of his mother and brother to the teacher and other pupils at

7. I am indebted to Dr. F. H. Allen for calling to my attention the motive of wishing to be different from his brother in connection with the boy's reading disability. Failure in reading as a covert form of hostility to a parent was mentioned by Pearson and English (33).

school, and to the therapist and other patients at the clinic, always neurotically recreating for himself the unpleasant and painful family situation which he was trying to repress from consciousness.

In the following case, we see how a later event may reactivate the unconscious feelings that surrounded an earlier traumatic one.

Case 3. Thomas was an eleven-year-old boy, failing fifth grade for the second time. He had made low ratings on group tests given at school. Individual tests showed that he had an I. Q. of 108 but was handicapped in doing both group tests and school work by a reading disability. He dated the start of his trouble with reading from the first part of third grade, when a teacher whom he liked very much had to go to the hospital for an operation. Since she did not return to the school, Thomas assumed she had died. He explained that he was so worried over the teacher's absence and her supposed death that he could not keep his mind on his work and so fell behind in reading.

This preoccupation with the question of the teacher's possible death becomes more intelligible if we know that when the boy was five years old, his mother had been away in a hospital, for an operation. He did not recall these circumstances about his mother's hospitalization, even when they were mentioned to him; he only remembered about the teacher.

In some of his therapeutic interviews, Thomas wanted to read aloud. It then became obvious that the content of reading often brought up his unconscious emotional conflicts. He would be reading fairly well when suddenly he would begin to make many errors until he stopped and talked of personal matters suggested to him by something he had read. After speaking out what had come into his mind, he could resume reading without excessive mistakes. For example, in reading a story about a dog, Thomas began making errors and continued to do so until he had paused to talk about a dog he once had owned. He had loved his dog very much indeed, he said, but he had not been permitted to keep it. After his dog was given away, he was very lonely; he cried and cried because he wanted his dog back and because he did not know what might be happening to it. "I was afraid my dog might die without my knowing about it," he explained. "It is awful to be wondering whether someone you love is alive or dead."

By the time his therapy ended, he could read without breaking down as described above. According to follow-up reports, during the next two years, his school progress was satisfactory.

The circumstances of the teacher's going to a hospital for an operation evidently revived the boy's feelings about his mother's hospitalization even though he had repressed the memory of his mother's operation and his anxiety about it. Reactivation of the emotional trauma was not the only reason for his trouble with reading, however, for from his interviews it was evident that reading content too frequently tended to stir up his unconscious conflicts. It does not take a very vivid imagination to realize that his feelings about his dog, for instance, were like those he had experienced when his mother was in the hospital. These feelings quite obviously were brought closer to consciousness when he read the story about the dog, even though it was a very cheerful one, just because the content contained the word dog many times repeated.

Both case 2 and case 3 illustrate the statements in the preceding general theoretical formulation concerning the ease with which reading content becomes associated with a child's unconscious emotional conflicts, leading to a break-down in reading skill, or to an aversion to reading.

An immediate effect of an emotional trauma connected with separation from the mother at a time when the child is entering school is illustrated by the next case.

Case 4. When Ethel was nearly six years old, her mother was forced to place her in a boarding school. Ethel's father had died two years previously and now the mother had to go to work so that she could no longer keep the child with her. At the school, Ethel seemed to have little appetite and would refuse to eat very much except when her mother visited and brought her food, which she would eat heartily. She did not learn to read during two years in first grade. She was brought to the clinic at the age of eight years, unable to read, still refusing food and having lost weight to the point where she seemed weak and ill and had to be kept in bed for considerable periods. Medical examinations could detect no physical basis for her symptoms.

In her interviews at the clinic, both her refusal to eat and her failure in learning to read soon appeared as symptoms of her unconscious conflicts over being sent away to school by her mother. At first she spoke of how much she loved her mother but soon in her play she began to dramatize her other attitudes of anger and hostility. She portrayed a mother doll sending her little girl doll away to school. The little girl doll was then angry with the mother, would not let the mother have anything to eat because she wanted to starve her mother to death, a fate that would serve her right for sending the little girl away to school. Immediately afterward, however, the little girl was punished for being so bad to her mother and also was described as being unable to eat and feeling weak and ill. Another drama with the dolls showed the little girl refusing to study or to read at school. Her poor school reports were sent to the mother doll, who decided that the school was no good and came to take the little girl home.

After this play with the dolls, Ethel could talk about how she felt when her mother placed her in the boarding school. She became aware of her idea that if she became ill or did not do well in her school work, she could force her mother to take her home again. At this point, she went on to explain that in reality, her mother could not take her because she no longer had a home. Since her father was no longer alive to take care of her mother and herself, her mother had to work to support them. She worked hard to earn money to pay for Ethel's school and her clothing. Ethel then felt very sympathetic toward her mother, who was tired from her hard work, and she was sorry that she had worried her mother by not eating and not learning to read. She announced that she was eating all right now but she had not been able to learn to read at school and she wished she could have someone to help her with reading. This request was seen as indicative of a change in attitude toward reading and special teaching was provided. Ethel worked hard with her tutor. She learned to read and began to make regular progress in school. At the time of the last follow-up report she was in seventh grade. None of her symptoms had recurred.

We might ask why this girl reacted so much more violently to being placed in boarding school by her mother than to her father's death. We can only guess at the possible reasons. Many children have less conflict over the loss of a parent through death than over separation from a parent through placement. Apparently placement is often taken as an act of aggression and rejection from the parent and therefore stimulates anger and resentment as well as grief. When a parent dies, love and grief over the loss need not necessarily come into conflict with other attitudes of anger and resentment. Serious conflicts over the death of a parent of course do occur when there was so much hostility toward the parent that a child feels guilty because of the hostile wishes before the parent died, as if they were responsible for the event. Thus a parent's death may or may not be a source of conflict to a child, depending upon the relationship that preceded it. On the other hand, placement often arouses conflict because it engenders hostility toward the parent while at the same time love and wishes to be reunited with the parent still persist.

While the next case also involves a child's conflicts over placement by the mother, it was selected for presentation primarily because it illustrates how errors in reading may provide a disguised expression and gratification of repressed wishes and drives, as was suggested in the more theoretical explanations of reading difficulties.

Case 5. Benjamin was an eight-year-old boy who had remained for two years in the first half of first grade without learning to write or read words. His efforts to write them consisted of reversals of letters or sequence, seemingly meaningless combinations of letters, or a series of peculiar marks. Other symptoms were a solitary withdrawal from social relationships and wetting and soiling himself, although when still living with his own mother, he had established bladder and bowel control. Regression to wetting and soiling began when he was about three years of age after the mother placed him.

Repeated medical examinations revealed no physical basis for his symptoms. There was no left-handedness nor left or mixed eye-hand dominance connected with his tendency to reversals in writing words. At the age of three years, before his neurotic symptoms appeared, he achieved an I. Q. of 95. When tested by the same psychologist at five and seven years of age, he achieved I. Q.'s of 75 and 74. At the end of therapy, after he had recovered from his severe neurosis, he was retested and his I. Q. then was 95.

Benjamin was placed in a foster home after the birth of a sister. Both children were illegitimate but the mother married the father of the second one. He did not wish to take the child by a former lover into their home, so the mother turned the boy over to a placement agency and then deserted him completely.

Benjamin was seen for nearly a year and a half, mostly twice a week. During these appointments, emotional conflicts about having been deserted by his mother were very evident. His feelings toward the mother were transferred to the therapist, whom he often reproached for sending him to live with strange people and causing his illness symptoms, saying, "I hate you for what you have done to me." He had various fantasy explanations of why his mother had deserted him. Since she placed him at the time of his sister's birth, he sometimes imagined that she had given him away because she loved girls better than boys. At other times, he suspected that she stopped loving him when she began to love the man she married, for it was after she had known this man that she gave up Benjamin. He hated his mother because he felt that placement was a proof of her ceasing to love him more than because of the placement per se. His hatred was expressed in certain fantasies associated with the symptoms of wetting and soiling; for example, he pictured burning up his mother with his hot urine or poisoning her by making her eat his feces. On the other hand, fantasies of being a baby, living with his mother and cared for tenderly by her, were also closely connected with his enuresis and soiling. Thus these symptoms concealed his love as well as his hostility and afforded gratification of ambivalent feelings toward his mother. Both his resentment toward his mother and his longing for her love had been repressed and were permitted an outlet only through his symptoms.

Benjamin regarded reading as evidence of being grown-up, but was blocked in his wishes to grow up because of fantasies that this could be achieved only by eating the father to gain his traits in magic manner. He was very guilty about such aggressive desires. But Benjamin's errors in writing words, like his other symptoms, were similarly disguised expressions of feelings toward his mother. He sometimes explained his mother's desertion as due to her not being Jewish, like himself, for he had heard that Christians were cruel to Jews. If his mother was not Jewish, the English language that they wanted him to write at school must be her language and he hated her so much that he did not want to learn it; instead, he wished to learn Hebrew, the language of Jewish people. He was unable to write Hebrew but he knew that it is written in the opposite direction to English; he explained that he tried to turn the English taught at school into Hebrew by writing it backwards. This was the reason for his reversals in writing words.

He called the peculiar marks that he sometimes made for words his "Chinese writing". He knew that the Chinese made peculiar marks to represent words; he had heard that Chinese tortured people whom they hated. When he hated his mother for deserting him, he elaborated, he felt like torturing her the way she had tortured him by letting him love her and then sending him away from her. His "Chinese writing" was a magic spell that would cause his mother to be tortured with sharp knives or in other ways and to be eaten by fierce animals.

These two types of errors in writing words—the reversals and the peculiar marks—were thus symbolic of his anger toward his mother, and his wish to hurt her. His other errors, in which he combined letters into what seemed nonsense, were symbolic of the love he still felt for his mother. For instance, he once wrote the following letter combinations—"As ur mor", which stood for the words, "Ask your mother". It developed that what he wanted to ask her (and the therapist, too) was to have a baby for him, as a proof that his love was returned. Then he need no longer fear that his mother loved the man she had married better than him.

It was only after he had produced all his imaginary explanations for his mother's having placed him and had become conscious of his repressed ambivalent feelings toward her, that he could realize there might be a different reason for the placement than those he had fantasied. Finally he accepted the reality that his mother had placed him because she could no longer take care of him. He then decided that he no longer needed to hate his mother, adding that this permitted him to love other women, too—his foster mother and his teachers at school. He explained that when he hated his own mother, he had hated all women, and so he had never wanted to do a single thing that his foster mother or his teachers asked of him. Now that he could love women, he wanted to do as they expected, so he would not have any more trouble with school work.

In thus describing how he felt about doing things for people because he loved them, this boy was confirming the psychoanalytic theory that the child first learns to please adults whom he loves. Of special interest was the fact that the reversals in writing words, often explained on a physical basis, in this instance were symbolic expressions of hostility and aggression. In two more recent clinic cases, reversals in reading and writing were similarly disguised forms of negative attitudes toward parents and teachers, accompanied by aggressive, destructive fantasies.

In reviewing the literature, there was a reference to a statement by Pearson and English concerning an inhibition of reading after a child had been forbidden peeping activities by parents. Our last case is that of a boy whose expressions of sexual curiosity and also of aggression had been stringently restricted. This case shows a reading disability developing from too severe limitations of instinctive drives.

Case 6. Jonathan, eight years old when referred to the clinic, had been living in the same foster home since infancy. He had for some time been a tense, hyperactive child, hardly ever still. After two years in school, he had not learned to read. At first it was difficult to maintain contact with him or carry on any connected conversation because of his extreme motor restlessness. He was always running around the room and never continued any one play activity or topic of conversation for more than a few minutes. It was soon observed that he often hunted among the therapist's books, as if searching for something in particular, but he never would tell what he was looking for, saying that he did not know, which was probably quite true. One day as he rummaged through the books, he came upon *Growing Up*. He seized it with the exclamation, "That's what I wanted," but immediately replaced it upon the shelf, saying he could not read it. When asked if he would like it read to him, he hastily disclaimed any such wish.

For some time after this episode, the interviews were taken up with some of his conflicts about living in a foster home and having no parents of his own. At first he tried to protect himself from the anxiety aroused by the knowledge that his own parents had died when he was a small child, by fantasies that the foster parents were his own. After awhile he gave up this defense and admitted the insecurity he felt at having no "real" parents like other children at school. Instead of running aimlessly around the room, he now began to do carpentry, liking to fashion swords, knives and guns out of wood. From his talk about these weapons, it was clear that they were symbols of both masculinity and aggressive tendencies, but he often had to leave them with the therapist because he was sure that his foster mother would object to his having them. Actually, when he did get courage to take home a sword he had made, his foster mother took it away from him. As he complained, she wanted him to act like a girl. His complaint had foundation in fact, for the foster mother told us that she had wanted the placement agency to give her a girl (although she had never mentioned this to the agency) and when receiving a boy instead, she had dressed him like a girl as long as he would tolerate it and still expected him to be feminine in his behavior.

After he had found some relief from the repression of aggression and masculinity imposed by the foster mother, he again sought out the book *Growing Up* and looked at the pictures, asking the therapist to read some of the pages. He was guilty about this until he had talked over how his foster father once read him this book—but behind locked doors and with a stern warning that Jonathan must never talk about these sex education matters with the foster mother or anyone else except the foster father himself. This was only one aspect of the foster father's need to assure himself the sole intimate relationship with the boy; he did not permit Jonathan to play after school with other children, visit them or invite them to his home. Once Jonathan had thrown aside the restriction his foster father had placed upon his speaking of sex matters to other people, his next interviews with the therapist were full of questions and talk about sex and babies, including repetition of all the slang words and phrases he had heard. He concluded this series of interviews by saying, "I wish I could have asked my mother these things and talked about them with her, but I didn't dare because it would have made my father so angry that maybe he wouldn't have kept me. I was afraid he would give me back to the agency." He also told how he had been eager to learn to read when he first went to school, so that he could read *Growing Up* by himself, only he was fearful that the foster father would not have liked his reading it, for he always kept the book locked in his desk.

After the therapy was completed, Jonathan was able to learn to read at school without remedial teaching. By then, too, he was ready for a move to another foster home where masculine and aggressive strivings were acceptable. Follow-up reports from the agency indicated that he was developing along normal masculine lines thereafter and when a young adolescent, he was seen for educational guidance tests and interview. At this later date, he could never have been recognized as the same repressed, effeminate boy who had come to the clinic years earlier.

It is interesting to raise a question as to whether this boy would have developed his reading disability as the result of limitation of sexual curiosity alone. To be sure, he was so guilty over wanting to read *Growing Up* and talk about it with his foster mother that he had to resist all reading, but it would seem that repression of aggression was also involved in his avoidance of reading. At least, it was plain in the therapeutic interviews that he could only admit his interest in sex questions, in defiance of his foster father's prohibitions, after relaxation of the repression of masculine, aggressive strivings. Apparently reading was not simply a way of acquiring knowledge but also was an activity that represented aggressive rebellion against the foster father's restrictions, and against his desire to keep the boy to himself.[8] The boy realized that aggression of any kind would meet with disapproval from the foster mother, on whom he had been very dependent as a young child. He was afraid also that the foster father might punish rebellious resistance to his domination by refusing to give him a home any longer. Hence it is little wonder that the boy had to repress aggression so completely.

Conclusion

In the clinical cases just presented to illustrate reading disabilities of a psychogenic nature, it seems possible to interpret the material in the light of psychoanalytic theories of reading and learning. But it also appears that there is no single situation or personality maladjustment, which can be isolated to explain the development of a reading disability as one of the child's neurotic symptoms. The background may be either traumatic or may reveal chronically unfavorable experiences; the personality difficulties may be severe (as in the case

8. In this connection, it is interesting to recall that Freud mentioned the sadistic nature of desire for knowledge in the obsessional neuroses (14).

of Ethel who made herself ill by refusing food, or Benjamin who was withdrawn from social relationships and had other serious neurotic symptoms, or Jonathan who was inhibited, passive and effeminate); or maladjustments other than the trouble with reading may be mild enough to be masked from ordinary observation and may become fully apparent only to the professional eye in therapeutic work with the child. These statements might not seem warranted as generalizations on the basis of the comparatively small number of cases included in this paper or reported in previous ones, except for the fact that other investigators have arrived independently at the same conclusions by accumulating statistical data on large numbers of cases.[9]

Both our individual case studies and the statistical findings of other psychologists suggest that a complexity of factors come together in a focal point around reading, particularly where the disability is of emotional origin. In this respect, the neurotic reading disability conforms to the psychoanalytic concept of neurotic symptoms generally as being over-determined. It also conforms otherwise to psychoanalytic theories of symptom-formation: for the repression of instinctive drives and existence of emotional conflicts forms the setting for the reading disability as well as for other neurotic symptoms; errors in reading may serve as disguised ways of gratifying repressed impulses just as illness-symptoms serve this purpose; failure in reading may represent a hidden antagonism to adults expressed in passive resistance rather than in openly rebellious behavior, and thus may also conceal repressed attitudes. To be sure, at other times the failure may result from a wish to avoid reading because it has previously stirred up feelings of guilt or anxiety, but here, too, it closely resembles a well-known neurotic tendency toward avoidance of imaginary dangers.

In considering that reading disabilities tend to appear as a center of convergence for several emotional factors, we probably need to take into account the timing of this occurrence. It is reasonable to

9. Bell speaks of research in this field as indicating that reading is related to many different factors and is a highly complex function of the personality; Jackson reaches a similar conclusion on the basis of his own statistical findings (1, 22). Gates (15) states that there is no single personality pattern among pupils of adequate intelligence coexistent with reading disability but that difficulty in reading may occur in all sorts of personalities, emotional patterns and parental relationships. Moreover, Gates points out, citing examples, that a factor which seems to be a chief cause of a reading disability in one individual may even be a strong motivation for learning to read well in another.

believe that reading is most apt to become involved in a child's emotional conflicts when these concur with the period of learning the fundamentals of the reading process in the early school grades. Once a firm foundation has been acquired, further proficiency in reading depends more upon enlarging the reading vocabulary than learning new processes so that disability for this subject is less likely to begin in higher grades, although it may have remained undetected until then.[10] It is possible, therefore, that the time element may have a bearing on whether a special educational disability will be for reading or for some other subject. Since in many cases personality maladjustments of children begin by the time they enter school or soon afterward, this may be one reason why reading disabilities are more frequent than others. But an equally valid reason, already mentioned, is the ease with which reading content, either directly or symbolically, can become associated with unconscious emotional conflicts.

BIBLIOGRAPHY

1. Bell, J. E. "Emotional Factors in the Treatment of Reading Difficulties", *J. Consult. Psychol.*, 9, May-June 1945.
2. Berman, I. and Bird, C. "Sex Differences in Speed of Reading", *J. Applied Psychol.* 7, June 1933.
3. Blanchard, P. "Reading Disabilities in Relation to Difficulties of Personality and Emotional Development", *Ment. Hyg.* 20, July 1936.
3a. Blanchard, P. "Reading Disabilities in Relation to Maladjustment", *Ment. Hyg.* 12, July 1929.
4. Blanchard, P. "Attitudes and Educational Disabilities", *ibid.*, 13, July 1929.
5. Blanchard, P. "Psychogenic Factors in Some Cases of Reading Disability", *Amer. J. Orthopsychiatry*, V, October 1935.
6. Blanchard, P. "Emotional Factors in a Disability for Reading and Writing Words", *Readings in Mental Hygiene*, ed. by Groves, E. and Blanchard, P., Holt, 1936. pp. 283-301.
7. Bronner, A. *The Psychology of Special Abilities and Disabilities*, Little Brown, 1921. p. 77.
8. Burt, C. *Mental and Scholastic Tests*, King & Sons, London, 1921.
9. Fernald, G. M. and Keller, H. "The Effect of Kinaesthetic Factors in the Development of Word Recognition in the Case of Non-Readers", *J. Educ. Research*, 4, December 1921.
10. Freud, A. "Psychoanalysis and the Training of the Young Child", *Psa. Quarterly*, IV, 1935.

10. Unlike arithmetic, where fundamental processes (addition, subtraction, multiplication, fractions, decimals, etc.) are being learned, one after another, through most of the elementary grades and lack of mastery of any one process can affect much subsequent work, so that a disability in this subject may develop as readily in later grades as in earlier ones.

11. Freud, A. *The Ego and the Mechanisms of Defence,* Hogarth, 1937.
12. Freud, A. and Burlingham, D. T. *War and Children,* Internat. Univ. Press, 1943.
13. Freud, A. and Burlingham, D. T. *Infants Without Families,* Internat. Univ. Press, 1944.
14. Freud, S. "The Predisposition to Obsessional Neurosis", *Coll. Papers,* II. p. 130.
15. Gates, A. "The Role of Personality Maladjustment in Reading Disability.", *J. Genetic Psychol.,* 59, 1941.
16. Gates, A. *The Improvement of Reading,* Macmillan, 1927. (Based on ten years of research on some 13,000 cases.)
17. Gates, A. *The Improvement of Reading,* rev. ed. Macmillan, 1936.
18. Gates, A. *The Psychology of Reading and Spelling, with Special Reference to Disabilities,* Teachers College, Columbia Univ., 1922.
19. Gray, C. T. *Deficiencies in Reading Ability: Their Diagnosis and Remedies,* Little Brown, 1922.
20. Hincks, E. *Disability in Reading and its Relation to Personality,* Harvard Univ. Press, 1926.
21. Hollingworth, L. *Special Talents and Defects,* Macmillan, 1923.
22. Jackson, J. "A Survey of Psychological, Social and Environmental Differences between Advanced and Retarded Readers", *J. Genetic Psychol.,* 65, 1944.
23. Jones, E. "The Child's Unconscious", chapter 36 of *Papers on Psychoanalysis,* Wood, London, 1923.
24. Klein, M. "A Contribution to the Theory of Intellectual Inhibition", *Int. J. Psa.,* XII, 1931.
25. Meek, L. *A Study of Learning and Retention in Young Children,* Teachers College, Columbia Univ., 1925.
26. Monroe, M. *Children Who Cannot Read,* Univ. Chicago Press, 1932.
27. Monroe, M. *Methods for Diagnosis and Treatment of Cases of Reading Disability,* Clark Univ. Press, 1928.
28. Nielson, J. M. *A Textbook of Clinical Neurology,* Hoeber, 1941, p. 235.
29. Nunberg, H. *Allgemeine Neurosenlehre auf Psychoanalytischer Grundlage,* Hans Huber, 1932. Chapter III.
30. Orton, S. *Reading, Writing and Speech Problems in Children,* Norton, 1937.
31. Orton, S. "Word-blindness in School Children", *Archives of Neur. and Psychiatry,* 14, November 1925.
32. Orton, S. "An Impediment in Learning to Read", *School and Society,* September 1928.
33. Pearson, G. H. J. and English, O. S. *Common Neuroses of Children and Adults,* Norton, 1937. p. 162.
34. Preston, M. "The Reaction of Parents to Reading Failure", *Child Dev.* 10, September 1939.
35. Preston, M. "The School Looks at the Non-Reader", *Elem. School J.,* 40, February 1940.
36. Schilder, P. "Congenital Alexia and its Relation to Optic Perception", *J. Genetic Psychol.* 65, 1944.
37. Strachey, J. "Some Unconscious Factors in Reading", *Int. J. Psa.,* XI, 1930.

38. Sylvester, E. and Kunst, M. S. "Psychodynamic Aspects of the Reading Problem", *Amer. J. Orthopsychiatry*, XIII, 1943.
39. Tulchin, S. "Emotional Factors in Reading Disabilities in School Children", *J. Educ. Psychol.*, September 1935.
40. Warren and Jones. "Effect of Acrophobia upon Reading Ability as Measured by Reading Comprehension and Eye-Movements in Reading", *J. Genetic Psychol.*, 63, 1943.
41. Witmer, H., ed. *Psychiatric Interviews with Children*, Commonwealth, 1946.

THE ANALYSIS OF A CASE OF
NIGHT TERROR

By JENNY WAELDER HALL, M.D. (Bethesda, Md.)

This paper was originally read, in a longer form, at a meeting of the Vienna Psychoanalytic Society in 1930. It was the first case of a child analysis to be reported in detail, and it threw new light on the psychogenesis of pavor nocturnus.

It was first published in the *Zeitschrift für psychoanalytische Pädagogik*, as "Analyse eines Falles von Pavor Nocturnus", in 1935. We feel it still valuable enough to reprint in translation here, not only for the benefit of English and American readers to whom the German language edition is inaccessible, but because it is outstanding among those few case histories of child analyses that have appeared in the literature.

—The Editors

I.

Anton was seven years old when treatment began. He was a small, nice-looking boy, moderately well developed physically. At first he seemed shy and anxious, but it soon became clear that he could also be very lively, confiding, and talkative. When the mask of shyness was put aside a vivacious street-urchin appeared. Anton had a good intelligence and a ready wit. His success in school (first grade) was only fair, but this was due to laziness. The slum environment in which he lived gave him practically no intellectual stimulus. His chief interest was in mechanical things; and for a boy of his years he had a very good grasp of them.

For weeks the boy had complained of piercing heart pains which appeared suddenly and which were independent of physical exertion. Hospital examination was negative; and in view of the night terror the boy suffered, the hospital referred the case to the Vienna Psychoanalytic Clinic for psychotherapy.

Night terror had occurred for about a year, at irregular intervals. The mother could not supply definite information about the first appearance. According to her story, the boy used to wake up screaming, or sit up and cry out in terror. He took no notice of what went on about him, nor did he respond to attempts to calm him. The mother used to apply cold compresses to his heart. After a while the child would quiet down and fall asleep, without having become fully conscious at any point. He had no memory of his attacks afterward. On medical advice Valerian drops had been administered in recent attacks, without apparent effect.

Just as alarming to those about him, though less conspicuous, was the child's general anxiety. He could not stay alone in a room. Following a recent burglary in the neighborhood he developed a burglar phobia; he explained his fear of remaining alone or sleeping alone by the possibility of a surprise attack by a burglar.

His mother traced his anxiety, especially his nocturnal attacks, to a fall from his bed when he was three years old. During the nights following this the child had been very restless, and she supposed that the blow to his head when he fell to the floor was the basis for the disturbance.

The child's social attitude must be examined in the light of his environment. His little world was made up of his family, the street, and, for the last half-year, the school. He was the only child of a poor family. We shall have occasion later on to speak of one sister who died at the age of five months—before Anton was born—as a result of a congenital heart defect. He often heard talk about this sister. His father, who was in his middle thirties, was an unskilled laborer. His mother was sometimes able to supplement the very meager family earnings. The parents were not happily married. There was constant quarreling which the child could not help witnessing, since the family had only a room and a kitchen to live in. No matter what happened, each parent blamed the other for it. They were united only in aggression against a third person. Aggressive though the father was, he could also be very affable. He was considered quite a dandy. He was vulgar, slightly hypomanic, temperamental, and witty. He had a flow of racy language which, as his wife said, would have fitted him for a sideshow announcer in the "Prater" (amusement park). He was industrious, and never avoided work in the home or outside it. He turned over his wages to his wife, keeping just enough for the tap room. He liked company along with his glass of beer. His witty talk made him popular, and so he was "treated" by others when he had no money of his own. But he did not carry his liquor very well: after his visits to the tavern he was quick to take offense, and quarrels were provoked all too easily at home.

As a father he was kind and thoughtful; but also ambivalent and inconsistent. He really loved his only son and wanted the boy's affection in return. His need for the child's love often made him oppose the mother by allowing the boy to have things she had just forbidden. As a result, the boy's attitude toward his father was exacting and disrespectful. This led to abrupt changes in the father's attitude. From tender affection he would pass to sudden rage, and menace the child. So, from an attempt to outbid the mother in an excess of indulgence, he could swing to the opposite extreme: he would whip the child for trifling faults, but when a firm hand was needed he would be soft and yielding. He would make promises that were never kept, and threats that were never carried out. Often when father and son began to wrestle as comrades, and the boy, taking the comradeship too literally, became too rough, the father would suddenly discover an insult to his dignity. The play that had seemed to begin in friendly equality would thus end in a sound whipping for the youngster. And so the father, too quick-tempered and intolerant to be a real comrade to his boy, too inconsistent and weak to be a real authority to him, ended by being neither. The boy could not take his father quite seriously; he was afraid of him, but with the fear was mingled contempt. On the other hand, the father had the advantage of possessing some qualities that the boy admired, namely, mechanical skill, wit, physical strength, and knowledge of many things that the boy wanted to know.

The mother was a pleasant and industrious woman. She also harbored considerable aggression which, however, was better controlled, with only occasional lapses. In the quarrels at home she was by no means always the patient sufferer. Undisguised aggression against outsiders was commonplace in the everyday life of the family. She suffered greatly from her poverty-stricken life, and had set her heart on improving it in order to be on a level with her sisters who had married into the lower middle class. She herself had been a cook in a middle class home, and this personal contact with another class of society had also fostered her ambition. Her attitude was expressed clearly in her two strongest desires, neither compatible with life in the slums—brass beds (a symbol of lower middle class status), and a well-brought-up child. Her striving for the "higher things" which were so far out of reach, only made her demands on husband and son more exacting.

The mother loved her boy more than anything else in the world; she sought in him compensation for all that life had withheld from her and, above all, for her unsatisfactory marriage. The child was her world. Young though he was, she confided to him her daily troubles and her marital grievances. When she quarrelled with her husband and there was no one else with whom she could "let off steam", she sought refuge in the child and incited him against his father. The boy, who idolized his mother, infuriated his father by openly taking sides against him. The mother was more consistent than the father in her training of the child. She was firmer and kept to her decisions, which the father very often took pleasure in upsetting. In general, the boy was much more obedient to her than to his father. Although he was afraid of being beaten by his father, he was even more afraid of losing his mother's love.

So much for the influence of the family on the boy. While boys of other classes remained in the shelter of the home, he, like most other slum boys, spent most of his time running wild in the street. There he sharpened his wits and learned much, especially of the seamy side of life. The aggressions in the streets in the outskirts of Vienna where he lived, the many fights which he had watched with fascination and of which he was sometimes the victim, fostered his sadistic tendencies, as did the similar situation at home. He often had the opportunity to watch love-making. What he saw in dark doorways, courtyards, and stairways, sharpened his curiosity and added to his understanding of the scenes so often witnessed between his parents.

II.

The only explanation given to Anton when he was brought to me for treatment was that the "Frau Doctor" would play with him. We played together with blocks and toys which I provided, and the child very soon felt at home. In the second hour he began to talk about the naughtiness of his schoolmates, who used an improper expression for one of the bodily functions. He was very indignant; he might possibly use the expression himself at home, but never at school, he said. When I told him he could speak just as freely with me as at home, he objected and insisted emphatically that he wanted to be a good boy. This little scene betrayed his conflict, his effort to be good despite temptations, and the defense he built up against them. Such small indications teach us that the indulgent attitude of the analyst may be interpreted by the child as temptation and may therefore be rejected.

In the third hour we touched the core of his most acute conflicts. Anton's mother came to me and discussed the following situation in the child's presence: For a long time the parents had felt that the boy should not be sleeping between them in their bed, but that he should have his own bed, even though it had to be in the same room. Up to this time Anton had stubbornly opposed such a plan. When he came into treatment, the parents decided to leave the decision to me. The sudden broaching of the matter by the mother made it possible for me to discuss the subject directly with the child.

Since the youngster felt his most vital interests threatened, he was carried away by his desire to protect his privilege and made statements that otherwise would certainly not have come out at the beginning of the treatment. At first he tried out his set form of resistance— his fear of sleeping alone, his need of protection against a burglar. He had also to protect his mother, and even his father against the burglar. We know that all this was not just mere rationalization, but had a deeper element of truth. When I expressed doubt as to the reality of the danger from a burglar and suggested that his father would be able to protect him and his mother against the burglar, he suddenly complained about his father. His father was no good, and teased his mother and him, especially in bed. At this point our session came to an end, and we arranged to continue the discussion the next day. When the hour arrived and we took up the subject again, the boy repeated his first arguments against sleeping alone, that is, his fears of a burglar. But he made no mention of his father's bad behavior toward his mother, probably because in the meantime he had become afraid that I might betray him to his father. I therefore reminded him of the other things he had told me on the previous day. I added that I knew what went on in children's minds and what they thought, and so I knew why he wanted to sleep with his mother. "You want to have your mother for yourself!" He answered with complete naivete, "Yes, of course, she belongs to me!" "Only to you?" "Yes, only to me," and, after a pause, "and to my father." I then said, "But you would like to have her all to yourself?" "Yes, because father is bad." . . . Father torments mother; there is no peace when he is around; he tickles her on the neck in bed . . . Anton did not like that . . . he could not stand it. Father teases him too, beats him, and is bad to him . . . Anton grew quite hot and excited during this recital.

As to the practical question of the sleeping arrangement, we agreed that for the time being he should yield to his parents' wish and sleep alone, but that we should continue to discuss the situation. Anton begged to be allowed to tell his mother himself about our agreement. It was characteristic of him that he told it to her in a distorted form, as I learned from her. He simply told her that I had said it was unhealthy for a child to sleep with grown-ups, and that he would therefore now sleep alone. Of course I had said nothing of that sort. Henceforth without any prompting on my part he kept to himself what went on in the hour and either refused to answer or parried his mother's daily questions on the subject.

For the most part he stuck to the decision to sleep alone, but occasionally reverted. Whenever this happened I had a fresh opportunity to discuss the situation with him. And these talks always followed the same pattern. To begin with, he tried anxiously to avoid any criticism of his father, obviously fearing betrayal; but finally his aggressive attitude to his father would break through.

Anton's play in the hour, his fantasies, and his unguarded chatter also centered around his father, though indirectly: he was either attacking a father figure or acting like father. This determined his choice of games: he would play a game in which he was a streetcar conductor acting peevishly or even rudely to the passengers. As a judge he was pitiless and imposed the harshest sentences; as a policeman he was always outrageously brutal to lawbreakers. At his suggestion we once played trains. As usual he was the conductor and I was the passenger. I gathered from the conductor's rude talk that in the train there were also children on their way to a vacation in Holland. I asked if I could speak to one of the children. He assented gruffly, left the car (i.e., the room) to fetch the child. The door then opened and Anton appeared in the role of the child. He was absolutely changed. The unfriendly peevish expression had given place to one of beaming pleasure. He came forward happily with a friendly greeting. He was somewhat reserved and shy in answering my questions, but always entirely friendly, just as he was with me in reality at that period of the treatment. When the interview with the "child" came to an end, the blustering, grumbling "conductor" returned.

My later acquaintance with his father confirmed the assumption that Anton was imitating his father. The man was always very pleasant with me, but whenever he spoke of his work and home life his face changed suddenly and had the same peevishness and expression of annoyance that Anton had shown.

Another of Anton's made-up games threw further light on his sadistic attitude. He brought his toy streetcar and motorcycle to play with. When he allotted the parts, I was given the streetcar and he kept the motorcycle for himself. He said we should ride around on the big table. He always managed to arrange a collision with the streetcar, that is to say with me, and in every instance the streetcar got the worst of it. It is difficult to convey the convincing impression which this scene made: the enormous satisfaction with which the child made the motorcyclist trample up and down on the overturned streetcar, his triumphant look of gratification in taking violent possession of the object. This game already seemed to supply evidence of the child's observation of his parents' intercourse, of his sadistic interpretation of what he has seen, and of his fantasy regarding his father's role.

One of Anton's games was called "Robber, policeman and judge". The roles should have been played by both of us, but actually he took all three for himself, because he could not let pass unused an opportunity for aggressive behavior. Once the game began with the fantasy of a criminal attack on a woman asleep in a sleeping-car. But usually it began with the second act, so to speak, with the policeman's pursuit of the robber. Anton took both parts and ran around the room, chasing himself, as it were. Then came the arrest, the court scene, the policeman's charges and finally the judge's severe sentences. The part of the game mentioned above, which occurred only once, "A man attacks a woman asleep in the sleeping-car", was interesting not only for its manifest content, but also because (as I learned later) Anton did not even know that sleeping-cars existed. Shortly before we had played dining-car, but the sleeping-car was his invention.

In the regular recurrence of certain themes in these games we can recognize the important role in his fantasy played by crime, pursuit, arrest and punishment. In contrast to this aggressive role was another that came out in some of his fantasies. Here he became the timid, fearful, anxious part of himself. He was soft-hearted, gentle, passive, anxious, sometimes even sad and melancholy. His voice became tremulous. This outward behavior fitted the content of the fantasies. I was able to keep a few records of such stories since I suggested as a game that he should tell his story while I wrote it down. An example follows:

"What Rudi dreamed." (Rudi and Mimi were characters from a school book.) "Rudi dreamed about a Christ Child." (Then in a singing voice) "Oh, but that was nice, we weren't afraid at all, at all. Naughty children are afraid. So Krampus (devil) will go after a boy. Oh dear, he is a cruel Krampus; so I am afraid; I cry, 'Mother, Mother.' Rudi keeps on calling out, 'Mother, Mother.' Mimi also calls mother four times. Oh dear, my heart hurts me. God above, don't punish me! I am afraid of the cruel Krampus. Go away! That is the end of the story."

The story reveals the motives of a wicked father and a protecting mother, the fearful child afraid of punishment, and the physical symptom of heartaches.

III.

Thus the first weeks passed. We had now come to the point where I could discuss directly with him the purpose of our meetings. I told him that he came to me to get rid of his anxiety; that to do this he must tell me everything that went through his head; that there were certainly things which he had not yet told, for I knew very well that every child had all sorts of things in his head which he does not like to tell to grown-ups.

His first steps in confession were typical. It was not he but another boy, his friend Franky, who had done and was still doing so many bad things. He represented himself as an inactive witness, who, unfortunately, was not in a position to teach his friend better behavior. But he kept laughing and was pleased and excited as he talked; and he admitted that what his friend did was good fun.

Franky, as I learned from Anton's mother, was a neglected child. His mother was dead and his father was a drinker, a brutal, unrestrained man who brought street-women into his room so that the child could not help witnessing their love scenes. According to Anton, Franky had assembled a little gang of boys who amused themselves with all sorts of erotic games in a huge empty furniture crate standing in the court of the dwelling-house.

These cautious approaches were meant to try me out. If I had shown indignation Anton would have been ready to pull in his feelers and hide everything away. So I gave no sign of displeasure and even showed interest. This led to a characteristic reaction. When Anton came to his hour on the next day he had a serious and solemn air. He stopped in the doorway and opened a book he had brought with him. It was a religious book for children. He began to read aloud from it, beginning with two prayers of a child who wishes to be good and pious so as to go to heaven. Only then did Anton come close to me, to show me pictures in the book. They were drawings of Hell and of devils. I remarked that there was no Hell and no devils. But he insisted, "There is a Heaven." He was looking forward eagerly, he said, to see the Heavenly Father. Then he looked in the book for a picture of Adam and Eve being driven out of paradise. The only picture he could find did not satisfy him at all, because the serpent was missing. He hunted in vain for one with the serpent in it, but there was none in the book. The picture with the serpent in it was very vivid, however, in his own mind. This behavior was understandable: I had listened to Anton's account of bad boys without criticism in order to avert his fear of punishment or moral condemnation; and I had wanted to relieve him of his burden of anxiety just enough to make him continue with his stories. But the result was merely that the fear I might punish him was replaced by the fear that I might entice him into evil ways.

I began by saying, "I know why you have got the book with you." He replied, "So that I wouldn't have to tell you any more." I explained to him he need not fear that our talking about such things would make him a bad boy. We had to talk about them to free him from thoughts that disturbed him. In this way I tried to show him that his fear of seduction was no more justified than his fear of punishment, since analysis aims neither to punish nor to give free rein to impulses, but to help the patient. This was not done with a single explanation; I had to repeat it very often. It is particularly difficult to make children grasp the fact that analysis does not mean punishment or seduction—these being probably the only two ways in which the child has known adults to respond to such forbidden thoughts or acts. I might mention here, in anticipation, a remark which Anton made almost at the end of his treatment when we were talking about masturbation. "You want to get that out of me so that you can punish me!" he said. And after my denial he went on: "Or perhaps you want me to do it?"

After such reassurances Anton brought further sexual material. He told of all sorts of games which the children played on the streets, and in dark corners, in imitation of what they had seen adults doing; or he reported the type of game which corresponded to the level of sexual development of children of his age. Every child of whom he told had some variation for the games; the result being that he had gone through the whole gamut covering practically every possible form of sexual activity. He still represented himself as the passive onlooker of the games played by other children in the furniture crate which stood in their courtyard. He himself was not even interested; he just happened to see what was going on through a hole in the crate. When asked how his eye had just chanced to arrive at the hole, he pretended to be indignant—of course it was his moral duty to spy on such goings on so as to be able to report them to grown-ups and to put an end to the whole business. (Of course he never did report them.) As he rushed ahead with his story with evident enjoyment he no longer kept close guard over what he said and made frequent slips of the tongue. He said "we" or "I" instead of "the other children". Putting the whole blame on Franky was not without some justification. Franky was in fact the leader of the gang who started the whole play in the crate and passed on to the other children what he learned by watching his father. Anton's indignation was not pure pretense for there was also a voice in him that spoke against such things.

Pushing forward in this way, under cover of Franky we came upon the first partial explanation of Anton's night terror.

The occasion was an outburst of criticism of his father followed by remorse—and an attempt to picture his father in the best possible light. Thus he turned his aggression against Franky's father. This man, he said, was quite different from his own father—this was really true—he had tormented his wife to death (Anton had heard from neighbors that the wife had pined away on account of her husband's behavior); he was a thoroughly bad man. In his mounting excitement Anton made Franky's father the killer of a whole regiment of women. At the peak of his emotion he exclaimed, "If I was in Franky's place and saw my father doing such things, I would not be afraid, I would jump up—even in the middle of the night, run out on the street in my nightshirt, and call the policeman. Then father would be arrested and I would be at home with mother alone." During the first part of his recital—up to the calling of the police—his voice was exceedingly high-pitched; he almost screamed; his eyes flashed, and his cheeks were flushed. But the last sentence was uttered in a completely different tone, in a somewhat slow and sing-song way, sounding like an expression of triumph after victory. He thus betrayed an important element of his symptom. In these nightly attacks he would spring up—as if "to call a policeman", to use his own words. The policeman, as is now clear, was to protect his mother from his father's assault.

I knew nothing at that time about such brutal assaults on the father's part. I had no reason to believe that the frequent quarrels between the parents were of sufficient violence to justify Anton's anxiety. Anton's reaction seemed to refer above all to the father's sexual attacks on the mother which he understood as something sadistic and which he wanted to stop. "Teasing" in bed meant to him the beginning of the sexual attack.

At this stage in the analysis the games which had been the basis of the treatment in the beginning gradually diminished in importance. Talking was now in the foreground. But there was not yet any frank, direct account of his own intimate concerns and thoughts, for he was still keeping up the fiction that he himself was not involved. His behavior in and out of analysis had greatly changed. He stopped pretending he was a good boy. His timidity disappeared; his aggression against me came more and more to the surface though it was still expressed in a devious way. It was directed against *other* doctors, and against the woman analyst who had referred him to me. The doctors were "silly fools", "dumb", "crazy". "They sit in school without learning anything so that later they cannot do anything and so they are not able to cure a poor little child. . . . The woman" (who referred him to me for treatment) "had better not come my way or else I will show her what it means to send a child to a treatment where he has to do nothing but tell things all the time." Once he even threatened to kill her with a hatchet. He expressed his lack of respect for a treatment in which no physical examination was made and no instruments used. But this attitude changed after I had recognized the approach of measles, because of suspicious catarrhal symptoms. I called his mother's attention to the probability that a rash would appear; and when the measles really developed I acquired great prestige in the eyes of the family. Anton also accepted the high estimate of my ability. Nevertheless this "ability" was of no help to me during the period of Anton's resistance. He no longer, to be sure, remarked that I was "no real doctor", that I was unable to cure a child. On the contrary he spoke with great respect of my knowledge of measles and sore throats but he had very great doubts about my knowledge in matters of the mind. "Of course, when a child has measles or sore throat you can understand it; but you don't understand what kind of thoughts a child has in his mind."

IV.

Material was plentiful in this phase of analysis. It gave insight into the child's life, into his sexual wishes and experiences. After he ceased to be afraid of talking of sexual matters, he found he could have his pleasure without danger as long as he remained on the outside, as an inactive but morally aroused onlooker. The gratification which he obtained from acting out was in general a hindrance to the analysis. (The means to an end became for him the end itself.) Any question about his everyday life was impatiently rejected with remarks such as, "What has that to do with what I have to talk about? The reason I come here is to get well and to tell everything. What sort of a treatment is it when one cannot tell any stories?" It thus became necessary to give up my attitude of innocent credulity.

His frequent slips of the tongue in saying "I" and "we" were sufficient to show I was right in assuming he had an active part in the games. Once in a somewhat orgiastic mood he threw himself on the sofa and asked in a provoking manner, "Well, what shall I tell you next?" evidently hoping that I would give him further opportunity to wallow in the material of his stories. I answered: "Tell me everything you all did." Although I put no accent on the word "you", and said it quite naturally and as a matter of fact, he jumped up as if he had received a shock and exclaimed. "What *who* did!" I answered quietly, "Why, you and the boys." Then came an unexpected reaction. The boy burst into tears and tried in every possible way to convince me that he was entirely innocent. He promised to bring me all his savings; only I must not believe that he could do such bad things. It was really touching when he offered me as hush-money all of his little savings of which he was very proud. The situation was clear. He suddenly believed himself in a trap. He supposed that I had acted as a kind and friendly helper just in order to draw out his secrets, and that I would now use these secrets against him. I would tell his father who would punish him and put him in a reformatory. So he wanted to bribe me to silence. I interpreted to him his behavior, tried to calm him, assured him that I did not think ill of him because of what he did, that other children did the same sort of things and told me all about them and that I never gave away their secrets to their parents. He calmed down after my interpretation and comforting explanations; his weeping and anxious behavior ceased. From this time on his aggression constantly increased.

The very next hour he began to do things which he thought I did not like. When he became too active, as for instance when he took up a piece of coal to throw at my head, I had to make him understand the difference between acting and verbalizing. I had to show him that physical violence could not be allowed if I were to remain intact to carry on my profession and fulfill my task of helping him. Children are not always so easily persuaded to confine their aggression to words.

Anton's indirectness and allusions soon stopped. He, no longer said, "I could say something if I wanted to," but expressed his opinion openly, however offensive it might be. His milder names for me were "Sheeny, Bohunc, Catholic" (all insults of more or less the same quality in his environment). I was "crazy", I had "a screw loose"; I "ought to be in the Steinhof" (the Vienna insane asylum). He expressed himself in a loud clear voice and with free and lively gestures. The more he realized that this behavior in analysis presented no danger to him, that I was apparently indifferent to his outbreaks, the more daring he became. There was no trace left of his original anxious attitude.

The paralyzing fear of his father had in fact been replaced by a lesser fear of punishment by me. In his fear of me he reacted with attacks against me. He vehemently denied any share in the games he had described. He shouted that he would not be insulted; it was not for that he had come for treatment. He wanted to intimidate me with screaming. He had learned from experience that he who shouts loudest is right. In his rage he acted as if an unjust punishment had already been administered against which he had to make vehement protest. But apparently he wished to express something else. He was trying to get the upper hand. He was doing what he expected I would do to him because of his naughtiness—scold him, shout at him, be furious with him.[1]

Apparently this mechanism came very easily to him because of his identification with his father. It was his father's habit to meet his wife with aggressive behavior when he had reason to expect reproaches from her. Anton's aggressive attitude was helped by a certain amount of disdain that went with his fear of me. His train of thought was: a grown-up who does not punish bad behavior in a child—aggressive

1. "Identification with the aggressor"—a line of thought developed by Anna Freud in an analogous case presented earlier in the Vienna Seminar for Child Analysis; later described in her book, *The Ego and the Mechanisms of Defence* (5).

talk as well as talk about sexual matters—is certainly no better than the child himself. Indeed, one must be particularly wary of such an adult for he will eventually lead you into evil ways. "Someday you will make me so bad that I'll call you a dirty dog!"

Besides, Anton felt that he had really suffered an injustice. It was true he had shared in the games, but that was in the past. Just now he was full of good resolutions and wanted to get credit in advance for them.

His aggressive behavior in analysis was of course repeated at home, since he expected to be allowed the same liberties there as in the treatment hour. But while the analyst could take his aggression for an hour a day, his parents could not be expected to take it for the rest of the twenty-four. I thus had to prepare the parents to win their cooperation and patience during this temporary phase which I could assure them would pass. Their cooperation was needed also to meet another danger, that the child's resistance would become so great that he would find means of getting away from treatment—even by simulating health. Anton tried to do this. For quite a long time he had no attacks of night terror. He assured me that he did not need treatment and that he preferred to stay at home rather than to subject himself to such insults. One factor that came to my rescue was his fundamentally positive attitude to me, which had been unclouded up to the outbreak of his aggression. But the thing that was of decisive importance was the determination of his parents not to let him interrupt the treatment until they felt certain that he was really cured.

As his fear of punishment faded his original good relationship came to the surface again, and with it the wish to show himself to me in a favorable light. Yet with this grew the fear of loss of love, which was just as strong a motive for not betraying his secrets to me as his fear of punishment had been.

V.

Although the resistance had shifted its source and form of expression, it was just as strong as ever. His abusive attitude gave way to good-natured blustering. What had been originally a spontaneous outbreak, an emotional urge finding release, became gradually a form of gratification, a pleasurable acting out which Anton had no reason to give up. It obviously amused him to grumble at me half in anger and half affectionately. To my question where this grumbling came

from, he answered laughingly, without hesitation "From father."
I pointed out to him that he was not really angry with me any more,
that he was just pretending to be angry because he enjoyed being
like his father and to order me around as his father did with his
mother. After initial resistance Anton had to admit that he was
playing father-mother with me.

From the very beginning Anton let fall isolated remarks which
could only be taken as expressions of transference. They became more
and more clear and numerous, and began to appear in his actions;
until finally a full-grown transference neurosis was apparent. In this
Anton's father, as we shall soon hear, played an important, perhaps
a decisive role.

At the outset of treatment Anton was friendly with me and
showed he was glad to be with me. In addition to this personal
regard for me there soon appeared transference phenomena. There
were fantasies in relation to an adult patient whom he met when he
was leaving. He concentrated his jealousy, aggression, and anxiety on
this "Mister Patient". He wanted to know if I did not give this
patient more time than I gave to him, whether the patient did not
come on holidays also, and so forth. Once he asked what I did with
the patient anyway. "Surely you don't play with Mister Patient."
Another time he asked, "If the patient is operated on, won't he come
here anymore?" "What sort of operation?" "But he is going to have
an operation, his breast will be cut open, here over the heart." "Why
do you think that I am going to operate on him?" "Because I am
sure you don't play with him." I tried to get more details of his
fantasy and learned that after the operation "the water which he
drinks does not come out below anymore, but comes out here" (pointing to the heart region). The full meaning of the fantasy became
clear later.

In addition to this general interest in the fate of this adult
patient, he showed quite open aggression against him. He was scorn-
ful of him, made fun of him; with clenched fist uttered a threat that
the patient had a lot coming to him when he, Anton, got his hands
on him. This aggressive attitude was probably the cause of his curious
behavior once when he was left alone in the room for a few minutes.
On my return I found him weeping and in a state of great anxiety.
He received me with reproaches. I asked him what he had been afraid
of. Although he knew no one was in the waiting room, he answered
that the patient might have come in and done something to him. In

Anton's fantasy the patient is given a double role; on the one hand he shares the fate of the boy himself (heart illness, operation), on the other hand he stands for the father (Anton's reaction of jealousy and anger).

With the "deepening" of our relationship Anton's affection became more and more evident, but it expressed itself in a special way. His show of affection was hidden wherever possible behind an aggression. He wanted to do me small favors, but tried to do so by grumbling and scolding. Once, for instance, he busied himself with putting the room in order and arranged the pillows and covers on the couch. But his field of activity was small, there was not much to "put in order". He managed however to make disorder, so that he could set things right again. All the time he grumbled away and once let fall the remark that "Here at your home the patients even have to do the cleaning up."

Much of his provocative behavior was due to his wish to make me reply in kind so that we could have the mother-father marital scenes. My sitting quietly rather spoiled the game. At this point something happened which made the transference situation more dramatic. A short time before, when his father was about to get a new topcoat Anton remarked that father must not come to see me in this new coat. He had been told once that a long time ago when his father got a new suit, his mother liked him so much in it that she married him. If I should now see his father in his new coat might not I fall in love with him? His father occasionally called for Anton after the interview. At the end of the last hour before Christmas the father turned up in his new coat. I gave him a small present for Anton, and asked him not to let Anton know he had it with him, but to put it under the Christmas tree as a surprise. The father hung the flat package on a vest-button under his coat. He found our mutual secret and the whole situation very amusing and chuckled to himself. Father and son left the apartment together and I did not learn until after Christmas of the tragedies which had occurred in the meantime.

In the first session after Christmas Anton appeared strangely altered. He brought me some things from the Christmas tree as a belated Christmas gift. He regarded me with serious mien, set himself solemnly on the sofa, and asked me if I could tell him why his father chuckled when he left me. I usually answered his questions with counter-queries to find out what his questions concealed. I tried counter-questions in this case too, but Anton insisted that I had to answer him first. He also rejected my proposal that if he would first tell me what he had supposed to be the reason I would then tell him facts. He remained very grave and stuck to his point that I must tell him first. I did not know what was going on in his mind, but realized this time it must be something very special. I did not want to provoke his anger and told him about the Christmas present. Then I asked him for his explanation. The boy began in a hesitating way, then getting more and more agitated, he finally said with great excitement that he thought his father had kissed me. When I asked him what made him think of such a thing I learned the following: when his father chuckled to himself in such a funny way, Anton's suspicion was immediately aroused that there was "something between us". This fitted in with his experience at home, on the streets and in the dark doorways. He was nettled, and asked his father why he was laughing—if he had something with the Frau Doctor? This idea seemed to have pleased the father and he answered darkly, yes, he and Frau Doctor had a secret together. This remark troubled the child all the more, and he asked the father if he had kissed me. The father smiled mysteriously and did not deny it. That made the child furious. He began to sob broken-heartedly, in the streetcar; all the father's efforts to quiet him were in vain. The scene was continued at home. He was shown the present and was told the exact truth in the hope that this would calm him. But he would not believe it now and behaved worse and worse. The mother grew afraid that I would be offended when he reported the situation to me and tried to smooth over the whole affair and to quiet him. But the father by making frequent remarks about me during the Christmas vacation saw to it that the boy's doubts were kept alive, that his fantasies were further aroused. For instance, his father remarked that he was not feeling well, that he had indigestion, that since I was also working as a physician in a general hospital he too would go to me for treatment. The more he succeeded in irritating the boy the more detailed and elaborate he painted his fantasy of how fine it would be if he too could come to see me every day, and so forth.

Anton insisted that he would not stand his father's coming to visit me again. With the phrase, "I won't have it!" he wanted to separate me from his father and prove his right to me. The intensity of his excitement made it advisable to comply for the moment. I said I saw no special reason why his father should fetch him and agreed that his mother might come for him every day from now on. But as might be expected the explanation did not help much.

The following hour showed that he had simply not taken in my explanations. He overwhelmed me with threats and reproaches. He had as yet no insight into the fact that his attitude with me was based on fantasy. He began to criticize his father, a married man, for doing such things, got more and more excited in talking against his father and threatened to call in a policeman. It was not the first time, he said, that his father had done such things. He had already had a "girl" and had at that time been "awfully mean" to his mother and to him, so that she had taken him (Anton) in her arms and had gone to the police station to complain. His emotion was too great to discuss the situation with him in detail at the time. But later I learned from him that his father had really had a "girl", that this had led to many scenes at home. One scene had ended in a bad brawl. His father had knocked his mother down and mistreated her. Anton, then three years old, had cried in distress and in his hurry to go to his mother's aid had fallen out of bed. Now I understood why his mother had traced his state of anxiety to this hitting his head when he had fallen out of bed.

Anton continued to rage against his father. He worked out the fantasy of a trip to a police station, conferences with the judge, and the final severe sentence on his father,—although the actual incident had ended in reconciliation between parents. That is, from this point on, Anton's fantasy "corrected" the facts. The father was subjected to sadistic punishment. Anton was now living out in fantasy all his anger, all his thirst for revenge for all his suffering. His ideas tumbled over each other. First his father was given ten years in prison, then this time was gradually prolonged to a hundred years, with dry bread, without water, standing the whole time, with no accommodation for sitting or lying down. And of course, all this time Anton had his mother to himself. Naturally all this aggression against his father was not without its risks. So occasionally he would add: "Even if my father shoots me or throws me out of the window, I don't care; but he has to be punished!" During this whole period Anton was free from attacks; his aggression was finding a direct outlet without having to wait for elaboration in dreams.

Anton's acting out was not limited to the analytic hour; he talked at home in great excitement about the situation. I succeeded in persuading his father to be more cautious in his remarks. His mother tried to convince the boy that his present suspicions had no foundation. Yet the incident helped to recall to her mind similar episodes in the past. She described them to me then for the first time and gave me much material that was valuable for later interpretation. The mother's description of the wild scenes which the little child had to witness made Anton's aggression against his father, as well as his fear of him, more understandable.

What made the greatest impression on those who saw it was the adult type of his jealousy. His mother recalled several scenes of jealousy years before in a tap-room, where a friend had sometimes asked her for a dance. The boy had reacted so savagely that the family had to leave the place with him—much to the amusement of everybody present. On this account the mother finally gave up going to the tap-room altogether. Anton's jealousy had imposed his limitation on his mother's life, and she had accepted it. It is therefore not surprising that Anton was so determined in his demand that his father should not come to see me anymore. In the tap-room episodes, also, he was convinced he was right: his mother should not have let herself be touched by strange men, nor should she laugh with them.

These recollections of the mother made it easy for me to open her eyes to some of the deeper things that were going on in the child's inner life. It was not mere theory for her; she had actually experienced it, and our regular conferences had made her able to see these facts— more so than other parents. This period was of the greatest importance in my relationship to the mother. In telling me all her troubles she became devoted to me and open to influence in her training of the child.

In the discussion of the boy's jealousy an important detail of his history came out. The mother recalled that at the beginning of her child's illness he had quite a different type of attack in which he "acted a part". The "act" was as follows: the boy sat up in his sleep and began to sing in a sort of somnambulistic state. At the time he had two favorite songs, both in his sleeping and waking state. "I Have Lost My Heart in Heidelberg" and "You, You, You Alone" (two well-known German love songs). Then he laughed and spoke in the Czech language which nobody at home understood; whereupon his mood changed, his gaiety turned into whining, and he cried out repeatedly, "My mother, my poor little mother!" Sometimes he started up, leaned forward and let out a loud flatus, often accompanied by raucous laughter. The scene always ended with expressions of anxiety, with tears, with shrieks of fear, calls for help, and sometimes with a prayer.

We can understand some of the details of this somnambulistic state (other details can only be explained later—for instance. the

Czech language and the loud flatus). We know that in the love songs he is declaring his love for his mother. "My poor little mother" refers to her ill-treatment at the hands of her husband, and the final anxiety represents his fear of his father.

The previous jealousy in relation to his mother was repeated in undistorted form in the analysis. But acting out now gave way gradually to fantasies. He realized at last there was nothing between me and his father. He now played with the fantasy that a strange man was following me on the street and courting me. Anton, now policeman, followed after to see that the man did not kiss me. If it happened, however, sergeant Anton would grab hold of him and take him to the police station.

Anton embellished his fantasies from day to day until they sounded like a romantic novel. The villain, having served his time, begins all over again. Anton tackles him like a hero and the fight is so realistic that the furniture is in danger. The fight ends, of course, with Anton's victory. The villain falls to the ground—dead.

Finally Anton came out into the open. He told me that he loved me, and that his father had said something very funny. When I asked him what, he answered, very much embarrassed, "That I should marry you." Naturally I took the matter seriously and asked, "What do you think about it, Anton?" In place of an answer came a movement of his fingers signifying money and an expression of resignation on his face—as if to say, "I have no money and you certainly would not want to marry a poor chap like me." Money seemed to be the only difficulty; he took my consent for granted. I remarked that a good character and a profession mean more in marriage than money—whereupon Anton played with the idea of becoming a male nurse in a hospital; he would then have a white coat just like a doctor. At other times he wanted to be a doctor and to have his consulting room next to mine; but reflected that to become a doctor involves much study, and that was not exactly to his taste.

Other fantasies and his behavior showed that he was not merely interested in a platonic affair. He showed exhibitionistic and voyeuristic tendencies towards me. One fantasy was that on a winter day I slipped on the icy streets and that my skirt flew up. A significant chuckle filled in the rest. This idea occupied him for several days and brought to light his annoyance with his mother when she told him to leave the room because she wanted to wash. At other times he would come from the toilet with his fly open and maneuver persistently to force me to notice it. When this failed he sat on the floor with his legs spread, and when I still did not look, said, "Why are you looking at me like that, what is wrong? Is my fly open?" at which he looked down between his legs. I was then in the position to interpret that he wanted me to admire his penis of which he was very proud. He was so disappointed at my response to his attempt at seduction that he gave it up completely.

Once Anton was convinced that his jealousy had no real foundation it was possible to explain it to him as a transference reaction. I could show him that he had always behaved in this way toward his mother and that was why he was doing it all over again with me. Anton retorted that it was true, that he was jealous about his mother before, but now he loved me and was jealous because of me. Why was I turning the talk back to his mother? "I will not have it!" I had to show him that this talk was necessary, to explain to him, how his feelings for me would pass one day, that he would return again to his mother and his jealousy about her was connected with his illness; if he refused to discuss this, his anxiety might return. Anton would always protest against my interpretations and make blunt remarks: "Leave me alone, will you?" He would doubt whether my mind was sound and would sometimes repeat his wish to have me shut up in Steinhof. Yet his later attitudes proved that he had grasped and worked out the interpretations.

At the beginning the transference neurosis brought abundant material to the surface. Gradually, however, this changed into playful acting and ceased to provide fresh material. Taking the interpretation of the transference neurosis as the starting point, I tried once more to find a connection with the first material of the analysis. But he frankly refused to tell me anything on the plea that then we would reach the end of the treatment too quickly, and he wanted to come and see me for a long time.

VI.

Fortunately a fresh turn in his home life helped to end the stalemate. Without any obvious reason in the analytic situation he showed defensive behavior combined with a whining form of aggression. This was a sign of a bad conscience, the causes of which were not known to me. It seemed that something was going on outside the analysis about which he was keeping silent. By probing long enough I learned from him that two changes had come in his life. Before the analysis began he had been forbidden to play in the streets because of his sexual games with Franky; but now his parents had moved into another flat and he had no playmates who could come to the house to play with him. As he was very lonely his mother allowed him to play again in the streets. The second change was the visit for several weeks of a grown-up girl cousin from the country. Anton was therefore forced, as he told me, to sleep with her, as there was no other bed available. I could learn little from him about these new developments. As regards the street, he played war games with other boys, looked at the motorcars, and took an interest in things in general. As to the new sleeping arrangement, my persistent questions drew either a defiant, "If you don't like my sleeping with the cousin you can buy me a bed!" or, in another mood, a suggestion, with love and hope in his voice, that if I didn't like it he could sleep in my house.

I tried in vain to get some clues from his mother. She said she found nothing striking about the boy, but that the cousin's visit was irksome. She was rather taciturn and I wondered whether she was losing her interest in the analysis.

Then one day mother and son came to the hour with a story that belied altogether the supposed state of calm at home. Both were very excited. The cousin, I learned, had given the boy a light slap; he had thereupon hit her savagely on the legs with a whip; the mother, beside herself, flew at him with clenched fists and in her own words "could have killed him". So much irritation for such a little cause, and such aggression from this particular mother, required explanation. But all I could learn further from her was that Anton had been very naughty lately and had forbidden her to tell me about it. He had screamed so much that she had given in to his wish.

This scene proved that something was going on which neither the mother nor the boy were willing to tell me. The analysis itself gave me no clue. The boy's resistance was serious. He threatened repeatedly to leave me unless I would leave him alone. This time there was nothing playful about his attitude—the analysis had become really unpleasant and he would have left me if his parents had agreed to it.

The appearance of a typewriter in my office seemed to offer some hope of moving on; I encouraged him to dictate stories for me in the hope that I would learn something from his fantasies. He was intrigued with the machine, and even said hesitatingly he was willing to tell further stories about the crate. This, in fact, was another sign that he was hiding more important things. We therefore made little progress. He added some further details about the games in the past but avoided the present.

Increasing tension at home and within himself led to another attack of night terror, although he had been free from attacks for a long time. He reacted to this attack with increased fear of analysis. He insisted to his mother with tears that I must not be told. He dreaded that I might ask him what he thought was the reason for the recurrence of his terrors. For he knew perfectly well what they were connected with, though he did not grasp the deeper meaning. His mother had pangs of conscience. His father said that if another attack occurred he was going to cure the boy by giving him a sound thrashing. He felt the boy's aggression, which the attack had revealed: When Anton's father had come towards the bed to calm the boy, his anxious screaming increased; he told his father to go away and asked for his mother. In the end, however, his father's aggression was what drew Anton close to me with an appeal for protection against his father.

The session began with the mother's faltering report that Anton had had another attack the night before. He had pointed to a corner of the room, as if he could see someone there, and showed marked anxiety. When I was left alone with Anton and tried to talk with him about what had happened he burst out crying. He knew nothing, he said. I should leave him alone or else he would go away. When I pointed out to him that the very reason that he had come to me was that we should try to find out more about it, he walked out of the room to his mother who was sitting in the waiting room. I called her in, leaving him alone for the rest of the hour. She was hesitating and confused. She attributed the attack to an incident at night, before the boy had gone to bed. He had broken a lampshade and had been fearful that his father would punish him. But she admitted that this was not in itself enough to explain the attack. Then finally she made a full confession. The boy had refused absolutely to share his bed with his cousin. He had talked his mother around to sleeping in her bed and even persuaded her to keep the whole thing secret from me. She thought this was the simplest way out because I might have been opposed.

It now became easy to understand a number of recent happenings. Sleeping in the same bed with his mother—a single bed—had brought Anton into conflict. On the one hand, he liked it very much, but on the other hand he felt disturbed. He blamed his cousin for the whole trouble and his irritation against her had reached the point where he finally lashed at her with a whip. His mother's sudden aggression against her son also became clear; she had realized that there was some connection between his sleeping in her bed and his behavior. She explained this in her own fashion by saying that the boy was "naughty" because he was being spoiled. Although the connection was not quite so simple, she had realized the cause and the effect. But having allowed herself to become an accomplice she had continued to be silent. Her bad conscience towards me, however, led to increasing annoyance with the boy until she had finally struck him. Not being able to come to me for help she had tried to manage the child according to her own methods, that is, by threats and intimidation.

It was just at this time that the newspapers were publishing long reports of the trial of a seventeen-year-old boy (Artmann) who had murdered his parents. The papers enlarged on the effects of bad upbringing and on the evil consequences of spoiling children. The mother thus saw suddenly in her little boy the great criminal of the future. She became very strict with him, saying that she could no longer tolerate his behavior lest he also should murder his father and mother. Her fears fitted in with Anton's own fear of patricide. For his mother's warnings showed that anyone who harbors such wishes "when he is small" will carry them out when he is "big".

In this way the situation was becoming more critical for Anton on all sides. The fact of his sleeping again with his mother directed his desires towards her anew and made it again more difficult for him to get away from her as a love object. This also increased his jealousy of his father and his aggression against him. And his father's behavior did not make things easier. The last straw was the Artmann trial, which was used to prove to him what became of bad boys.

In the next hour I turned again to the subject of his night terror and again met with Anton's resistance; but this time he did not risk leaving the room as he knew this meant remaining alone while I talked to his mother. So he decided to let me have my way. He told me that he had talked to his father about a shark and that he had been afraid that the shark might eat him up. I asked whether he did not fear his father more than the shark and he unwillingly agreed. I then brought in the Artmann trial and said it had scared everybody and maybe that was why he was so frightened. At first he denied vehemently that he could have anything in common with Artmann, and tried to change the subject, but finally he said he would dictate into the typewriter. The story which I give here in the original wording was dictated in three sessions. There were preliminaries each time before he could bring himself to continue his story.

The Artmann-story, first part[2]: "I thought about Artmann, that Artmann killed his mother. But I got up early in the morning.[3] I look at the picture of Artmann and saw that he killed his mother. And, but I dream again at night, that Artmann killed his mother because I looked at the picture and it went again through my head." ("What was the picture like?") "The picture looked like this: the man and the woman and two policemen and the lad. The man and the woman had been killed. The policeman took him with them immediately and dragged him immediately to the police station. He is sentenced from seven to ten years; if he behaves well he gets seven, and if badly ten years. And he has behaved well and has improved and he has got seven years."

In the story it is striking that he talks of the killing of the mother, but not about the father. In answer to my question as to what the picture was like, he reported truthfully, but talked of the "man", not of the father. He avoided talking about what concerned him most, of what touched upon his own fantasies and wishes. His identification with the criminal is still very marked; he pities him, and lets him be good so as to get the less severe sentence. (The verdict of from seven to ten years, in accordance with the criminal's behavior, corresponded to the facts.)

Second part: "And, after all, he has not improved. He has only been just a little good and thought he would go free; but he did not get out and got ten years punishment. Ten years are a hard punishment, seven years are a slight punishment. I wouldn't like to become a thief, and I would prefer to become a coachman or a chauffeur."

This second day's story shows a real change of attitude. Anton tries to detach himself from the murderer. The superego is becoming more strict as is shown in the severity toward the delinquent: Artmann has not improved; he gets the heavier sentence. But still there is some understanding for the murderer. Anton says, in rather a sorry voice, that ten years is a hard punishment. As the last sentence shows it is the fear of punishment which reinforces his wish to be an honest

2. The poor syntax is partially due to the dictating. Since I type much more slowly than he dictated, he got into a muddle and repeated the phrases so that nouns and verbs no longer agreed.

3. The family fought over the morning paper; Anton's interest was first to see the pictures of the trial.

person. This new ability to hold himself aloof from the criminal resulted in Anton's becoming much lighter-hearted. He came to the next
hour in high spirits and brought me the drawing of the motorcar
which he had done himself. ("I would prefer to become a chauffeur
and not a thief.")

Suddenly he remembered how the night terror had come about:
before going to bed he had felt such a strange wish to discuss with his
father what it is like when a burglar breaks into a house—whether he
shoots "the man" immediately. His father explained to him that the
burglar only threatens to fire without doing it, that he quickly col-
lects the booty, and so on. I wanted to know the source of his increasing
interest lately in questions of this kind. "Maybe," he ventured, "so
that when I become a man, I will know what to do when a burglar
comes."

Third part: "Why Artmann killed his mother and murdered his father.
I never have seen such a 'suicide' (Selbstmord—self-murder) and so I
thought that Artmann was a wicked man and murdered father and mother.
But I for my part thought that Artmann was such a wicked devil. If I had
been the judge I would have given him a punishment of a hundred years.
Because I do not see the reason. But I for my part was very angry with him
because he killed his mother. But I for my part, did not think that Artmann
was such a wicked man. But I for my part, was angry because he had not
obeyed his parents, in consequence of which he was such a wicked man,
that he did not obey his parents. And because he is such a wicked man
I am angry with him. Because he was such a bad boy, when he was small
and his parents let him have his own way; therefore he became such a
wicked man when he was grown-up, and murdered his parents. He was so
wicked because his mother had given in to him when he was small."

This third part of the story shows t emendous progress toward a
greater strictness of the superego. The identification with the criminal
has been given up and there is complete identification with the parents.
Such expressions as "for my part", "in consequence of which", and
"because I do not see the reason", which were not at all his way of
expressing himself, must be attributed to this. Only when he had got
to that point could the patricide enter, for Anton himself was no
longer the murderer. The latter was an entirely strange person with
whom he had nothing in common, whom he absolutely condemned,
much more so than anybody else, much more than the judge himself.
("Had I been the judge, I would have given him a punishment of a
hundred years,"—again a "hundred years" as in the case of his father.)
He repeated his parents' words that this crime was the consequence

of Artmann's having been a bad child and of the indulgence with which his parents had treated him. Naturally one cannot expect the superego to be strengthened so much already that the child could really and finally discard the identification with the criminal. There is a little backsliding in the words "And I, but I was so angry with him because he killed his mother,"—as if to say, "Killing father is all right, but why mother?" Hence the very severe sentence of a hundred years. Only by meting out the very severe punishment could he save himself from the pressure of his wishes and thus protect himself from anxiety. What kind of anxiety it was he revealed immediately afterwards. When I asked him in what way Artmann had been a wicked child, Anton answered, "I do not know because I am not a boy." As I began typing that (as a part of the story) he showed uneasiness and insisted that that should be rubbed out. He blocked it out on the machine himself and then with one finger typed out the words, "But I am a boy all the same." This slip as well as the earlier one—*suicide* in the place of murder—show how close to one another are crime and punishment. The time was now ripe to analyze his castration fear.

With analysis, his castration fear diminished and he became able to admit his masturbation. The question arises whether it would not have been feasible to open up this problem at an earlier stage of analysis. An opportunity to do so had in fact presented itself in an earlier game: "bad" Anton goes out of the room and "good" Anton comes back. When he entered the door he made a slip, introducing himself with the words, "Here is Mrs. Anton." The slip showed how he thought a bad child is turned into a good one. The organ with which the child sins is cut off and he is then able to be good. He had added, immediately after, the words, "My heart is aching." My careful attempts to follow up this slip had been rebuffed. Anton did not wish to touch this delicate subject, but the slip "Because I am not a boy" gave a better opening when resistance was at low tide.

VII.

Taking as starting point his words "I do not know that because I am not a boy" we discussed the difference between a boy and girl. Anton gave the usual answer that the difference lies in the clothes. In answer to my second question, whether changing the clothes would be enough to make a girl into a boy and a boy into a girl, Anton showed he knew all about the anatomy of sex. Obviously he had inspected the female genitals with the greatest interest in the crate

To my question how it happened that a girl looked different from a boy he replied that the girl was born like that, that there was nothing that could be done about it. "Nothing more grows on to it," he said. "And what about a boy?" "That is different, a boy can be changed into a girl. Of course, the father cannot do it, nor the doctor, nor the policeman; but a criminal, he can do it."

This answer explains not only his fear of burglars but how this fear developed. His words, "Of course father cannot do it," etc., had only gradually become a matter of course and perhaps it was not quite yet a matter of course. In the first stage it was the father who could change a boy into a girl; then the doctor was added who treats children's bodies, and has horrible knives; and finally the policeman became the punishing authority. Anton's capacity to discriminate had reached the point where he knows father, doctor, policeman cannot cause such injuries. But what about the criminal? He does not care whether a thing is forbidden or not. He will stop at nothing, so there is no final safeguard against him. The whole castration fear is thus centered on him.

The discussion of this subject took a fairly long time. We talked over the question whether a burglar was really likely to castrate a child. When Anton realized how improbable it was, he understood my interpretation of the growth of his anxiety. The result of the talks was his admission of masturbation.

The way this came out was typical of Anton. The fear of punishment was still strong enough for him to try to funk the responsibility. He said casually that he had done "something of the kind" but that was when he was quite a small child. He showed with a circular motion of his hand how far his head had been above the ground at that time. But his hand slid gradually so close to the floor that it made him little more than a baby, so little that he could not be made responsible for his actions. Besides, there could hardly be a punishment for sins so ancient. Moreover, he maintained that he had done "such a thing" only just once. This partial confession hedged by so many qualifications made me think that his father must have reacted to his masturbation with quite open threats of castration.

The talk with his father was interesting because it showed exactly the same mechanisms as his son had shown in the analysis. At first the father—like Anton—met my questions with an indignant denial that his son had ever done "such things". Then when I had turned the talk to his work as member of a School Parents Committee and slipped in an appreciative remark about his cooperativeness and understanding of children's problems he felt remorseful. Like Anton he turned to Franky as scapegoat and blurted out, "Oh, I just remember, Franky did such things and maybe I scolded him and Anton overheard me." He paused and then suddenly burst out, "I better tell you the whole truth, Anton played often 'down there'. I was very patient with him at first, I told him that it is dangerous and unhealthy. But it didn't help. I just had to tell him that I would 'cut off' his 'dirt-slinger' (a very vulgar expression for penis)."

It was clear how much the boy had to suffer because of his masturbation. He could not give it up, despite his father's threats. He continued, as I learned later, to do it in secret. Though he was able to hide it from his father, he was still full of fear of punishment, in case he should be found out, and of the diseases he had been told would result.

It was now essential to have these facts brought into analysis by Anton himself. When I approached the point he raised his fist as if to hit me and made angry threats. I told him I did not want him to be a ruffian. It was the first time I had been critical of him. He grew thoughtful, sat down on the floor, which he only did on serious occasions, and he began to talk half to himself: "If I tell everything I can get quite well again. I can then be a policeman or a chauffeur or a fireman. If I do not say everything I will come to a bad end; I can only be a criminal." At these words his eyes lit up—"But I shall have a revolver too." Then he added after a pause, "But then nobody will love me. Not mother, not Frau Doctor, not even Aunt Betty. So I prefer to tell everything." Then suddenly taking hold of himself he said: "I have played with the 'birdie' three times."

Despite the heroic gesture, this was of course far from being the whole truth. But the little monologue opened up a wide vista on the facts of real life. A large number of instinctual needs may be satisfied in various ways. Which way is chosen depends, among other things, on the individual's relation to the world about him. Anton's wish is to possess a revolver, to be a tall, strong man who need not to be afraid that something might happen to him. This can be attained by becoming a policeman, a soldier or a criminal. To become a policeman or soldier is a goal which demands sacrifices (being good, studying, getting well—and, first of all, speaking up now). The path which leads to becoming a criminal, who also possesses a revolver, is on the contrary easy to follow and full of gratification. One can be naughty and take everything one wants to have; but for that one has to pay by losing the love of human beings. And it is this love which ultimately prompts the child to renounce so many gratifications easily obtainable, to take on himself the hardships of school and to accept the high demands of those about him. This is an old truth but it is here given impressively by a child.

The analysis now moved forward into a phase when the child began to speak far more directly and frankly, thus indicating that the end was not far ahead. To reach that stage the child's anxiety had to be analyzed and overcome. Thus the greater part of the analytic work was already behind us. This material supplemented and completed the fragmentary knowledge we had obtained before. Above all it provided the possibility of summarizing, putting in order, reformulating more effectively—working through—the interpretations which hitherto had been offered sporadically and piecemeal. The subjects mainly covered in this phase were: masturbation; the oedipus situation and the primal scene; and the sexual games with other children, which led on to the analysis of his cardiac symptom.

As regards his masturbation, Anton told me that though his father's threats had troubled him a lot, he could not give it up. Fearing punishment by his father, he had found a way out by doing it in secret. This led on to an analysis of his sleeping ritual: he had to hold his mother's hand before falling asleep. This ritual was not, as I first suspected, a protection against the temptation to masturbate. The boy masturbated under the blanket and asked for his mother's hand when he had enough of it. By holding his mother's hand he hoped to keep her away from his father. If she tried to get her hand away to go to bed with his father he would wake up.

This led to his observations of what went on between his parents at night. He said he had never actually seen anything. It was too dark for that. But he heard noises, and his own experiences and what he had learned from Franky told him what was going on. It was agonizing for him; so he tried by every possible means to put a stop to it. If he woke up and saw his mother in his father's bed, he said, he either began to cry and asked his mother to come into his bed or he called out sharply, "Go away from father, you have no business there." (All this was confirmed by his mother.) He now repeated what he had said in the beginning of the analysis about being upset by his father caressing his mother, teasing her, tickling her on the neck or touching her in any way with his hands, because he was afraid "the rest" would follow.

Passing on to the crate games, Anton now told me that he had not merely been a passive witness, as he had tried to make out before. He was indeed a very active member of the Crate Club. He was very unhappy when he was discovered by his father because he was forbidden to play anymore with the children. On that occasion he had not been punished by his father, who knew that Franky had been the seducer.

At this point an earlier fantasy of Anton's which I had not understood, became clear. He had played the game that he had a great number of children, ten, twenty, thirty, and all of them two years old. I had told him that twins, triplets, even four children, were possible at one birth, but never as many as he claimed. But he had only laughed knowingly. He now told me about a game in the crate which he called "making babies", in which the children said, "Now I give you another baby, the tenth, the eleventh," and so on.

Something that Anton experienced in the crate, which he now told me, helped me to understand an important element in his cardiac symptom. One day the children were almost caught at their sexual game; they shook with fright and their hearts beat violently. Anton noticed the heart poundings of one of his playmates who was very thin. Anton knew that he also got palpitations when he was sexually excited. His father's words, "Such games are bad for your health," gave him the idea that the palpitations must be a manifestation of a heart disease caused by sexual games. This observation on his playmate also explains a remark Anton had made, that he was suffering from a heart disease because, as he said, "I have looked into my stomach." For children, the stomach region often includes the region of the heart. In fact this idea had already occurred in the earlier fantasy, that I would operate on the heart of another patient and the water would then flow "out of the heart instead of down below". We connected up with this two other components of his fears about his heart: first his mother's nervous heart condition; and the death, long before his birth, of his baby sister from a congenital cardiac defect. The sister was thus in his mind doubly crippled, in heart as well in genitals. ("Girls are born like that, they cannot be changed into boys; nothing can grow on to it.") The supposed heart disease of his mother was another confirmation to him that women are defective in both regions. His idea that the penis ceases to function when a patient has a heart operation (the water comes out of the heart and no longer "down there") shows his identification of heart with genitals.

The misunderstandings were of course cleared up. He was informed that palpitations occur after any kind of excitement and so with sexual excitement, but that this is no sign of heart disease. His connection of heart with genitals was explained to him, and he was told that his sister's heart defect had been a pure coincidence from which he had drawn wrong conclusions. Finally it was explained to him that his own heart symptoms were really self-punishment. Of course these interpretations were not made all at once; they were given from time to time at points where explanation was needed and always in a form which he could understand.

During this last free-flowing phase in analysis transference fantasies became increasingly open. One day Anton made a direct proposal of marriage. I dwelt upon my age and my thought that he would certainly drop the idea when he grew up and was in the position to marry me; for I should be much too old for him by that time. Thereupon Anton said pleadingly, "Then marry me little." I answered that he certainly knew that the law forbade it and that the minister would refuse to marry us.

Laws are abstract things; it is difficult to fight against them. It was easier to take revenge on the minister. And so following this the transference fantasies centered around the stubborn priest; the object was to coerce him into performing a marriage ceremony. There were scenes resembling wild-west films, with pursuits, escapes, battles, and the final vanquishing of the priest. One of these fantasies ran thus: after much fighting, Anton succeeded in overpowering the priest who was always running away. Anton picked up an axe that was lying on a bench. In the first version he slew the priest. Then he was overcome by guilt and gave a different ending to the story. It was the priest who took the axe in order to defend himself; but he was unlucky enough to drop it and cut off his big toe. So he could not run away anymore, and said he was ready to marry us.

It was much too dangerous, after all, to go against the priest because of his connection with God. So the original idea of killing the priest was softened down to a mere slip—and this on the priest's part, not Anton's. But his conscience was not really stilled by this compromise—as was shown by anxious behavior in his sleep, about which his mother told me, though he had no recollection of it himself. He cried out uneasily in his sleep "That's the bird, sitting there." His mother asked where, and he replied, "On my big toe." Thus the open aggression against the priest was not without conflict. There was still the fear that "If you want to cut it off your father, he will cut yours off." His "big" toe—the seat of the bird—is in danger. Yet he has made progress. It was only an anxiety dream and did not develop into a full attack of night terror.

We talked more about his castration fear. He was reassured to hear that other little boys did the same, that they gave up the habit as they grew up and that their health did not suffer from it. The parents were also instructed in this respect and asked to avoid open or veiled threats of castration.

At about this time Anton had a dream which showed that he no longer had to express his aggressive wishes against his father in the form of symptoms. One night after his father had been to see me the boy had the courage to dream an active castration dream against his father without reacting with anxiety and screaming. (The few dreams of this analysis almost all occurred in the closing stages of the treatment; before that the impulses had led to an attack of night terror. What he had reported as "dreams" in the first year of analysis had generally been daydreams.) Anton laughed when he told me the dream: "Father came from you and brought a long pencil with him. I took a hatchet and cut the pencil in two, so that only a tiny bit was left; then I got some glue and stuck a bit on it." He had understood the dream perfectly well without interpretation and was much amused by it. As the dream shows, he was still jealous of his father; he did not want him to pay me a visit and punished him for it. But the dream was free from anxiety.

The analysis of another dream which Anton had at this time filled in a further gap. When he had been allowed to play once more on the street, he had found a partner for sexual activities. This had been going on for some time—since the episode with the cousin—but Anton was only now ready to talk about it. The dream was as follows:

"I drove in a sledge with Karli. Two dogs were harnessed to it. I had a whip in my hand and a cord, and I had tied the cord around the dogs' bellies like a saddlegirth and whipped the dogs with my whip. There was a steep mountain, it got steeper and steeper, and we tumbled down. The other boy was killed and I was wounded."

Karli, he said, was the playmate in the street with whom he had played "horses". As the dream contained distinct allusions to sexual activities I inquired more closely and learned that Karli was also his partner in sexual games. Karli had recently slipped on the street and broken his arm and been taken to a hospital; Anton regarded the broken arm as a punishment for the sin, a warning to himself. I tried to explain to him the mechanism of self-punishment. Maybe Karli had a bad conscience and a need for punishment, and maybe this was a reason for his slipping. He answered, "When I am very much afraid because I have done something wrong, then my hand shakes and I drop the glass and then I think that is the punishment." We can substitute "lamp-shade" for "glass"—the lampshade which he had broken on the evening before the night terror in order to provoke punishment by his father. It seemed to me that the analysis of self-punishment was of decisive importance for the therapeutic result.

VIII.

When Anton was finally persuaded to leave his parents' bedroom the analysis seemed to draw to an end. Anton tried to make some profit from his agreement, and at first promised to agree if I bought him a rocking-horse to keep him company when he slept alone in the kitchen. I explained to him that this would not help us much, because we would not know whether he agreed to sleep alone because he was already quite well or because he wanted the horse. But I promised that I would buy a rocking-horse for him after the end of the analysis. Nevertheless this offer proved that he was well to a certain extent; because a year before not even rocking-horses could have made him agree to sleeping alone in the kitchen. His mother, who was not at all sceptical about the treatment, had said time and again that analysis might perhaps remove his anxiety, his night terror, but never make him willing to give up his parents' bedroom. (Perhaps her own secret wishes were behind her scepticism.)

Anton's exodus from the bedroom proved to be a success. Only once, his mother reported, was the boy very restless; he had complained of being frightened and so was allowed to get into his father's bed, the latter being away. When his father returned he had to sleep in Anton's bed in the kitchen. The discussion of this alleged return of anxiety differed greatly from others on similar occasions in the past. Whereas, with genuine attacks, he had vehemently declined to talk about them with me, he now told me all the facts freely. At night there had been a quarrel between his parents. His father went to a tavern and his mother began to cry. The boy knew what usually happened in such a case: the father would come home rather tipsy;

the mother would reproach him rather spitefully; they would take up the quarrel where they had left off, only the storm would be worse because his father would be drunk. Anton thus reckoned quite logically that perhaps he could prevent a great scene by pretending anxiety, thus getting into his father's bed and forcing the latter to pass the night in the kitchen. The next day the father would be sober and quiet and the whole affair settled. Although his procedure seemed quite sensible and by no means neurotic I had to remind him that his mother was married to his father and not to him and that his father would not harm her. He had to wait until he grew up; he then would take a wife and sleep with her. He would not be pleased if *his* son were to interfere with *his* married life. Thereupon Anton became thoughtful, sat down pensively on the floor and talked to himself in a low voice. "Firstly I am not married to Mother; secondly I am not Father; thirdly I am not the Boss; fourthly I am not the Master; fifthly I need not sleep with Mother; sixthly I have my own things; seventhly I need not be so foolish." In this meditation he briefly rehearsed the desires leading to his neurosis and added his renunciation. Although I had succeeded in taking down in shorthand what he was saying, I said to him, "That was very sensible, what you said just now. Dictate it to me. I shall write it down; because, you know, there are times when you are not so reasonable. I shall then read it out to you." Thereupon he dictated as follows: "Firstly I am not the boss; secondly I am not the master; thirdly I am not the chief; fourthly I need not be stupid; fifthly I should not be silly; sixthly I must have sense."

Between the first and second version repression interfered. In the second version he omitted his correction of the very wishes which had led to his neurosis, i.e., his rejection of the wish to usurp father's role, to be married to mother, to sleep with her, and the consolation that he had "his own things"—masturbation. I felt however that the repression was no longer of a pathologic nature. The magnificent renunciation ("I am not married to mother, I am not father, I need not sleep with her") and the consolation ("I have my own things") seemed to mark an important step forward to recovery.

Now at last it became possible to explain to him the full meaning of his night terror. All the material seemed to dovetail. I could bring together his seduction by Franky with its stimulus to his sexual desires, and the further stimulus by what he saw in the bedroom of his parents. He wanted very much to be a good boy; but this experience, and his love for his mother, stimulated his sexual desires towards her. This

made him more anxious when she seemed to be threatened by his
father (sadistic interpretation of intercourse). This recalled the scene
several years before, when the boy had seen his father struggling
violently on the floor with his mother, and Anton had been knocked
down. Hence his wish to get rid of his father, to have him imprisoned
for a hundred years or to kill him on the spot. He felt he ran a great
risk, even perhaps of castration by his father; and so he was overwhelmed by anxiety.

We may now analyze the symptoms—the somnambulistic act—
as they appeared before the analysis began. The boy starts up in
terror at night at the time when he knows that his father is taking
his mother into his bed. Anton is in the positive oedipus relation. He
wishes to have his mother to himself and interrupts his sleep with an
aggressive impulse against his father. He begins with the declaration
of love for his mother (love songs); but he also wishes to play out
with her what the children did in the crate (the obscene words in
Czech); then comes the idea that it is not he but his father who is
doing this to his mother and that she is in danger (the tearful exclamations: "My poor little mother"); hence the impulse to have the
father taken away by the policeman (the jumping up in bed; the
interpretation of this detail is offered by the boy's explanation of what
he would do if he were in Franky's place); and the impulse to kill
him (the loud flatus, which in the children's games meant shooting).
This is followed by great dread of his father. Thus his starting up
in bed is above all an attempt to prevent his parents from having
intercourse, to warn his mother against his father, to protect her from
his attacks, and to remove his father by means of the policeman or the
burglar and then to be alone with his mother. All this has been pushed
into the background by his fear of his father (burglar, Krampus-devil),
who threatens to come and castrate him. And at the same time there is
an attempt to flee from the dangerous situation.

Anton had finally grasped the meaning of analysis. He had been
in analysis for about a year and six months. At the beginning my interpretations had seemed uncanny to him; he attributed my knowledge
to supernatural power. He thought I possessed a kind of telephone with
which I could look into the distance. One incident had made a great
impression on him. It dated back to the time before his confessions
began. I had asked him what Czech words Franky had used in the
crate (after I had learned from his mother that Anton spoke isolated
Czech words in his attacks). For a moment he had looked at me in

terror; but as usual he regained his poise quickly and said indignantly, "But Franky does not know any Czech." He saw I doubted him and added, with an air of injured innocence, "If you don't believe me you can ask Mother." He brought her into the room and asked her a little anxiously, "Say Mother, Franky does not know Czech, does he?" His mother answered, "No," and left the room. She very soon returned and apologized. The boy's sudden question had so surprised her, she said, that for a moment she had forgotten that Franky's father was Czech and that this was the only language spoken in the family. Anton was not at all downcast at being found out, but flew into a rage, demanding to know how I could have known. I was a witch; I could not have heard over the telephone what was spoken in the crate. But in the end he repeated the words laughingly—they were dirty words in Czech. I explained to him how I had guessed. This explanation, and other experiences he had had during the analysis gave him a deeper understanding of the analytic procedure. He became aware, for instance, of the fact that when he got excited he would always let out things he wanted to hide, because, as he put it, "I drop a careless word that is going around in my head." And then I would guess the rest.

He even had some inkling of the difference between what was fully conscious and what was preconscious. Once I encouraged him to tell the things that were in his mind. Although he seemed to be in a rather cooperative mood, he promised to do it "sometime later". "Why not now?" "Because I do not know it now," was his answer. Seeing my surprise, he then gave the following explanation: "I have it in my head, but I don't know it."

IX.

We come now to the last weeks of Anton's analysis. His cooperation was still found to contain some elements of resistance. He wanted to get through with analysis not only because he felt cured, but in order to hide from me some fresh "sins". But once again he dropped "a careless word" from which I gathered another crate had turned up in the courtyard, and Anton could not resist the temptation to repeat his former experiences with other children, this time as the seducer. With Anton's consent we asked his mother to get him admitted to a day-care center so that he would not be exposed to such temptations. He was helped to become a "good" boy as he had wished to be in the beginning of the treatment. At this stage Anton seemed to be entitled to educational help of this character. Before we had arrived at a satisfactory understanding of his conflicts in all their ramifications our efforts had been constantly directed toward making the unconscious conscious. But this having been done, and the boy well on the way to recovery, the educational help was both permissible and necessary. His ego was not yet strong enough for him to be able to keep firmly in the saddle and to make himself obey the command, "You ought not and you must not," if temptations were too strong. If fresh adverse influences could be avoided there was more hope of a real *rejection* rather than an unsuccessful *repression* of undesirable tendencies.

We no longer concerned ourselves with matters of which he preferred not to think ("If I walk through the street I want to look at the beautiful things in the shop windows and not always think of such filthy matters.") We also discussed his rather aggressive attitude toward other boys and his behavior in the settlement where he spent his afternoons. And I soon felt that he was able to go on his way without further analysis.

Among the educational measures there was one to be undertaken by the parents. Anna Freud has pointed out that threats of castration can be best undone in children by the person who has uttered them. I therefore set myself to persuading his father to take back his earlier threats. I had to be content with a partial result. The father's inhibitions were too strong for him to discuss this point openly with the child. So the solution was that one day, when the family was gathered together, the mother casually spoke of the many new things which even grown-ups can learn. She herself had believed, for instance, from her childhood on, that it was bad for children's health if they played with their genitals; but now she had learned that it is quite common for little children to do this, that it does not harm their health, and that as they grow up they give it up by themselves—while the father sat by mumbling, "Yes, yes, that's right." Although the father did not expressly give his permission, the fact that he listened to the mother without contradicting her had the effect of undoing his former threats.

The mother treated the subject with such frankness that after the end of analysis, when I was no longer available, the child turned to her in delicate matters like these.

After the analysis was over, in March, 1930 (it had begun in the autumn of 1928), I had an opportunity to see the boy on a number of occasions at intervals of a few months. In November, 1934, I had an extensive interview with him. In this time the family's financial position had grown much worse; the father had been out of work for years, and the mother had lost her job as janitress. The boy's physical condition had not always been satisfactory. In 1931 he showed tubercular symptoms. He had been taken to a sanitarium and later had been under the medical care of the tuberculosis center. He had been sent to the country every year for a month or two. In 1931 a tonsillectomy had been performed. In spite of all these unfavorable conditions the boy had remained psychically well. Night terrors had not recurred. There was no trace of his previous anxiety. He was then nearly fourteen years old, in puberty, and gave the impression of being a stout-hearted, manly youth. When this review was made he was asked about his former symptoms. He almost took offense at the idea that he had once upon a time suffered from anxiety. It was only gradually that the whole thing came back to him; it seemed to him strange, as if it had not really anything to do with him.

A second examination at the end of 1937 showed no signs of recurrence of the symptoms, and apparently normal puberty.

BIBLIOGRAPHY

1. "Die Entstehung des Pavor Nocturnus bei einem Kinde". Von einer Mutter, *Zeit. f. psa. Päd.*, I, 1927.
2. Deutsch, H. *Psychoanalysis of the Neuroses,* Hogarth, 1933.
3. Fenichel, O. *Outline of Clinical Psychoanalysis,* Norton, 1934.
4. Freud, A. *Introduction to the Technique of Child Analysis,* Nerv. Ment. Disease Mon., 1928.
5. Freud, A. *The Ego and the Mechanisms of Defence,* Hogarth, 1937.

HYSTERICAL TWILIGHT STATES IN AN EIGHT-YEAR-OLD CHILD[1]

By BERTA BORNSTEIN (New York)

The following case of an eight-year-old girl who suffered from twilight states demonstrates with special clarity the meaning of the infantile sexual trauma, the fixation to the oedipal conflicts, and as far as our material permits, some of the pre-oedipal problems.

Sonja began her analysis at the age of eight years. The first attack had occurred at the age of six; several attacks, varying in length of time from half an hour to two days, followed. In such states the child usually would leave the house, beckon men who were driving by in cars and, in a very coquettish manner, would ask for a ride. If her mother prevented her from leaving the house, she would become hostile, threaten her with a knife and eventually turn it against herself. She responded when she was called by name, and recognized everybody but her father. When the attack subsided, she whined and whimpered, clung affectionately to her mother, and pleaded for protection. Afterwards she showed complete amnesia for these events.

In her normal state she seemed well adjusted, though somewhat shy and subdued. She was intelligent, loved school and could not understand why she should be prevented from attendance, as had been advised previously.

The mother was uneducated but lively and intelligent, and Sonja resembled her in many ways. The father was a hard-working small businessman with the grandeur of a Southeastern squire. Amused by Sonja's coquettish and courting manner, he used to praise her beautiful eyes, and once had promised her a career as a movie actress.

The girl's early childhood was described by the mother as easy and uneventful, her relationship to both of her parents as close. A second girl was born when Sonja was four years old. About half a

1. From a course of lectures on "The Psychopathology of the Child" given at the New York Psychoanalytic Institute 1945/46.

year later it was discovered that Sonja had contracted gonorrhea, which was treated at home with douches, to which the mother referred as "baths".

A medical examination of the family revealed that a young uncle, the mother's brother, was also infected. He had been brought up in Sonja's family and was treated by Sonja's mother like a child of her own. Although sexual relations between the child and the adolescent uncle were suspected, details were revealed only in analysis. The mother protected her young brother as well as her child by saying that, after all, both of them had only been children at the crucial time. She blamed herself because she had failed to supervise them properly since all her attention had been needed by the newborn child.

Some of the psychiatrists consulted had diagnosed the child's state as psychotic and hopeless. However, the mother's genuine love for Sonja, and her strong feeling of guilt, kept her alert and determined to find help for the child. In her search for a cure, the mother resorted to analysis. After a short trial period the mother left the child in a boarding school and returned to her family. The child was reluctant to let her go, one of her fears being that then nobody would prevent her from killing herself during an attack. She had to be promised that I would be on call whenever such an attack would occur.

It was expected that a connection would be found between the child's symptom and the seduction, which was assumed to be the traumatic factor. Surprisingly enough, the sexual scenes with the uncle were not completely repressed, and the child remembered parts of them with relative ease.

As a reward for her surrender the uncle had promised her a ride in a car, but lacking money, he had defaulted on his promise. His promises had stimulated daydreams in which she fancied herself as an actress riding in a car with gentlemen. These gentlemen could easily be recognized as substitutes for the father and his brothers. The analysis of her daydream revealed that riding in a car was meaningful only if she, as a bride, drove up to her father's door.

The daydream turned our interest to the child's father and to the role which he might have played in the development of the child's symptom. Not before the last few months, however, did material come to the fore which gave insight into the genesis of the twilight states.

It centered around two dreams. The first one occurred a short time before the sister's birthday, and contained the following material:

Lying on sister's bed is a tennis racket of chocolate.

It is a present from father and mother.

The color of the tennis racket led to memories in which the child saw her mother give enemas to her sister and spank the little girl for soiling. It revived memories of a "brown smelly stuff" which the parents had used in the treatment of Sonja's gonorrhea. This was the first time that the child mentioned the treatment. Details, however, were not obtainable; to cautious questioning the child reacted with weariness and sadness and a kind of confusion which resembled the onset of her twilight states. She was, however, willing to tell us more about the tennis racket and produced associations of ball games. What appeared to be a screen memory showed her father in a hilarious mood taking off the mother's slipper and throwing it at the mother, and the mother angrily throwing it back.

Recollections of these scenes of lively action show the child as a mere onlooker. Scenes in which one person is overpowered by another reinforced the child's conception of the sado-masochistic character of sexual relationships. The fact that the tennis racket in her dream is a toy indicates the child's attempt to reduce the danger of masochistic genital experiences to playful child-like activities that will not result in a disease.

The interpretation given to the child was confined to the element of jealousy. The approaching birthday of the sister, the presents that she would receive while our patient was absent from home, had revived this jealousy, which had originally been aroused by the mother's preoccupation with the baby. "Mother never had time. She always had to clean and to feed the baby," Sonja complained. A reference to her present attitude contrasted to her usual intolerance of any emergence of jealousy brought about resistance and negative transference reactions which for this child were uncommonly strong. She accused the analyst of putting "bad thoughts" into her head, and held her responsible for a possible relapse into her "foolishness", as she called her symptom. She confirmed, however, the fact that it had been shortly after the sister's birth that the sexual contact with her uncle had begun.

The second dream leads us further into the theme of jealousy:

Sonja, her young uncle and her parents are in one room. She is lying on a table. Suddenly it is not she who is lying there but the little sister who has to undergo some kind of treatment. The sister opens the mouth, two matches are put into her throat. Her uncle plays with fire.

This dream was a reaction to a letter in which her mother announced that she would arrive with the little sister who had to undergo a tonsillectomy.

The doubt expressed in the dream as to who is the one to be operated upon led to discussions of the advantages of sickness: if one is sick, mother is always extremely nice, as Sonja had experienced during her own sickness.

In the dream the sister opens her mouth and two matches are put into her throat. This led Sonja to speak again of the treatment of gonorrhea, and this time we learned more about "the baths" her mother had mentioned. For two years the child had received vaginal douches. While these were administered by her mother, her father had held the struggling child. The two matches in the dream are recognized by the child as father's fingers with which he spread her labia apart. The memories of this treatment, to which the child had been exposed between four-and-a-half and six years, had up to now been completely repressed, and not even the resumption of treatment of her gonorrhea during her analysis revived memories of her former experiences. The uncle's play with fire in the dream referred to the child's observation of his masturbation and his sexual excitement. It led further to the arising of memories of the burning sensation during urination and to her own sexual excitement which she had felt during the treatment administered by the parents.

Upon the interpretation that the dream fulfilled her wish for a repetition of these experiences, new material came into the analysis that may be abstracted in the following way: Will her sister receive the same treatment? Has the uncle, by any chance, played with her in the same way? Has he infected the sister? Is that the reason for her tonsillectomy? Or is she herself responsible for her sister's disease? After all, she, too, had played secret games with her sister in the garden. To be sure, she remembers them as harmless—though one scene in which she recollects her mother's interfering and scolding her suggests that they may have been less harmless than remembered. It sufficed temporarily to interpret the child's feelings of guilt as referring to these masturbation games, modeled after her experiences with her uncle.

This opened the way to the child's predominant fear, the fear of infecting others—to which fuel was added by one rule imposed on her in the boarding school: not to use the bathroom the other children used. She was overly conscientious about observing this rule—even when it was declared unnecessary after the successful cure of her gonorrhea.

Considering the play with her sister, we understand that the child's fear of infecting others contained the element of the contagious character of "badness". The "badness" referred to her desire for sexual contact against which she tried to protect herself by her over-conscientiousness. The following transference reaction demonstrated that especially clearly. An insignificant injury on my hand aroused her fear that she might have infected me. Questioned as to how she could have done so, she confessed having had the desire to kiss or touch me.

Beneath this fear, the same curiosity and jealousy that had been revealed in the dream of the operation, became evident. If what I said was true, that not she was responsible for my injury, who then had infected me? Who was treating me? Was it the doctor who treated her? Was it, by any chance, this doctor who had caused my infection? She had grasped that the consequence of her play with her uncle was bad. Thus "badness" became related to satisfaction as experienced in her secret play with her uncle and her sister, as well as in the gonorrhea treatment by her parents. Her disease appeared to be the natural consequence of badness; and badness, satisfaction and punishment became so identical that toward the end of the analysis she asked whether, after all, it was not the treatment by the parents which had caused her gonorrhea. In her fantasies, consequently, the sister's operation was likened to her own treatment by the parents.

From discussions at home she had learned that gonorrhea may lead to sterility. That meant to her that she could not be like her mother. To be unable to have children appeared to her as the main punishment for her badness. When she was finally reassured by the doctor that the treatment had removed this danger, a new factor was added to the positive side of the ambivalent feelings about the treatment and what had led to it: though bad—it made it possible for her to have children. When the sister now was to have an operation, she had to undergo something disagreeable, something bad, but at the same time she shared also in what was good and desirable about such an experience — satisfactions which Sonja did not want to share with anyone.

The genesis of Sonja's hysterical twilight states hinged on all these factors enumerated, which could even be better understood on the few occasions when the child produced her symptom in the course of analysis. She had four attacks, all slight, and short and free from the dramatic conditions by which they originally had been marked. The first one occurred in the initial state of analysis when we discussed the necessity of a medical checkup and treatment of her gonorrhea. The second occurred after she told me that a boy had given her a ring and proposed to her, but secretly had given a similar ring to another girl. The third attack occurred when Sonja once brought her favorite candies which her father had sent to her and suggested that she share them with me. After she had offered some to me she lapsed into a brief twilight state. The last time she produced her symptom was when she saw a visitor of mine arrive in a car.

All these scenes have one element in common: they awaken conflicts which the child cannot face consciously and which lead into the analysis of the oedipus complex.

The first attack was not analyzed, but was understood later, in the course of the analysis. The second attack brought to light the following facts.

The boy's proposal and gift aroused memories of her uncle's promises. Our little patient would have wished to experience sexual play with the school-mate as previously she had with the uncle. But now, at the age of eight, this desire met with the objection of her ego and could not find conscious expression.

We could deduce its existence, however, from a specific reaction which increased whenever she had to ward off her desire for the boy. At such times the rigidity of her conscientiousness with regard to the use of a separate bathroom was augmented. Although she was apprehensive that the boy might thus find out about the gonorrhea, she rigidly observed the rule even after it had already been lifted. The child says, as it were, if he knows about my disease, he will not like me —and as long as I am infected I may not have any physical contact. Her preoccupation with the idea of infecting others subsided after she had accepted the interpretation that she needed this over-conscientiousness as a protection against an eruption of her sexual impulses. The attack itself was produced when she related that the other girl had accepted the ring although she knew about Sonja's "engagement". What she could not bear was the fact that the beloved person was not her sole possession. The little rival's "unethical act" aroused Sonja's aggression. Simultaneously, however, it called to the fore the recollection and the criticism of her own covetousness for her father. Both, incestuous desires and aggressiveness, could not be tolerated and resulted in the attack. In her actual behavior toward the envied rival she did not allow her aggression to come through. She did not accuse her, but instead helped her with her homework, shared secrets with her, and tried in many ways to win her friendship. This behavior may not only have served to ward off the aggression toward the girl friend but may have had an additional motivation: it represented a hostile and revengeful action against the boy, attempting to isolate him, and she enforced this isolation by withdrawing her interest from him also.

We have here a complete reproduction of the child's reactions toward her parents. Before her sixth year her relationship to her father was very close. After the onset of her twilight states, she showed exaggerated affection toward her mother and alienated herself from her father. This alienation had a double motivation: on one side it protected the child from the eruption of her incestuous drives toward her father; at the same time it expressed her hostility toward him. (She felt rejected by her boy friend, as she had felt rejected by her father.) In the symptom of her twilight states the alienation was increased to the point of not recognizing him. No signs of aggression toward or jealousy of her mother became visible in her normal state. In her twilight state, however, her aggression broke through. As soon as the mother prevented her from pursuing her libidinal aims, the girl became angry and tried violently to free herself from her mother's grip. If unsuccessful, she threatened to kill her mother with a knife. But immediately she turned it against herself, whimpering and whining: "I must kill myself," or occasionally, "Don't kill me."

The same factors of aggression and jealousy also became evident in the scenes that had led to the other attacks, during analysis, the candy incident and the incident at the arrival of my visitor. They reveal even more plainly the elements of the oedipus complex. These two attacks took place after her treatment of gonorrhea had just been concluded. The termination had stimulated her hope for the approach-

ing end of her analysis and for her return home. Sonja became conscious of her longing for her father, and recollections of their loving
relationship emerged.

She attempts to share father's candies with me: one may assume
that sweets in particular may have played a part in the seduction scenes
with the uncle although this was not confirmed by the child. Some of
the child's oral sex theories were ascertained however—e.g., that the
father has to give "something good and sweet" to the mother in order
to impregnate her. Sharing her father's gift is equal to sharing his
love with mother. If in her attack she is sitting helplessly, unable to
eat the candies in her hands, she expresses both the defense against
her wish to get a baby from father and the defense against her impulse
to remove the rival. At the same time, by means of the attack, she
spares herself the pain of seeing her rival enjoy her father's gift.
The girl's inability to remain the excluded observer shows even more
strongly in the scene at the arrival of my visitor which occurred at a
point of her analysis when our interest was focused on details of the
twilight state like the beckoning of men in cars

In all four scenes the elements stemming from the oedipus complex are merged with details that have their origin in the seduction
scene with the uncle.

It must be asked what part the seduction played in the patient's
neurosis.

The seduction had occurred shortly after Sonja's mother had given
birth to a second child with whose care she was preoccupied. Envious
of the satisfactions which her sister received and hurt by the mother's
seeming withdrawal, Sonja reacted with a depression. Her uncle, an
adolescent in the beginning of his puberty, having also lost Sonja's
mother to the baby, was in a similar situation. Searching for substitutes,
both children found consolation in each other. Sonja told how she liked
to lie in bed with him and to be cuddled. She perceived the sexual play
to which she was initiated as an equivalent of what her mother did with
her sister. She remembered in particular that her uncle held her in his
arms and cleaned her with a wash rag which she took as "playing washing". Our assumption was that this "washing" may have happened
after an ejaculation, but this was not confirmed by the child, and it is
possible that this part of the scenes—in contrast to other details—had
to be repressed in line with the douches administered by the parents.

The seduction seems to have passed without immediately noticeable traumatic effect; at least no neurotic symptoms or behavior dis-

orders were observed during and immediately after that period. Nor did the discovery of the contracted gonorrhea and the numerous cross-examinations by parents and physicians seem to have been pathogenic. Details of this period came into analysis without particular resistance.

However, the discovery of the gonorrhea had another consequence. It led to the termination of the child's sexual play with her uncle. This frustration was compensated for by the subsequent vaginal treatment by the parents. The treatment, as we know from the dream of the operation, was experienced not only as a continuation of the satisfactions received from the uncle, but also, and chiefly, as the realization of the child's oedipal wishes. Whatever desires the uncle's play may have satisfied originally, there is no doubt that it accelerated the development of the child's phallic phase and stimulated genital wishes related to the oedipus complex.

That she could tolerate the satisfaction experienced in the gonorrhea is understandable if we consider the circumstances. The vaginal douches were administered by both parents. The douches appeared to her like the enemas which her sister had received. They were a necessity like "washing", on which the parents insisted, and they spared the child conscious feelings of guilt which were still more dulled by the pain which she temporarily experienced.

The sudden cessation of the gratifying treatment repeated the frustration experienced at the sister's birth. At that time it sufficed to devaluate the mother's significance as an object of love. By turning to her uncle the child behaved as if she were aiming only at some gratification of her pregenital drives. At the age of six, spoiled by the sex play with her uncle and by the subsequent treatment which provided excessive gratifications, she had become especially demanding. Now her wish centered on her father and she was not able to relinquish the desired satisfactions, nor to content herself with a substitute or with autoerotic gratifications.

The conclusion of the gonorrhea treatment just at this time aroused the feeling that her incestuous demands for the father were even more disallowed than were the secret games with the uncle and sister which the mother had interdicted. In order not to lose her mother again she identified herself with her mother's moral code and tried to repress her incestuous impulses. In the resulting conflict between these impulses and the internalized demands, the ego resorted to a compromise solution which found its expression in the symptom of twilight states. The first attack appeared a short time after the termination of the treatment.

In summarizing all these factors we must conclude that it was the deprivation resulting from the termination of this treatment that had the traumatic effect and that precipitated the neurosis. The twilight state permitted the discharge of the patient's incestuous wishes, although only in distorted form.

In a recent paper on fugues, Geleerd, Hacker and Rapaport (7) discuss the ego-superego relation during the fugue. They suggest that during the state of fugue the superego function is changed, the superego is eliminated. Our case does not confirm this hypothesis. To be sure, we gain the impression that during the attack the superego relaxes its censorship, but as in a dream it is neither paralyzed nor eliminated. Our patient could permit herself the attainment of her aim only if it was unrecognizable to the ego. This disguise took place under the influence of the superego. The censorship of Sonja's superego was so strong during the twilight state that she could not recognize her father.

The treatment of the venereal disease which gave her such intense satisfaction was conceived by her as the fulfilment of her oedipal wishes. It is understandable that under those conditions the passing of the oedipal phase as well as the consolidation of the superego were delayed. In addition it should be mentioned that the standards of sexual morality were not stringent in Sonja's native town. The children's sexual play, for instance, was somewhat excused; the fact that her uncle had acquired gonorrhea before the age of fourteen made the boy a man in the eyes of his male relatives, and Sonja herself was by the same token, so to speak, taken into the world of grown-ups.

The combination of exceedingly strong incestuous impulses and an as yet unconsolidated superego developed in so relatively indulgent an environment may explain the particular form of symptom in Sonja's case.

The patient could achieve the continuation of the accustomed gratifications only if she were not responsible for her doings, which was the case in the twilight states. The child remembered that her mother had excused her earlier sexual play by saying that they were only "foolish little children", who *did not know what they were doing*. By being foolish and irresponsible, like a little child, Sonja bribed her superego and soothed its objections in the identical way that her mother had. She called her symptom her "foolishness".

We want to repeat that Sonja's ego and superego were weakened only with regard to the management of the oedipal strivings. Her pregenital impulses, for instance, were mastered by well functioning reaction-formations. Her intellectual development was excellent and she drew considerable pleasure from successful sublimations. She considered her symptom of twilight states as a foreign body of which, consciously, she wanted to rid herself.

After eleven months of analysis the child was freed from her symptom and the analysis had to be terminated, although the solution of some problems involved had not been reached. We did not succeed in lifting the amnesia veiling the period preceding the birth of the sister. At various periods during the analytic treatment material was expected to emerge that would lead to the primal scene. These expecta-tions were not realized and we had to content ourselves with screen memories and reconstructions.[2] We were only able to make assumptions concerning the pre-oedipal relationships. The depression which Sonja developed after the birth of her sister, the way in which she escaped the painfully frustrating situation, suggest that her ties to her mother had been particularly strong. (She escaped from her mother to her uncle.) We further must assume that her way of managing her hetero-sexual conflicts was formed on the same pattern. After a renewed frus-tration at the age of six, when the treatment administered by the parents was stopped and her desire for the physical contact with her father was no longer fulfilled, she formed her symptom in which she actually ran away from the house and tried to replace her father by strangers.

The intolerance of frustration and the attempt to leave the place of temptation appear to be typical of twilight states and fugues.

2. How well, however, the child understood that the observation and jealousy of her parents' sexual relationship contributed to her symptom is evidenced by a letter which the child wrote to the analyst one year after the termination of her analysis. The letter reads: "Today mother called father 'Yingele' (the Yiddish word for 'little boy'). Then I thought that my foolishness was coming back. So I thought I'd better write this letter to you. Hugs and kisses.

Sonja."

A postscript by the mother said that the child had on that day shown signs of rest-lessness such as had preceded her twilight states, but that she had calmed down and kept in good condition after writing the letter.

Contact with the family was sustained during the subsequent five years. In that time the child remained free of symptoms and developed well, according to her parents' communications.

BIBLIOGRAPHY

1. Abeles, M. and Schilder, P. "Psychogenic Loss of Personal Identity: Amnesia", *Arch. Neur. & Psychiatry*, XXXIV, 1935, p. 587.
2. Abraham, K. "Hysterical Dream States". *Selected Papers*, Hogarth Press, London, 1927.
3. Breuer, J. and Freud, S. *Studies in Hysteria*, Nerv. Ment. Disease Publ., New York, 1936.
4. Fisher, C. "Amnesic States in War Neuroses: The Psychogenesis of Fugues", *Psa. Quarterly*, XIV, 1945.
5. Freud, S. "General Remarks on Hysterical Attacks", *Coll. Papers*, II.
6. Freud, S. "The Aetiology of Hysteria", *Coll. Papers*, I.
7. Geleerd, E. R., Hacker, F. J. and Rapaport, D. "Contribution to the Study of Amnesia and Allied Conditions", *Psa. Quarterly*, XIV, 1945.
8. Janet, P. *The Major System of Hysteria*, Macmillan, 1907.
9. Jones, E. "Remarks on a Case of Complete Autopsychic Amnesia", *J. Abnorm. Psychol.* IV, 1909, pp. 218-235.
10. Menninger, K. A. "Cyclothymic Fugues. Fugues Associated with Manic-Depressive Psychosis: A Case Report", *J. Abnorm. Psychol.* XIV, 1919, pp. 54-63.
11. Stengel, E. "On the Aetiology of the Fugue States", *J. Ment. Science*, LXXXVII, 1941, pp. 572-599.
12. Stengel, E. "Further Studies on Pathological Wandering (Fugues with Impulse to Wander)", *J. Ment. Science*, LXXXIX, 1943, p. 224.

EXPERIENCES WITH ENURETICS

By ANNY KATAN, M.D. (Cleveland)

Enuresis is one of the most frequent neurotic symptoms. Difficulty is apt to arise in the beginning of its study because constitutional disposition as well as various traumata may play a part in it. One often finds in the history of enuretic children that siblings have wet up to the age of five or six; with the siblings the symptom disappeared then, without apparent reason, while in the one child it may have persisted up to the age of ten. I remember one family in which seven out of eight children suffered from enuresis. The parents found it comparatively easy to accept this situation, as they themselves had suffered from the same symptom. There are other cases, however, in which only one child in a family has been unable to achieve bladder control.

Experiences with non-treated cases are contradictory. One frequently hears of cases in which the symptom has been removed by talks, explanations, threats, or punishments; and of others in which the symptom obstinately withstands any attempt at interference. There is a widely accepted view that bedwetting disappears by itself at puberty, especially in girls with the onset of menstruation. This is true in some cases, but unfortunately it is not the rule. As a result of army medical examinations we are now in a position to know better than we did that the number of adult bedwetters is much greater than is commonly supposed; nor is the number of grown-up girls small in whom the symptom continues after the onset of menstruation.

Cases also vary a great deal in regard to the time when the symptom appears. With many children who develop normally at first and are dry at night for some time, enuresis sets in later on. In these cases one can frequently find a traumatic experience preceding the appearance of the symptom; in my experience, these respond most favorably to treatment. There are children, however, whose condition I consider to be far more serious, who have continued to wet from babyhood up to the time of treatment. Then again, some bedwetters can keep dry under certain conditions, e.g., when on a visit, after giving a promise, etc.; or in the company of certain people. They may succeed for a few days or for as long as the summer holidays. They are able to control their symptom for a time with great energy, but usually relapse sooner or later.

Anyone who has had experience with enuretics can amplify this material with similarly confusing, contradictory observations. Many years of experience enable one, however, to distinguish certain groups of cases, according to the nature of the trauma, and this is of great importance in practice.

A.   One group consists of little children whose training in cleanliness had been completed by a beloved person from whom the child has now been separated. After the loss of the love object the child regresses, relinquishes the newly acquired developmental step, and begins to wet again. In cases such as this one cannot yet speak of a symptom, but rather of a passing educational disturbance. If it is possible to replace the beloved person by another suitable object the child will achieve control again for the sake of the new object. He will give up a great deal of satisfaction in order to gain love. Such children make up for what they have missed and merely reach the aim somewhat later than others.

B.   In a second group the symptom appears after the birth of a baby brother or sister. Jealousy of the baby plays a very large part here, since the baby is given a great deal of love and care by the mother who makes no demands upon it in return. It is precisely by being dirty that the infant forces his mother to give him attention— and so it is difficult for the older child to understand or accept the fact that in order to win his mother's love he must forego his infantile satisfaction. Were he able to put his feelings into words he would probably call out, "Why are you making it so easy for him and so hard for me? If I start wetting again, you will have to give me all your love and attention just as you give it to the baby." He regresses to an earlier stage of development, trying to become like the baby. Such regression must be regarded as an attempt to win the mother's love. If his reaction is correctly understood, and he is made aware of his feelings and wishes he will be dry again without too much delay—assuming, of course, that at the same time his need for love is satisfied, and that he is helped to understand that his mother especially appreciates his attempts to give up instinctual gratification, and loves him the more for it. In this case we can consider wetting to be a temporary symptom. If, however, the mother is unable to understand the child's reaction and deal with it accordingly, the enuresis persists. If then she is provoked to anger and punishment, the symptom is intensified by obstinacy and aggression against both mother and baby. A vicious circle is created. The child feels neglected, unloved, and builds up fantasies to explain the reason for this. This complex of conflicts soon links up with the child's masturbation conflicts, and so bedwetting becomes an established symptom.

C. In a third group of children the symptom appears at the discovery of the difference between the sexes. This trauma may coincide with the birth of a baby brother or sister. In these cases also, the right measures applied without delay lead to a rapid termination of enuresis. If treatment is undertaken it is generally successful. At the Child Guidance Clinic (The Hague, Holland) where we have dealt with a very large number of enuretics we have gradually learned to select cases such as these, as they can frequently be helped by brief treatment. (See below, the case of Wim.)

D. Trauma and illness are far more serious where the sex differ- ence has been observed not in another child but in an adult. The case of a thirteen-year-old bedwetter described by an earlier paper[1] of the author is an example. In that case the trauma had not been known to anyone. At the age of three the child had been taken to her grand- mother in Yugoslavia for the summer holidays, and left there by her parents for several months. The child's development had been normal, and bladder control had been established. During her stay she had an unexplained illness accompanied by vomiting and fever. This was fol- lowed by nightly bedwetting which obstinately resisted the various attempts to stop it. In the Analysis, ten years later, it became possible to clear up the amnesia and to bring trauma to consciousness: a gypsy had induced the little girl to follow him; he had exhibited his penis before her, made her handle it, and had undressed her and touched her genital. (See below, for another example, the case of Grete.)

E. A form of enuresis for which extensive treatment is neces- sary is caused by operation traumata. Whenever the symptom appears after an operation we can expect that the disturbance is not slight. In these cases the children usually have experienced the operation as a castration; even after a long analysis they cling to the fact of their castration and, simultaneously, to the enuresis. The cases in which enuresis appears following treatment or operation for phimosis clearly take a special place.

---

1. "From the Analysis of a Bedwetter", *Psa. Quarterly*, IV, 1935.

The time when the trauma occurs is naturally of greatest importance. The effect is very different, according to whether the child undergoes an operation in babyhood, at the height of the oedipal conflict, or during latency. It also makes a tremendous difference whether a child has been prepared for the operation or whether he has been overwhelmed by the doctor without preparation. The manner in which the operation is carried out is similarly important—where a narcosis or an analgesic is used the trauma is considerably slighter than it is where the child has to bear all the pain, the sensation of being cut, the sight of blood, instruments, etc. This unfortunately still happens very frequently, and has the effect of a confirmation in reality of all the child's castration anxieties. Boys who meet with this experience usually escape into a passive-feminine attitude. If being a man evokes such dangerous threats, they no longer find masculinity desirable. The woman's fate appears much safer. She is not threatened by similar dangers, and can still enjoy pleasure in her own way.

In all cases it is of great therapeutic value to bring the masturbation fantasies into consciousness. They are usually extremely numerous and varied, pleasurable or full of anxiety. Freud early pointed out the most pleasurable fantasy: the jet of urine has the meaning of sperma; the act of wetting means coitus.

In all cases of enuresis we find the fantasy that the genitals are damaged and, like a broken water-tap, cannot retain urine. In serious cases this fantasy is followed by passive feminine wishes. Bi-sexuality plays an important part here, but it need not form the basis of the symptom.

According to my experience there is another pleasurable fantasy that is based on a bi-sexual disposition and opposes therapy with great tenacity. It is the fantasy of being man and woman simultaneously. Those enuretics who have it perform coitus in the act of wetting. The jet of urine represents sperma and is therefore pleasurable in a masculine sense; at the same time, the child experiences the warm flow like a woman who is being impregnated. Here masculine and feminine tendencies are satisfied simultaneously. A kind of pleasurable equilibrium is produced, which the child is unwilling to give up. The trauma of the primal scene frequently contributes to the fixation of this fantasy, and is elaborated in it.

It is obvious that while some enuretics are at the genital stage, others have regressed to earlier stages of development. Their fantasies show this clearly. The warmth of the urine may for instance have the meaning: the child lies curled up against his mother's body and takes the breast.

I have made the symptom of bedwetting the center of my considerations, but I should not like to give the impression that I see only the symptom and not the neurosis. In many cases enuresis is only one symptom among many. We frequently find it in combination with learning disturbance. In such cases the child often has the unconscious idea that someone who has not achieved so simple a task as bladder control cannot possibly master a task as difficult as learning. The idea of having an insufficient or damaged genital becomes displaced to the head, the seat of intelligence. The same idea has an entirely different result with other children. Many years ago Freud and Jones drew attention to the ambition of enuretics: they have to prove that they are able to do everything else particularly well, because they are unable to master something as simple as bladder control.

The energy with which children fight their symptom varies a great deal. It does not solely depend on the attitude of their environment nor on the degree of pleasure or displeasure the child himself experiences. Where the fight against the symptom reflects the child's fight against masturbation, the severity of the superego plays the most important role, and leaves its imprint on the child's personality.

As an example of the type of case described under C., I should like to describe a case treated by a young colleague, Dr. van Meurs (Holland), who has kindly allowed me to do so.

Wim was not quite eight years old when he was brought to the Child Guidance Clinic. He suffered from nocturnal enuresis and was anxious and withdrawn. His aggression was inhibited. Wim's father emphasized this fact especially, and reported that the mother constantly suppressed the child's aggressive tendencies.

The mother had had a very unhappy childhood. At the age of sixteen she had been raped by her brother. Following this, her mental disturbance was such that she had to remain in a sanitarium for years. Her mother, to whom she had been very much attached, died during this period. The girl returned home to look after her father, but he decided to live with a woman with whom he had had a relationship of long standing. She then stayed with an older brother until her marriage. She and her husband were happily married at first; more and more difficulties made their appearance later on. It seemed that they were caused by her character disturbances.

Wim seemed to develop very well at first. He was dry at night at eighteen months. His enuresis began when his baby sister was born, and he was not quite three years old.

This history made it likely that the child's inhibitions had been caused by the mother: that she unconsciously saw her brother in her boy, and that her unconscious fear made it impossible for her to stand the child's aggression; so that she had to suppress them forcefully, whether they were directed against herself or against his little sister. We were soon able to ascertain that she really did suppress all of Wim's instinctual manifestations, in fear of a repetition of her own traumatic experiences.

Treatment of the child seemed impossible without simultaneous treatment of the mother; in this case it seemed best for mother and son to be treated by the same physician. The aim of the mother's treatment, to make her sufficiently conscious of her own conflicts and fears and to enable her to tolerate her son's aggression and instinctual manifestations, was reached. I here confine myself to giving an outline of the child's treatment. Wim was seen twice weekly for three-quarters of an hour. He had fifteen sessions in all.

As could be expected, Wim behaved very nicely during his first sessions. He talked a great deal about the toys he had at home, and about a friend he played with. He was sorry to have a sister, he said; he would much rather have a brother—but not a baby, of course, with whom one cannot play. He also told about his visits to the zoo, asserting that he was not frightened of wild animals as long as they are safely behind bars. Then he said good-bye politely.

In the following hour he started with similar conversations and stories. Only a few of his questions were enough to show the problems he was concerned with: Is the earth round? Does it turn, and don't the people fall off? How was the earth made? His father had made a drawing of Adam and Eve with the apple and a lot of animals; he didn't know the story exactly—who was it really who took the apple? He talked about school, mentioning that he had to miss a few hours in order to come for treatment. The analyst then asked if he knew why he had come: Wim mentioned his bedwetting and his hope of being cured. After this he was inhibited, but yet seemed relieved. In the next session he showed very clearly that he wished to talk about pleasant things only, and that he warded off all conflicts. This was interpreted to him, and in the following hours he gradually began to talk about his bedwetting, and about his actual conflicts and fears. He was afraid of ghosts and of the dark. Talking of ghosts led him to Santa Claus and Black Piet, his black servant. He insisted that Santa Claus does not really exist but that Black Piet does. The analyst told him that this sort of fairy tale is often told by parents to children, as if it were true. Wim finds this difficult to believe: he is sure he has seen Black Piet. Once while he was asleep on the divan, Black Piet had come and brought him toys; afterwards, his father had told him, he (father) had tried to wake him up, but Wim had been so fast asleep that he could not be awakened. But Wim was not quite sure whether his father had believed the story himself, or had made a fool of Wim.

In the following sessions he admitted having been told the story of the stork when he had been younger, but said that recently his mother had told him that children grow inside their mothers. He wanted to know if this was true, as he had been deceived before. During these sessions he always talked about his bedwetting, which now was occurring irregularly.

Gradually he began to talk about actual events . . . his sister was punished much less than he . . . Sundays are very boring . . One is always expected to look nice and tidy, one isn't allowed to play wild games, etc. He talked about church and faith in God. He had asked his father about God and Creation, but had not understood the answer, as his father had avoided answering directly. Wim wanted to know what happens after death; he had heard that souls rise, and wondered if this was painful. The analyst told him that many people believe in these things, but that nobody knows for certain.

Later it became clear that Wim wondered whether one might lose certain parts of the body, legs or arms. Could one live if one's head were dead? In this connection he talked about the war and bombs. In his street there was a boy who had lost a leg—Wim thought it might have been caused by a street accident. During this period he was delighted to report that he had been dry for some consecutive nights, and went on to tell about further fears . . . he dreaded falling into the water from a bridge . . . he was very careful when fighting, lest he fall and hurt himself. Suddenly he raised the question of how rain is formed. He had imagined that two clouds bump into each other and make a hole from which water drips. Here the analyst linked this fantasy with Wim's wetting and with his anxieties. After this interpretation Wim was dry for twelve nights.

Simultaneously he became much more aggressive toward his sister. He admitted that he still could not help thinking that Black Piet had been in his house that day, as he had told him, and that it had been impossible to wake him. It was pointed out to him that he must be very frightened if he believed that so much can happen during sleep; he was reminded of his fear that harm might be done to his limbs; maybe he had thought that somehow his penis had been damaged, and maybe just this fear was connected with his bedwetting. At first Wim did not accept these interpretations. He was wet again one night. He talked a great deal about accidents, enumerating all the parts of the body that one might lose, except the penis. He gave many opportunities, in the material he produced, for the analyst to repeat the interpretations of his fear.

At this time he celebrated his eighth birthday, after having been dry again for ten consecutive nights. He began to talk about a girl in his class —she was not a nice girl; she had such a crazy name, Ada; she was not a bit strong; she wet her bed every night. If one were strong, one would not wet the bed. Here the difference between the sexes was discussed with him. He was told that it was not true that girls wet more often than boys; that being strong had nothing to do with it really; and that it now seemed clear that he was afraid of being weak himself, just like girls, and that was why he had been wet. Wim felt very happy and relieved after these interpretations were given, and did not wet again.

He asked for more sex information, and was told about the father's role. He gradually became more courageous and aggressive. His mother gradually became able to accept this. At this point treatment was stopped. Later inquiries showed that the positive effects were fully maintained.

The symptom had developed not only as a result of the sister's birth. Several other factors may be assumed to have played a part: the witnessing of a primal scene, as the cloud fantasy seems to show; the traumatic discovery of the sex difference; and the suppression of the child's instinctual and aggressive drives by his mother. However, the symptom does not appear to have become linked up with the masturbation conflicts resulting from the oedipus complex. Had this been the case success would not have been achieved so quickly. Interpretations could not have been confined to his fantasy of being damaged as, he thought, girls were. It seems that this boy had developed fairly normally, while his fantasy had remained isolated, like a foreign body.

The age at which the child experiences traumata is of course very significant. Had this trauma occurred when this child was at the height of the oedipal conflict, a far more serious illness would undoubtedly have resulted.

The trauma experienced at the sight of an adult's genitals, as described under D., is illustrated in the following case. The case was reported to me by the child's mother, herself an analyst, who on account of war conditions was forced to conduct a brief analysis of her own daughter.

The little girl, Grete, was three-and-a-half years old when her family was driven from home (in Holland), and for months had to live in very cramped quarters. Eventually they lost even this kind of refuge, and had to separate. The little girl and the mother remained together, and spent the first five months of this period of separation in a strange town. It was here that Grete's enuresis began. The landlady of the house in which the mother and child were staying was very disturbed by it, and as there was no other possibility at all of getting treatment for the child, the mother undertook it herself.

During the months preceding the appearance of the symptom and the family's separation, Grete had appeared changed. She was often excited, shouted to get attention, etc. These changes in the child's condition seemed sufficiently explained by the emotional state of the adults about her at this time. However, her excitement and fear became more obvious in the new and quieter surroundings when a little incident occurred: one day a twelve-year-old boy gave her two small live fish. Grete was overjoyed, and had to abreact her excitement in play. At first the whole experience had to be repeated in her play exactly as it had happened in reality, and each time the mother had to express her astonishment and surprise. Then the child pretended that it was her mother who had bought the little fish for her in a shop. Then she pretended that she was a married woman; she would phone her husband at his office to tell him of the happy fish story, and he would come quickly by car to admire them. Later, she was a school child, and there were little fish in the school room to be looked after . . . the kind teacher gave her two to take home . . . again the mother had to show her happy surprise. After this, Grete became a Red Indian girl who goes fishing and catches two little fish that she brings home to her mother. In between times, Grete once more became a married woman who had a baby. She had long telephone conversations with the doctor, the nurse, and her husband, telling them to come quickly—on the occasion of this happy event, she was presented with two little fish. All these games came solely from the child's own initiative and imagination. The mother was entirely passive, and merely carried out the child's suggestions.

One wonders why such a little incident should have caused such great emotion to a child. Was it due to the big new friend or to the fish? It turned out that the possession of the fish was far more important than the person who had given them. In her games the friend and the husband did not play a prominent part. The gifts came, rather, from the mother or the teacher. But eventually even they were excluded: not the boy gave them to her, nor the mother, but Grete herself was able to get the fish, and she brought them to the mother. In her marriage, too, her husband played an unimportant part; he might come and admire the present but he might not have a share in her emotion. That role was saved for the mother: she had to show emotion—the happy surprise—and then Grete could identify with the mother's pleasure. It seemed that she had retained her early attachment to her mother, and in it played an active role. She tried to retain the happy affect by means of her fantasy. Her mother had to enact it over and over again, but her role was confined to just this showing surprise—otherwise it was passive. The actual separation from her father made the little girl cling to the active mother relationship. Her excessive amount of emotion, however, indicated sexual over-excitation, the cause of which was quite unknown.

Several days after this game was played, Grete built up a fantasy in which she showed great sense of humor. She told of a family, Mr. and Mrs. Biblbabl and five little Biblbabls. In this family everything was topsy-turvy, just opposite to the way things are in an ordinary family. Mother Biblbabl, for instance, washed her children with black boot polish instead of soap, etc. They also had an incomprehensible language, to say nothing of their table manners. And amidst laughter Grete asked her mother if she knew how the Biblbabl family got their children: it was the father who got the babies, and he had two little pink things where the milk comes out to feed them. The mother is the man of the house, and only gives orders as to how everything should be done.

The little girl tried to win her mother's love in this humorous fantasy. The center of the fantasy, however, does not seem to show progressive development, but denial. In the Biblbabl family education is ridiculed. Wishes that had been warded off return as permissible actions. Cleanliness here became an excuse for smearing dirt. Anything that must usually not be mentioned could be said in this family whose language was not intelligible. Good table manners were transformed into bad manners. This was followed by the birth fantasy.

Grete had reached the point where she knew that all women look alike, but she did not accept the fact that they get babies: first, because possession of a penis seemed to her more desirable, and second, because birth seemed an obscure and dangerous affair. Therefore she had to castrate the man, in her fantasy. A remark the child had made some time earlier now had new meaning for the mother. A few months before, during a visit, Grete had seen a naked newborn boy. She had declared, "Jan has girls' legs." At that her statement was assumed to be a denial of the sex difference, and the opportunity had been taken to tell her facts of sex, to which she had listened quietly. Grete's last comment was more than denial; it contained a castration.

One might wonder whether her Biblbabl fantasy could not be regarded merely as a joke, as if she were to say: I know well what reality is like, but it would be nice if it were different; or whether it should be taken as marking the beginning of a neurosis. Further development proved the latter to be true. Grete began to wet her bed two days after she expressed this fantasy.

Once more the mother discussed the sex differences with her, and inquired about possible fears in this connection. Grete confessed that often she could not help thinking that when she had been small she had been in bed with her mother, that the mother had played with her (Grete's) penis until it had fallen off. Here the mother reassured the child about her own play with her genitals.

Two nights later Grete was awake and already wet at 10:30 p.m.— and laughed at her mother provocatively. There was no doubt that this time she had consciously and deliberately wet the bed. The mother reacted with displeasure intentionally. She told Grete that she knew all about it now, and obviously wanted to make her mother angry. The mother did not at this point go further into the question of aggression, as she still hoped the symptom might be a passing one. This hope, however, proved false. From then on Grete wet several times each night while she was fast asleep. There was no alternative but to attempt treatment, although the mother was fully aware of the difficulties she would encounter in the analysis of her own child.

It was necessary to avoid, if possible, letting the analysis extend over the whole day, and to confine treatment to a single hour. This was especially difficult as the child had no other companions. She would have to work off the aggressions that the analysis would free, on one and the same person, turning against her with provocative behavior and disobedience. There was a danger that by discussing and sharing her sexual fantasies with her mother, her sexual attachment to the mother, at this time her only love object, would be further increased. A disturbance in her development might easily result from this.

Grete had previously seen children coming to her mother for treatment. She was pleased that now she too would have "talking hours". She understood completely the aim of these interviews.

In the very first hour it became clear that, as was to be expected, Grete had not observed the sex difference for the first time in baby Jan. During the past months, living in restricted quarters, she had found occasion to watch her almost grown-up brother undress; this had probably had a traumatic effect. She told about her jealousy, her wish to rob the penis not only from her brother, but also from her father and from other big boys who now shared the house she lived in. She wished for four penises—one in front, one in back, and one on each side. All the boys should become girls and then she would get married, but only in the topsy-turvy world. (Biblbabl fantasy.)

When in the course of the day her mother happened to use the expression "thrilled to death", Grete said, "You must not say that about death. It makes me think of Daddy and that he might be dead. I dream about it with my eyes open and I don't want it and I still dream it."

It became clear in the analysis that she had fantasied inheriting her father's place and being married to her mother. She had to imagine in detail the sad news of the father's death, and how she would have to cry. She was dry during the night after this conversation. During the next day it was noted that she shouted excitedly instead of talking as usual. When asked about this she said, "It's all got something to do with that." "What do you mean?" "When I'll be the big Daddy and be married to you, and I lie in bed with you, then I'll shout like that because I'll be so happy!" For one more night the child was dry, but then the symptom reappeared. In the following hour she told her further fantasies: she always thought that men must be making very big "puddles" and very big "sausages", and that Daddy had wet his bed every day in the old flat . . . she interrupted herself with the question, "Mummy, when you go away from here, will you leave me alone? I'm so frightened that you will go alone and leave me, and that I won't be allowed to see you ever. Perhaps it is because I'm Daddy and married to you that I've got to think these things."

Interpretations that followed were all accepted by Grete. They were to the effect that because she had such bad wishes against her Daddy, and wanted to take everything away from him, her bad conscience did not allow her to enjoy being alone with her mother; this was why she had to be punished; her mother might not think her nice enough, and might leave her just as she (mother) had left Daddy and did not visit him now.

During this period Grete loved best to play wild Red Indian games.

Another game that had been going on for some time was that of the married
Grete: she got a baby very realistically in the presence of a doctor and nurse.
But she did not have to stay in bed more than a day; then she came to visit
her mother with her new baby, who frequently was already able to walk.
Grete would stay with her mother for lunch, would ring her husband at
his office to tell him that she had a baby and was invited to her mother's,
and would ask him to come too.

The baby, like the little fish earlier, had to be shown to her mother;
the mother had to express surprise. The baby and the fish had to be regarded
as penis substitutes.

Grete was wet every night, and each time would laugh defiantly. She
defecated three times a day and was very interested in the size of the
"sausages" she produced . . . big men do the same. She admitted finding it
wonderful to be dirty. On one of these days she met her big boy friend in
the street with a water pistol, and proposed that he exchange it for her
kitten. He did not give her the water pistol, but a bow and arrow instead,
and she spent hours playing Red Indians . . . she said Red Indians never
wet their beds, not even the babies. That night, when she was in bed, she
asked her mother to give her diapers; they would keep her dry and the
mother would then have no trouble. She accepted instead her mother's
interpretation that she would like to return to the time when she thought
she still had a penis. Grete said she always seemed to think it had been
taken off when she was one year old. The advantages and disadvantages of
being a baby were now discussed with her.

Her bedwetting grew worse steadily, and was always accompanied by a
provocative laugh. She seemed compelled to make her mother cross and then
to fear being left. At this time she showed a great deal of interest in dogs;
perhaps she imagined it easier and less forbidden to rob a dog's penis.
She asked once more to be told about babies, and was afraid that her mother
might get one. Grete thought that if it were a boy his penis would be taken
off. It seemed to her mother, rather, that she was afraid that just this would
not happen, and therefore Grete was so cross, and so defiant generally that
she continually forced her mother to be angry with her.

We see that her fantasy of being left alone was the most important
of all her fantasies. Being left alone was her greatest fear. Probably it had
to be understood as a result of her having been left by everyone except the
mother—and it was just the mother against whom she felt furious for not
letting her have a penis; therefore she had to wish her dead now. But
how can a child have death wishes against the last beloved person who is
still with her? Grete struggled violently against them, and it could be
foreseen that this would lead to an undesirable fixation to her mother, which
expressed itself in her masturbation fantasy (Mummy has played with my
penis until it came off). The mother was faced with Grete's pre-oedipal
mother-attachment, which was reinforced by the disappointment in the newly
developed oedipal attachment to the father. That was why the father, too,
must be wished dead. But the death wishes against the mother were hidden

behind this. In her relationship to her mother she was a boy: she shouted to show her masculine strength; her favorite Red Indian games were boys' games; Red Indian babies were not incontinent; therefore she so much wanted to be a Red Indian herself. But to wet was masculine, too . . . the big men make such big puddles and big sausages. To be naughty and disobedient is boyish, too. And finally, her fantasy of being left is also an identification with her father. It is noteworthy that in her attempt to make an exchange with the older boy, the water pistol seemed to her more valuable than the child (kitten).

In all this there was an undertone of anger for not having been given a penis by her mother; and now that it had become clear that her mother also had none, contempt was added to anger. Grete's provocative behavior and her deliberate wetting certainly seemed to be connected with this. The fantasy that was nearer to her oedipal wishes was to get a baby herself; here she minimized her fear—she stayed in bed only one day, and then visited her mother to show the child. Competition with her mother, as well as the wish for a penis, can be seen in this fantasy.

After a few dry nights Grete was less defiant. She asked her mother for advice, seriously: "When Daddy is dead, how can one get his penis, cut it off with a big knife?" It seemed as if the wish to spare him pain was part of this fantasy: I don't want to hurt Daddy, so I'll do it when he is dead.

After a few wet nights she expressed her great wish for a scooter. "If I were a man and could be in bed with you, you would surely buy me a scooter." She often asked whether, if scooters were available again, her mother would give her one, which the mother promised she would each time. Grete must have suspected that she might not be given a scooter because she was a girl. She showed her jealousy in other ways, too: she so much wanted another child; her former nurse already had two children; could not her Daddy be her husband so she could have children with him? The mother asked what would happen to her in that case, but Grete knew a way out: the mother would become a grandmother and help Grete with her children, so she (mother) would not have to die.

On the same afternoon that she said this she also expressed her longing for her father for the first time. "I miss him so much, he used to call me tiny little dromedary. I wish he were here." But these positive love wishes disappeared soon again, and made place for the aggressive wishes instead. Again she herself was Daddy and made giant puddles. She asked if her Daddy had a walking stick; she thought that if she were Daddy and married her mother, the mother would surely give her one as a present, and she would be able to play "old man" with it. Her fantasy probably expressed: If I were allowed to sleep in your bed I would be dry, but like this, it isn't worth while. Grete doubted whether she might not regain the penis her mother had robbed her of. Her coitus fantasy seemed to be that men make large puddles into the bed . . . if she were a big man, her mother would never be angry about her naughtiness and disobedience. She would find everything all right. Sometimes she wondered whether it would be better to cut off, bite off, or tear off the penis. Her wishes for a child ran parallel with these fantasies. She wanted many, many children; two would by no means be enough. She tormented her mother, wishing to drive her away by her aggression, and simultaneously dreading that she might succeed. She was angry because her mother had not given her a penis and because her father was her mother's husband and not hers. She seemed to cling desperately to these fantasies; over and over again she imagined that her genitals were damaged because her mother had robbed her penis. Finally the mother asked if Grete could not believe in her at all. Grete answered with a sigh that she had many worries; that it was such a pity the summer was coming to an end and the geraniums would soon be fading. "Sometimes I think that you won't be quite dead, but that you will come back when I can listen better to what you say." Her not being able to listen was surely connected with her not being able to listen to her mother's interpretations. The mother now interpreted that Grete could not and would not listen because she would then have to believe what she heard, and that would mean giving up her bedwetting which she enjoyed so much. It meant pleasure and revenge at the same time, and one doesn't like to give that up. After this interpretation Grete was suddenly relieved and friendly, kissed her mother spontaneously—a thing she did rarely during this period—and said suddenly, "Mummy, I should so love to do something to please you."

She was dry for three nights after this interpretation; then her penis- and death-wishes gained the upper hand once more. She wet again, laughed about it, and returned to her former spirit of anger. Father and mother should both be dead; then at least she could be sure to keep the stolen penis. Anxieties and dreams appeared in which wild animals were eating her up; they disappeared when her oral aggressive wishes were interpreted. Then she imagined she had a room full of flowers and that her mother had a room without any: her mother was furious about this and took all her flowers away. A slight hint was enough to make Grete understand the meaning of this fantasy. She said: I want to hide the penis inside my "pipsi", then it is quite shut, and no longer spoiled. Grete assured her mother that she wanted to have all the penises of all the boys in the whole world to decorate her room with. From then on, although at first her moods still fluctuated, she remained dry.

After about eight dry nights she saw two boys urinating in the street. She asked if the boys had water pistols hidden in their trousers. When she heard the correct explanation she became silent at first, then provocative and tormenting. At this point the mother interpreted everything once more: the child's jealousy, her anger, her fantasy of being damaged, etc. She added that Grete should try to remember this well, as she might otherwise wet her bed again. But Grete stood the test and remained dry.

Three weeks after this, she had a setback. Her big brother visited suddenly, and this obviously excited her sexually, and renewed her aggressive fantasies. Her envy was discussed once more, and she admitted still being cross occasionally, feeling that her mother had stolen her penis, and thinking that she would take a sharp knife and cut off her mother's nose and mouth.

"I'll get yours then, and you can have my little ones. Sometimes I think that I eat you all up and swallow you, but you have a knife and cut my tummy and you jump out again."

Now Grete remained dry. Three years have passed since her treatment and there have been no educational problems worth mentioning. The treatment had lasted about six weeks.

The favorable course it took was certainly due to the fact that it was begun soon after the appearance of the symptom. Had this not been the case, and the child, instead of being able to express her numerous conflicts, fantasies, and affects, had had to repress them, a serious neurosis would have resulted. She would have been a problem child, and a long analysis would later have been necessary to achieve what was accomplished in six weeks. If cases such as this can be treated early enough, they need not become serious.

A CASE OF
SUPEREGO DISINTEGRATION[1]

By ANNA MAENCHEN, Ph.D. (Berkeley)

The main factors hampering the development of the superego in wartime have been studied thoroughly by Anna Freud and Dorothy Burlingham (2). The children under observation in the Hampstead Nurseries were mostly of pre-school age, that is their development was beyond the appearance of the formal superego function (5) and before the integration of the superego. During this period the child is occupied with the complicated task of mastering his destructive and aggressive wishes. Exposure to the destructiveness of war makes it extremely difficult for him to achieve this. The child does not become cruel and aggressive because of these conditions but may remain so because of them. A second factor is the often abrupt separation of the child from its mother which is inevitable when an area has to be evacuated at a moment's notice. Subsequent wandering through evacuation centers, hospitals, and nurseries, from one pair of hands into another, throws the small child in a "no-man's land of affection" in which the feelings of the child are turned inward. There is nobody whom the child loves enough and with whom he can identify. As one small boy in the Hampstead Nurseries expressed it, "I'm nobody's nothing."

We in this country had little opportunity to observe the impact of the war on the developing superego. It is true that here, too, many homes were broken up as a consequence of the war. But in those cases the damage done to small children was not different from that we meet so frequently in our social agencies' cases, those children with a history of a dozen foster-homes behind them. And it makes quite a difference whether a five-year-old is actually dug out from a collapsed air raid shelter or whether he just listens to the machinegun noise over the radio.

Although American children were not personally subjected to bombing and fighting, some pre-adolescent children were profoundly affected by the ideological aspects of the war. The superego of the pre-

---

1. Read at the meeting of the San Francisco Psychoanalytic Society, October 23, 1943.

257

adolescent child, and even that of the adolescent, is not firmly established and may undergo partial reversal. Cases like that of a twelve-year-old patient of mine were, perhaps, not rare. But few of them are likely to have come under analytic observation. The case is presented only insofar as it has an immediate bearing on the subject.

Peter's most conspicuous symptom was his fear of being "destroyed". He was convinced that everybody was against him, first of all his parents. In the first interview he told me that the other day, when he was with his father, he had heard a rhythmical noise in the kitchen and was scared to death. He thought his father had put a time-bomb there to "destroy" him. In telling me of his experience, he stressed that he knew that it was not true and could not be true; but he was not sure that he would not get the same idea in a similar situation. He asked me to help him to get rid of his "worries".

He was in constant fear of an impending disaster. Somebody was going to do something to him. He was always anxious to find out what was going on behind his back. For hours he remained glued to his radio. When it was turned off, Peter would burst · into tears. How could he ever know what he had missed? It might have been vitally important to him. It might have given him "power" to overcome the sinister designs of his enemies, to take away *their* "power". He was intensely interested in hypnotism, the mastering of a technique by which one get's "power" over other people. The original fear that his parents could read his mind had become more and more impersonal. It was "Nature" that had to be outwitted. "Nature" did not want him to get what he wanted. When he wished something very much, he pretended to himself that he wished just the opposite. "Nature" then ·read the pretended thought, denied it, and thus granted what he really wished.

His parents sent the boy to me, first, because they were frightened by his anxieties, but also because he was such a dismal failure in school. He had the greatest difficulties in learning to read and write despite an I.Q. that made him "near genius". He was, indeed, a most intelligent child. By listening to the radio and living with his intellectual parents he had acquired an amazing vocabulary, ranging from *sophistication* to *claustrophobia*.

The fantasies which accompanied his masturbatory activities were frequently of outright passive-homosexual character. When he thought of big strong men, he had erections. His dreams swarmed with biting snakes to which he felt exposed in an exciting and pleasant suspense. And he was able, he said, to turn off the dream at the most dangerous moment like a radio.

When, in the fall of 1941, I took Peter in analysis, he lived most of the time with his mother. His parents, whose only child he was, had been divorced four years earlier. Although both parents observed meticulously the legal agreement that gave each of them definite rights to the child and imposed definite duties upon them, they never ceased fighting over him. The problem of divided loyalty, common to any child in such a situation, was aggravated by the war.

Peter was the child of mixed parentage. His father was German, his mother American. The father had immigrated many years ago and had long been a citizen. Although he was not a Nazi, he regarded himself as a German and probably did not hide his sympathies. The boy's mother was an American patriot and even before the war advocated all-out help to England. And each of the parents wanted the boy to be on his or her side.[2]

Peter could not make up his mind. He was thoroughly bewildered. He did not know whom to believe. After each visit to his father, he talked about the strength and efficiency of Germany. After a few days with his mother he would, with the same eloquence, defend the opposite side. But most of the time he just did not know what to think about the war. Who was right? What is right anyway? At this period his speech consisted mostly of interrogative sentences. In entering my room, e.g., he did not bid me a good afternoon, but asked whether it was the proper time to say good afternoon; or was it, perhaps, too late for that? He asked constantly whether somebody should do this or that. Would it not be better, fairer, juster? Even his simplest statements sounded like questions.

This period of indecision came abruptly to an end when, as potentially dangerous, Peter's father was removed from the West Coast. In the following months the boy changed in a remarkable way. Until then he had made himself a nuisance in school by driving his teachers to despair with his almost uninterrupted questioning. Otherwise he was more or less well-behaved and unaggressive. Now his behavior became "impossible". He picked quarrels, provoked and insulted adults and children everywhere. In the analytic hour he behaved not quite so aggressively, but aggressively enough.

Until then the boy had taken, if not an intensive, still a considerable interest in other people. Now he became almost completely self-centered. Anything not directly concerning him he shoved aside. A discussion might start on any subject; it led, in no time, to him. Politically he was now completely "neutral". Everything was "just bunk". When his mother wanted to join an auxiliary corps, he implored her not to. She must not buy war bonds. Not because Peter was any longer for his father's or against his mother's country: he laughed at all patriots of all countries. He was neither for nor against anything or anybody. He was only for himself.

The pronounced narcissism and the rapidly developing aggressiveness were evidently the result of the heavy blow dealt to his ego and a far-reaching disintegration of his superego. Neither his ego nor his superego had ever been strong and well-integrated. The general hostility by which the boy felt himself surrounded was not entirely the product of projection. He was an unwanted child, and felt rejected. His mother, ambitious, absorbed

2. Lauretta Bender reports the case of a boy with a Catholic-Italian father and a Jewish-German mother who found himself in a whirlpool of conflicts not unlike Peter's. This Catholic-Jewish-Italian-German boy chose a radical way out of an unbearable conflict. He denied the unpleasant reality and declared himself a Filippino.

by her professional work, gave the infant the bare minimum of bodily care. He was left strictly alone except when he was fed and bathed. This was supposedly required by "progressive education" of that decade. He had no toys as a toddler. His room was bare. Maids would come and go. He was locked by one of them in a closet for hours, hungry and soiled. No wonder that the child was late in talking. His speech has, phonetically, remained somewhat babylike, in striking contrast to his amazing vocabulary. He was still wetting when he was three. His aggression against both parents, but mostly against the mother, originated largely in the pre-oedipal phase.

Living in a loveless world, the child did not learn to love. The only object with which he succeeded in establishing a modicum of relationship was his father. The ego-formation was, thus, disturbed at a very early time.

When the boy entered the oedipal phase, his parents were already alienated. After their divorce, Peter lived with his mother. He won. The rival left. It was a victory. But he could not enjoy it. The fear of revenge of the father became so strong that he almost abandoned the wish to take the father's place. Not quite. He was still vacillating between masculinity and femininity. The motive to grow up, to become an adult, to become like the father, had lost much of its strength. While the fundamental hostility against the mother interfered with the full formation of the normal oedipal love, the partial success over the father interfered with the process of identification with him.

In the normal development of the child, the pre-oedipal identifications are intensified by those identifications which compensate for giving up the love objects in the oedipus situation. But Peter carried no intensive pre-oedipal identifications into the oedipal phase, in fact, hardly any identifications at all. As, furthermore, the object cathexes of the oedipus complex were not completely given up, the superego could not attain to normal strength. In addition to all these factors the parental authority, the predecessor of the superego, itself was divided.

The loss of the father was the loss of the only love object the child had ever had. According to his archaic ego formation it had served as an ego-substitute. When he lost it, he became unmanageable and aggressive. But the fall of the father was also a very heavy blow to the unstable superego[1] of the boy. The man whom the small child had thought omnipotent and whom the twelve-year-old admired for his position in society, his knowledge, his professional skill, his income, his father was, overnight, thrown from his pedestal. He was humiliated,

---

1. I am aware of the various attempts to differentiate between superego and ego-ideal. They seem to be of little value. The superego embraces all the forces by which the ego judges itself. Its prohibiting and punishing and its ideal aspects are closely interwoven. See Fenichel (1).

banished, he became an outcast. The boy's superego, weak and un-stable as it was, shattered.

We know that the energy with which the superego is endowed has two origins. It is, first, a continuation of the punitive energy belonging to external, parental authority. But it is also endowed "with that part of the child's aggressiveness against the parents for which it can find no discharge outwards on account of its love-fixation and external difficulties" (4). As soon as this aggressive energy ceases to be in the service of the superego, it flows back into the id. The aggressive id impulses liberated by the breakdown of the superego are augmented by those which are set free in the very process of superego disintegration. The suddenly increased aggressiveness of the patient was, to a very high degree, the consequence of the partial disintegration of the superego.

This explains also why at the same time the ideas of being surrounded by enemies gained greatly in strength. The stronger the aggressive wishes became, the more had the ego, this poor, weak, undeveloped ego, to fear. The projection served as a defense against heightened aggressiveness.

Into the formation of the ego-ideal large quantities of narcissistic libido are drawn. The self-love which the ego enjoys in early childhood is directed towards the ideal ego, with the result that the ego-ideal is cathected with narcissistic libido (3). When it falls to pieces, this narcissistic libido is liberated and flows back to the ego.

The fascist ideal was refused on the battlefields. The ego-ideal of Peter was arrested by the FBI. A fighter for freedom can become a martyr. The superman on trial becomes a laughing stock. The marked narcissism of the patient after the relocation of his father can be understood as the result of the destruction of the ego-ideal.

In spite of all the individual features of Peter's case it is, perhaps, typical. What happened under special circumstances to this American boy is happening, mutatis mutandis, to millions of young people in the defeated countries. The group ideal of the Hitler Youth and the Balilla has fallen to pieces. The basis on which these young people have identified themselves with one another in their ego is destroyed. The Führer or Duce, whom they had introduced into their superego, is no more. Will they become even more aggressive than they were taught to be? Will they become narcissistic cynics? Only the future will tell.

BIBLIOGRAPHY

1. Fenichel, O. *The Psychoanalytic Theory of Neurosis*, Norton, 1945.
    p. 106.
2. Freud, A. and Burlingham, D. *War and Children*, Internat. Univ. Press,
    1943.
3. Freud, S. "On Narcissism", *Coll. Papers*, IV. p. 51.
4. Freud, S. *New Introductory Lectures*, Norton, 1933.
5. Waelder, R. "The Problem of the Genesis of Psychical Conflict in
    earliest Infancy", *Int. J. Psa.*, XVIII, 1937.

HEADLINE INTELLIGENCE

By CHRISTINE OLDEN (New York)

There are people who when we first meet them, appear to be interested, well-educated and well-informed. At closer acquaintance we find that their information is very superficial and that they do not feel inclined to learn more about any subject.

Intellectual inhibition has been very thoroughly discussed in psychoanalytic literature and the following remarks are not meant to contribute anything new to the question of causality or etiology of this neurotic disturbance. We shall only deal with one type of intellectual disturbance, stressing one kind of pathological solution of the male castration complex.

The main characteristics of this disturbance are: gathering catchwords or headlines in one dashing glance; a certain ability to combine the few and superficially collected bits; an ability to apply these pieces of knowledge in a skillful way so that they appear to be profundities. These people have the tendency to condone their own kind of intellectuality and furthermore to be proud of this specific technique of quick grasping and applying; they are incapable of thorough studying and learning in any one field. The symptom we are speaking of need not necessarily be obvious to the average individual, and under favorable conditions need not seriously interefere with the life of the person involved.

We had the opportunity to analyze this specific form of intellectual deficiency in three male patients, one man and two little boys in their latency periods. The case histories of these patients will be given only as far as they are related to the particular symptom mentioned above.

The adult came to analysis because of various character difficulties; Johnny, the eight-year-old, because of eating troubles and extreme anxieties; Charlie, the nine-year-old, came because of enuresis, stuttering and reading difficulties. In the first two cases the symptom of intellectual inhibition was more obscure than in Charlie's case. His difficulty had already assumed more concrete form.

The three patients had very similar family constellations, they all were the youngest in the family, the only boys; they all had sisters, rather weak and yielding fathers, and domineering, possessive mothers who inclined towards compulsive neuroses and serious depressions.

In their attitudes these three patients had much in common. They had a certain type of undemanding and charming friendliness. They tried to fool people and told jokes apparently unaggressively. The two little boys were very clownish; the grown-up remembered that he was clownish throughout his childhood and into his teens. The three patients were extremely restless in mind and body, impatient and fidgety; the two little boys hardly ever could sit still or stick to an occupation or discussion for any length of time. The interest span of each was exceedingly poor; they jumped from one activity or topic to another.

Extreme sensitivity was another quality the three patients had in common. Both in and out of analysis they were always ready to take anything that was pointed out to them about themselves as an accusation.

The three patients all loved to argue. Not only because this was their infantile aggressive way of handling their relationships, but also because arguing had the purpose of proving desperately that they were in the right.

The most obvious and persistent symptom was their complete denial of causality. This was displayed by Charlie, the nine-year-old, when he said: "I wanted this because I wanted it, period." Johnny, the eight-year-old, was even more decisive about it: "The words 'why', 'because', and 'reason' are ruled out from our discussions!" The adult for more than a year was altogether inaccessible to suggestion as to why he did or thought or felt one way or another. He managed to isolate the person he was today completely from the person he had been yesterday if yesterday was responsible for what he did or felt today. He had repressed the greatest part of his childhood. He entirely rejected the idea of the past as being something mysterious like the "disgusting fairy-tales". The fear of the past went beyond his personal experiences; he for instance could not bear to hear about history or abstract science. Anything that was not tangible and contemporary was upsetting to him.

The three patients were very much interested in inventing things, the idea being to combine many functions in one object. Both boys independent of each other thought of a machine that was an airplane, an anti-aircraft gun, a ship, a submarine, and a tank, all in one.

All three of them were very secretive. The two little boys showed their secretiveness in their play. Charlie put a secret room in all of his block buildings, and Johnny in his drawings made a "mysterious part" which he generally covered with paint before I was allowed to look at it. They said "This is my secret and you can't guess it."

The three patients had several obvious neurotic symptoms in common: passivity, eating troubles, and phobia of germs and sickness whenever they had the slightest physical ailment. They then became panicky and regressed into infantile behavior.

When they first came to analysis they all lived more or less on baby food: milk, eggs, toast, etc. They were suspicious and afraid of any new tastes.

The passivity of the little boys showed up in endless dawdling. They had a slouching posture and their favorite reaction to nearly everything was, "Who cares?" They had very few wishes, and they were not able to really enjoy anything. They wanted to be babied and taken care of all the time. They were inert, effortless, and as Johnny so well put it, "I have no motor going inside of me." The adult patient had his "sleepy periods". He then was in a kind of daze and almost inaccessible to any suggestion.

As mentioned above, this man was the youngest of his family, his three sisters being four, six, and eight years older. The sisters, he said, were constantly teasing him, and acting as though they knew everything and he nothing. He did not remember ever having seen them undressed which does not seem probable since the environment was poor and narrow. He finally did remember his feeling of helplessness against his sisters' provocations, and his desperate effort to compete with their standards of knowing. He could not remember that his father played any important part in his life except that he came home drunk at times. The patient did not remember either where the father slept nor any other sleeping arrangements in their little apartment. The mother was a very rigid, stern, and religious woman with a limited number of friends, who concentrated possessively on this little boy whom she warned of the world's evils, the greatest one being sickness. The mother caught him once with another little boy while they were starting some mutual masturbation; this incident ended by her threatening the boy with hell and death and by prohibiting him from ever again playing with other children. The patient was thus kept isolated until he entered school which he experienced as a shock. He fell sick very frequently during his grammar school days, but still managed to get through somehow. In high school he was very popular, in spite of his dislike for athletics. Yet he did not form any close friendships. He managed to get through high school, partly because the other boys helped him along and partly because of his ability to quickly collect bits and quickly apply them at a given opportunity. He never sat down to learn anything systematically and lacked the fundamentals of general education. He nevertheless had the reputation of being a bright boy and was persuaded to go to college. Amazingly enough he managed to get through the first year. The second year when thorough studying could no longer be avoided, he walked out. He held various jobs and shifted from one to the other very easily. In every job his habit of grasping things quickly made him a success. He became a source of information on what was going on in the personnel department, in the rival firm, etc. The idea was always to reveal a large piece of knowledge very quickly, "at just a glance". Most of his free time was spent looking at newspapers and magazines, where he mainly read the advertisements. He never read a book. "You can never survey in one glance what's in a book; the closed pages are hiding the stuff." When his analysis eventually revealed his sex fantasies, we found his idea that the fetus in the womb was the penis that the mother had bitten of the father's genitals and swallowed. But it was not only the pregnant woman that he fantasied as having a penis. "Intellectually I can believe that women are born without a penis, but I really cannot believe it," he said.

Johnny in his analysis at an advanced stage said: "I am two people; I know that nothing will happen to my penis, but the other does not know." He had one sister, four years older than himself; and he remembered, and his parents remembered also, that his sister had threatened him quite overtly with cutting off his penis. He was very much afraid of his sister, and jealous of her; at the same time he admired and loved her very unhappily indeed. His mother was a much more understanding woman than the mother of the grownup patient. But her suppressed aggressiveness which he felt frightened the little boy terribly. The father was kind, indulgent and undemonstrative.

When Johnny came to analysis he had eating troubles which cannot be explained here at length—just so much that his idea of the devouring woman, of red mouths with terrific teeth, showed up in his paintings, his fantasies and dreams about the woman with cannibalistic customs. His birth fantasies served as insurance against death. They were stimulated by the Grimm tale "The table, the ass and the stick". When the donkey dies his stomach bursts and out come many little donkeys which also can spit gold stones. The young donkeys put their gold pieces into the dead one's mouth whereupon the donkey is resurrected. This idea in different forms was being applied to everybody or everything that would die or be destroyed. Money can bring everything to life again, but for this sake, alas, it had to be swallowed by the dead. But on the other hand death then creates abundance.

Johnny fought desperately against his penis becoming erect because then his sister, or the mother, or other girls, would become aware of it and would castrate him. He quite consciously avoided being enthusiastic about anything in order not to get himself excited.

Johnny knew a lot and he knew nothing really. In school he had difficulties with writing and spelling, but mostly because he never could listen to the teacher's explanations. His reading was all right, but he used it only for advertisements in the magazines. He surprised the family with his knowledge about the latest cleansers and the most practical kitchen gadgets, and the most inexpensive food. He would know and notice things that his sister did not know: any change that occurred in the neighborhood, something new in the room, or the new dress of Mrs. X. He observed sharply, and joined casually in the conversations of the adults with a remark on some new kind of airplane or woman's make up, etc. And the visitors said: "This boy certainly has his eyes open." But Johnny never could utter any more than just this one remark, because he would never want to know more about any subject. It became especially clear in his analysis that he was not only afraid of probing any deeper into one or the other problem, but that learning also meant to him not yet knowing, a state that made him feel very insecure and restless.

Charlie was of the three the intellectually most disturbed patient. He had a sister four years older than himself, who was bored by the little one, felt deprived on his account and took it out on him in teasing him a great deal. His mother was over-anxious, over-tense, over-insisting, compulsive and always full of guilt feelings. Never could she take anything casually. Her greatest fear was that Charlie would be intellectually inadequate and every free minute she practised reading and spelling with him. His father was a kind man, very passive, not interfering with the child's education. Charlie had great difficulties at school. When he came to analysis and for a long time after, he did not look upon reading as a means of gaining knowledge; syllables and letters were strange pictures to him, which he was afraid of. He read with fear and great effort, without any accentuation. He felt as though the mighty women, his mother and first teacher, made him face a catastrophe. On the other hand he wanted his mother to help him with his reading; he then felt protected and secure. As much as he was afraid of her he still wanted her to do everything for him and baby him as she did when he was sick as a young child. He very definitely refused to grow up mostly for this reason: he was relatively safe as long as he participated in his mother's omnipotence. Alone he was helpless. His idea was: the women know or rather, they hold the great secret which they keep in their genitals as a powerful weapon. He played "secret" in endless variations and was secretive in his behavior. While he was still in analysis he had heard about vaginal *secretion,* and what it meant. He asked me to spell it for him. "You see," he exclaimed, "its coming out of the secret." For a long time in his analysis he refused any sexual enlightenment, as he refused any other real knowledge. He played the dope because he wanted to be considered as a baby; but on the other hand he had developed an ability to pick up bits of information which he surprised the grown-ups with, mostly the mother and sister. His teacher once said: "For a child who does not read, Charlie is amazingly well-informed." Which was true. He caught sentences from the grown-ups' conversations, from the radio, from the schoolboys. He found out about stocks that his mother was interested in, he knew the latest war news, and about the latest war weapons. But it took a relatively long time in his analysis before he was able to discuss these things even superficially. "Skip it," was his favorite reaction.

Charlie had developed this capacity to pick up pieces of knowledge because his sister and mother provoked him in a teasing way. This was his sister's way of expressing her aggressiveness toward him, and his mother tried by joking to fight her real fear that her son was an idiot. In despair he took up the competition with the women who held the secret, in the urge to prove to them that he knew too.

These three patients had all the advantages of being the only boys in the family and all the disadvantages connected with this situation in general; the disadvantages in their specific cases were: living among the older and jealous sisters, living with extremely aggressive mothers and with fathers who did not back up their sons. Their anxiety was based on the idea that they being the only little boys were continuously endangered by the devouring women.

The identification processes of these patients were complicated and never resolved themselves because of the subordinated role of the fathers. The mothers and sisters were the only love and identification objects the patients had. They could not identify with the aggressive quality of the mother because aggressiveness to them was equal to sexual impulsiveness, equal to masturbation activity, which was forbidden and dangerous. They only identified with the teasing, provocative attitudes of mothers and sisters.

Their castration fears made them regress to a very early stage—the stage of babyhood—which was probably the fulfillment of an unconscious wish of their mothers. The idea: "I must not look closely but I nevertheless must know" was a result of the patients' picture of the women's attitude. This in effect was: We know what you cannot know. We can see your penis and therefore can castrate you; whereas you cannot see our penis, and you cannot injure us. We are protected, you are not. Don't dare to come too close, or else——.

Out of despair the patients were driven to meet the provocations of the women: I am not allowed to know the truth, and I don't dare to really know it. But knowledge is power and protection. Therefore I will collect as much information as I can get on the surface and use it against the sisters. In addition there will be some satisfaction in arguing with sister and mother and holding ground even in this fragmentary way.

Being urged to compete with the challenging women apparently saved these three patients from pseudo-debility. The thirst for knowledge was incited by the need to fight the women of the family. On the one hand, the patients' impulse to look, though repressed, had to break through at times because of the drive to investigate what was so interestingly put to them as the great secret. On the other hand, the thirst for knowledge could not really be satisfied, not only for fear of the threatening women, but also for fear of learning something terrible: I don't want to know the truth which might be that women have no penis. What I see and hear must be just on the surface and no deeper else my illusions could be destroyed.

The fear of terrible discoveries, such as the female genitals, was the basic source of the intelligence disturbance in these three cases. It was also recognized that they each had a fear of surprises, i.e., a compulsion to immediately know something about everything and to quickly "label" it in a neurotic way. After they recognized the type of the new discovery they lost interest in it and dismissed it. The fear of surprises is frequently based on the fear of one's own excitement. This became quite obvious in Johnny's fear of erections.

The analysis of the mother and sister relationship resulted with Johnny in a complete removal of the symptom of learning disturbances; and although for external reasons treatment had to be discontinued with the grown-up patient and with Charlie, both patients were relieved from their disturbances to a certain degree.

BIBLIOGRAPHY

Bornstein, B. "Zur Psychogenese der Pseudodebilitaet", *Int. Zeit. f. Psa.*, XVI, 1930.

Bornstein, B. "Beziehungen zwischen Sexual- und Intellektentwicklung", *Zeit. f. Psa. Paed.*, IV, 1930.

Freud, S. *Three Contributions to the Theory of Sex*, 1905.

Freud, S. *Inhibitions, Symptoms and Anxiety*, 1926.

Klein, M. "Zur Fruehanalyse", *Imago*, IX, 1923.

Landauer, K. "Zur psychosexuellen Genese der Dummheit", *Zeit. f. Sexwiss.*, 1929.

Mahler, M. "Pseudoimbecility: a Magic Cap of Invisibility", *Psa. Quarterly*, XI, 1942.

Schmidt, W. "Entwicklung des Wisstriebes bei einem Kinde", *Imago*, XVI, 1930.

Special issue of *Zeitschrift für Psychoanalytische Pädagogik* on "Intellektuelle Hemmungen", IV, 11/12, 1930. Contributions from B. Bornstein, E. Buxbaum, G. Bychovsky, P. Federn, I. Hermann, M. Schmidelberg, H. Stern, H. Zulliger.

A CONTRIBUTION TO THE PROBLEM OF PSYCHOSES IN CHILDHOOD

By ELISABETH R. GELEERD, M.D. (New York)

I

The diagnosis of psychosis in childhood is made when children before puberty show in their behavior many similarities to the adult schizophrenic or manic-depressive patient. The nearer these children approach puberty the more does this disorder resemble the psychosis as described for adults. Those psychoses in childhood that are classified as schizophrenia generally are considered to have a bad prognosis.

In this paper the author wishes to draw attention to a group of children who not always are considered psychotic. They behave overtly as if they may be suffering from a milder behavior disorder. (In all these cases organic disease has been ruled out.) The author shares in this respect the view of Bender (1) and Despert (7), who have described similar symptomatologies among other more obvious psychotic symptoms.

For reasons that will be elaborated upon later the author wants to consider the disorder of these cases to be psychotic, and most likely a forerunner of schizophrenia. These disorders may resemble the ones Potter (21) considered to be pre-psychotic. Of the ten cases described here, three were diagnosed as schizophrenic in adolescence. Friedlander (10) has described analogous conditions. However, the other cases in this paper ranged between the ages of six and thirteen, and have not been observed long enough to permit a definite prognosis. Also, the fact that they have received psychoanalytic or psychoanalytically oriented treatment may have favorably influenced the course. In spite of these unknown factors, the author wishes to direct attention to this type of childhood disorder. Early recognition and treatment may prevent deterioration of the condition and may bring

---

1. The material for this paper was studied in the Menninger Clinic and Southard School in Topeka, Kansas.

improvement, and may make these children less disturbing to the normal child with whom they are in contact.

The behavior and symptoms of these children will be described in detail, and their case histories presented. First, however, certain general traits will be mentioned.

These children display a far lesser degree of control over their aggressive actions than do other children of the same age. Also, they show a lack of control over their anal and sexual impulses such as one would expect in a much younger child. In most of their activities they tend to present uncontrollably impulsive behavior, although to the casual observer they appear to be just full of mischief. In any group situation they become either uncontrollably aggressive or completely withdrawn. In contrast to this inability to participate in a group is their pleasant behavior, their alertness, their intelligent conversation, their charm and wit when alone and undisturbed with one adult.

Often, when they feel frustrated, they have serious temper tantrums which differ from those of the normal or neurotic child. Their aggressive behavior is more dangerous to both the child and his environment. The child is out of contact with reality and believes himself to be persecuted. He cannot control his aggressive behavior as the more normal child can if he wishes, nor does he react favorably to firm handling as the neurotic child does. This child, on the contrary, becomes more paranoid when treated with firmness. He considers it proof of his paranoid ideas. But a loving, soothing attitude of a familiar, affectionate adult will bring him back to normal behavior.[2] The tantrums increase in violence with the age of the child; the child becomes more difficult to handle because of his greater physical strength and resourcefulness in the choice of weapons.

These children show little interest in their human playmates, but often they are extremely interested in animals, varying from dogs and cats to frogs, snakes, turtles, etc. Closer observation reveals that the feelings for these animals are much stronger than those for children. But this does not prevent many of them from being very cruel to animals. In addition to their feeling for animals they often have excessive interest in trains, motor cars, sewers, heating plants,

2. The phenomenologic description and dynamics of these tantrums as a withdrawal from reality and a break-through of paranoid ideas have been presented in an earlier paper (15).

and other inanimate objects, about which they often accumulate a vast amount of knowledge—in contrast to their generally poor scholastic knowledge.

In the clinical history of these children it became clear that almost all phases of their development have shown deviation from the normal. Although not all cases described demonstrate the fact, many had an infancy characterized by disturbances in feeding and sleeping, and by their being either difficult to manage or too apathetic, or both. Toilet training was achieved with difficulty; some had never become really clean; training would break down at the slightest physical or emotional provocation. Those children who went to nursery school were described by the teachers as being unmanageable and unable to play with the other children so that they were outstanding either through their aggressive behavior or through their complete withdrawal. Despite their continuance in the nursery school they showed little change in behavior. The aggressiveness and withdrawal always persisted throughout their later school careers. In addition, they showed neurotic characteristics, such as many phobias; nightmares; compulsions; tics; disturbed eating, sleeping, and toilet habits, etc.

II

A few case histories are given to illustrate the above.

Case A

Age: 12 years

A, a good-looking boy, had finger nails one inch in length. He refused to have them cut because he said he needed them as a weapon and because he dreaded the process of cutting them. His hair was long and worn combed over the forehead. He wore the same clothes winter and summer and would never wear underwear (this was related to a hidden obsession).

All his time he spent in his room either drawing pictures which no one was allowed to see, or listening to his phonograph. He refused to learn, rejecting even a tutor. He would join the teacher only if she promised to discuss furnaces, smoke or snakes. He provoked and teased younger and weaker children; but of older boys he was very suspicious and afraid. When he felt frustrated, he would burst into such severe rage that he lost all control of himself and would endanger not only his own life but that of others as well. During these tantrums he was paranoid and felt that he had to defend himself against his "enemies". Only a loving attitude could bring him out of the tantrum.

He was able to build up a relationship with a few warm, maternal women who treated him with almost complete indulgence.

Cn the father's side of the family schizophrenia was suspected in a few members; the mother was a maladjusted woman.

The birth was uneventful. The child was breast-fed for three days and then was easily put on the bottle. When he was six months old, he sucked his thumb, a habit which was broken temporarily by aluminum mittens. He was described as an easy baby, but intense in his reactions.

A nurse took care of him in his infancy. Once he so irritated her with his crying that she put her hand over his mouth until he became blue in the face; then she threw him on the bed. (This may well be an indication that in spite of the fact that his early development seemed fairly normal, a basis was formed for later maladjustment.) He was bowel-trained at one year of age and bladder-trained at eighteen months. When he had a bowel movement, he used to sit with his hindside turned around.

When he was sixteen months old, he walked with his arms over his head. After he had an appendix operation at eighteen months, he had to learn to walk again. Once he was terrified by a large bulldog who hurt him, since which time he feared large dogs.

His mental illness began when he was two years old and his mother became ill. He started again to suck his thumb; he bumped his head when he was frustrated; he threw toys around in a rage when presented with the wrong one; he developed a pot-belly posture; he began to smear his feces and play with his urine; and he began to develop many phobias.

In the hope that it would cure him, he was put in a nursery at the age of three. There he screamed, was fearful of the other children, and would only rock himself.

He remained in nursery school until he was seven; then he continued his poor adjustment in a private school. He was incapable of any group participation. In spite of his superior intelligence, he had great difficulty in learning. He resented all authority of the teacher and, to antagonize her, he would speak up loudly in the class. He was afraid of the other boys who, he was sure, would attack him and beat him up. Close observation, however, showed that he actually provoked them to attack him. He used to spend hours alone, drawing pictures and fantasying.

Since the age of two he had been extremely sadistic toward animals. For example, after speaking endearingly to his beloved toad, he killed it; he squeezed his chickens too tightly; he put mice in his slippers to squash them; he put his puppy in the oven to burn.

He always complained that he was picked upon and then he would indulge in sadistic fantasies of revenge, some of which he carried out with intense pleasure. As soon as he felt frustrated, he would burst out in a severe temper tantrum during which he was paranoid and out of contact with reality, and dangerous both to himself and others.

Case B

Age: 7½ years

B was an attractive youngster except for his generally sloppy, dirty appearance. His clothes were torn, his shirt tail was out, his shoes were untied, his face and hands were unbelievably dirty. Constantly in motion, he squirmed a great deal and made shaking movements with his hands. He sometimes defecated on the bathroom floor, smearing the feces all over.

Toward all women he was very affectionate. But as soon as he had to share their attention with another child or they had to forbid or frustrate him in any way, he would immediately go into a severe temper tantrum. He could not learn; even tutoring was hardly accepted. He would not eat. He would indulge in all kinds of "naughtiness", such as playing with fire, playing with tools and guns, easily wounding others or himself without caring. He indulged in sex play with other boys. When he was naughty, he seemed to be overcome by an impulse to go on and to do even worse things; he would laugh excitedly, look anxious and appear to have lost control of his actions. Any attempt to stop him would produce a severe tantrum in which he would become increasingly destructive, anxious and paranoid. Only a loving attitude could restore him to normal.

He was very imaginative and creative. As soon as he started to develop his fantasies in stories and writing, they would become increasingly frightening to him. At such times the slightest provocation could set off a severe tantrum. The visits of the doctor also produced tantrums, especially when an injection had to be given.

The patient was born as the second child of neurotic parents. Birth was normal. He was bottle-fed, but a poor eater. However, his mother felt that he should eat his prescribed formula; it would take her more than an hour at every feeding to make him empty his bottle. He was toilet trained at two months, stopped soiling at one year, with the exception of many accidents, and stopped wetting at three. He had a very strict nurse who did not allow him to play with other children because, according to her, they were dirty. But she smothered him with a possessive love.

When he was three years old, he developed a great interest in feces. He would say to his brother: "Eat grunt." He played with the dog's feces, with his own feces; he would put his hand into the toilet bowl. He became destructive. When he wet his pants on a few occasions, his nurse tied him against the radiator to punish him. She put tabasco sauce on his thumb to stop his thumbsucking.

At the age of five he was sent to kindergarten. There he did not adjust to the children at all. He shoved them around and threw spitballs at them.

The only way he functioned well with children was in being the leader when they played out his own fantasy games. Because he resented the authority of the teachers he disobeyed them; but he was described as being more manageable when alone with them. He spent most of the time alone drawing, fantasying, and talking to himself. After he left kindergarten for school, he did not do well in spite of his excellent intelligence. His attention span was short; he would walk through the classroom throwing water at the children. In a summer camp he became very much excited when he saw other boys undressed. He grabbed their penises, chased them with feces on a stick and masturbated openly in front of the adults and children. Subsequently he was sent to a psychiatrist.

Case C

Age: 12 years

C was a very sloppily-dressed boy, with his heels out of his shoes. He kept his shoes untied purposely so that when he had a tantrum, which occurred upon the slightest frustration or assumed rejection, he could throw them through a window. As with the other cases described, in his tantrums he seemed completely out of touch with reality and believed himself to be persecuted: he appeared to defend himself against a fantasied attacker.

He swore all the time, tantrum or not, teased smaller and weaker boys and seduced them to sexual games. He was a chronic bedwetter.

In spite of his high intelligence, he learned very little. Whenever he believed that another person might know more than he, he ran away from the class. After a temper tantrum or when he believed that he had lost out in a competition, he would describe himself as a worthless individual and become dangerously suicidal. He was extremely restless and hyperactive. His span of concentration was very short. He spent most of his time listening to the radio while eating candy and masturbating at the same time.

This child was born of a mother who later in life became psychotic. Neither the father nor his family were mentally ill. The child's early development was supposedly normal up to the age of three-and-a-half when a sister was born. Then he became mischievous and would urinate and defecate on the floor to spite his nurse.

He was sent to a nursery school where he would only roam about the room making faces and disrupting the class. When he went to grade school, he became more and more behind due to lack of concentration and illness. Then his father died and his behavior became worse.

He would take possession of everything upon which he could lay his hands. He became such a nuisance that he was sent to boarding school, where he would strike and kick the other children, spit in their faces and swear at them. He had no conception of personal property: he would give away his most valuable possessions but he would also go through the drawers and pockets of other people.

He ate everything, like rubbish from the floor, toothpaste, tops of fountain pens, pencils, erasers. He had no idea of personal care; he openly masturbated in the midst of a group. He behaved well on vacations with his mother or when in the company of one adult. He loved to play with fire and at a summer camp set fire to an expensive building.

Case D

Age: 6 years

D was a very tall boy with a large head and protruding teeth. No clinical verification could be found for a suspected organic disease.

He was an alert child, well-oriented. Despite his excellent memory, his stories of real happenings easily became mixed up with fantastic tales about his heroic deeds. He constantly jumped from one topic to another. A sample of his conversation is given: "When I was a little boy, my father went hunting and found me a duck to play with. And I said to the duck, 'Will you please go and find my balls' and the duck laid eggs in my bed. I said to the duck, 'Will you please go up, there is a passenger in the tree.' The duck caught him by the hair and swung him round and round and then he fell into the garden and died."

At the age of six he had no sense of danger and only with very skillful handling could be dissuaded from jumping off bridges or roofs. He would cross the street without noticing the traffic and would walk into strange houses and enter into a friendly conversation such as the one described above.

He was unable to do any school work. He had no concentration. With other children he never got along; he would push them around and kick them in the genital region. Following very slight frustration, he would display tantrums; it made no difference whether the frustration were real or supposed, the effect was the same. He was very impulsive, stubborn and negativistic.

When the child was about four, his father had become schizophrenic. The mother did not appear to be a maternal woman. Breast-feeding was never attempted. Feeding was exceedingly difficult; he had to be gavaged and it was hard to find a satisfactory formula. At eight months he had a severe case of diarrhea and since then had had constipation mixed with a mild diarrhea. At eight months he spoke simple words but he never learned to speak distinctly. He could walk at one-and-a-half years, but he always had an awkward gait. Although sphincter training was begun at six months, he still at the age of six was not clean, during either the day or the night. Between two and three years of age he smeared feces over his face and on the walls; at six he trampled his feces into the carpet. He urged his younger brother to wet his pants as he himself did. He had always been excitable, disobedient and destructive.

Case E

Age: 13 years

This intelligent and good-looking boy hated everything connected with cleanliness. He smelled distastefully of urine which he passed in his pants apparently without any awareness. Over-active and restless, he could not be in one position for more than two seconds. He always chewed edibles or non-edibles, smearing them all over and putting them into his mouth again. In public places he was loud and boisterous. He was very suspicious of everybody and especially of kindness in people. He was always dissatisfied with everything that was done for him and always felt slighted. When his suspicion or feelings of frustration were aroused, he would have tantrums in which he would pick up articles and throw them dangerously and at the same time express paranoid ideas. He complained about lack of concentration in his school work. Most of the time he spent in reading and in listening to the radio. He liked music. He showed no disharmony of emotion.

According to his mother, E had always been different from his two brothers. Although it was hard for her to identify the difference, she felt that everything with him had always been more difficult and that he had always caused her worry and concern.

Until he was four months old he was breast-fed; then until he was two years old he was bottle-fed. There was no apparent difficulty in weaning, but since then he would eat heartily only special dishes which his mother prepared. Bowel and bladder training was started at six months. From the beginning he resented bowel training and it was not completed until he was three years old; bladder training was never successful.

He seemed independent at an early age, but it was an independence which could not be influenced by anything. He was not cognizant of consequences adequate to his age. He could not dress himself until he was nine years old.

He went to school at five-and-a-half years. There he always did well in his studies, but he was never liked by the other children. He tried to bribe them with gifts but he never succeeded in having a friend. A physical coward, he did not dare to fight. He seldom carried through what he started. Regardless of what his mother did, he always felt that his brother got more than he did.

Case F

Age: 10 years

F was a small, meticulously-dressed boy who talked constantly in a high-pitched voice. He spoke a great deal about his own and other people's appearance and especially, of his own and their hair. He carried around a small pocket comb, and if permitted, would spend all his time combing other people's hair, discussing the color, the permanents, the type of curls, etc. After a while the combing would become rougher and rougher. If anyone refused to have his hair combed, the child would react with gross irritation which increased and became a temper tantrum. Sometimes while combing he would touch his pants in the region of the penis. When he combed, it was very obvious that he was not merely satisfying the desire to make the hair look neat. Mainly he wanted the touching and the process of combing. If no one were present, he would comb his own hair.

He stated openly that he would have preferred to be a girl. He was very excitable and giggled about everything. When taken out to visit or on a shopping trip, he behaved in a loud, silly manner. He avoided the company of other children because he feared they would beat him. He refused to do class work and instead spent his time drawing curls. He stated openly that he did not want to grow up because he wanted to be taken care of all his life. He asked questions compulsively and constantly without listening to the answers. He was preoccupied with religious ideas. He ate poorly.

The mother of this patient was mentally ill; the father was normal. The child's early development was described as normal, although he sucked his thumb until he was eight-and-a-half years of age. Then his mother applied restraints.

There was much parental discord; when the patient was two years old, the mother went to live with her own mother. There the patient was left a great deal to himself; at that time and throughout his life, great stress was laid on being well-dressed and socially well-behaved. When the patient was three years old, the parents were divorced. The mother was highly disturbed during the divorce proceedings; she lived in constant fear lest her former husband kidnap the boy.

The boy learned moderately well at school but was transferred from one school to another, each time in the hope he would adjust better. He never could get along with other children in groups and always disrupted them. Generally he would seek out one adult and try to spend all his time with this person.

He had the compulsion to wind all clocks and watches lest they stop. After seeing a movie concerning spies and amnesia, he became very much excited, complained about being blind, could not hear and had hallucinations about his mother and two cousins. He called himself a bad boy and dismantled his mother's clock. After being scolded about this, he became happy and hyperactive. He talked baby-talk and started to suck his thumb excessively. Gradually the episode subsided.

Cases A through F were diagnosed psychotic when the battery of intelligence and projective tests were given and interpreted as described by Dr. David Rapaport (22).

The following three case histories are those of patients who were diagnosed as schizophrenic at the ages of fifteen, seventeen and nineteen, respectively. The histories previous to the psychotic break seemed similar to the histories of the Cases A through F.

Case X

Age: 15 years

The patient's birth was normal; the family history seemed normal. The patient was breast-fed until he was nine months old. He was then abruptly weaned. He was toilet trained at eighteen months with difficulty.

When he was eighteen months old, his parents went on a trip and left him with a nurse. All through his life his parents were gone most of the time. In addition, the parents got along very badly and had arguments in the presence of the child. There were quarrels also between the grandparents and the parents.

The patient was always slow. When he was four years old, he developed a lasting speech defect during one of his parents' quarrels. At five-and-a-half he went to kindergarten, but he did not make a good adjustment. He never played with the other children. In grade school he did not mingle with other children either and said that he had "enemies". His mother felt that his not mingling with other children was due to his too great dependence on his parents. Therefore they sent him away from home with the result that he felt "more shut out than ever" and became more and more dependent on his mother. He read a great deal, loved music, and spent hours listening to his phonograph. His irritability increased, or he had spells in which the family described him as emotional, alternatively laughing and crying. When he was taken out of school for a while and tutored at home, he did much better scholastically. When he was thirteen years old, the family quarrels increased. He became hostile toward his parents and compulsive in his habits. He then had homosexual conflicts and felt embarrassed about the development of his secondary sexual characteristics. He refused to go to school. He would dress up in his mother's clothes and became compulsively erotic toward his mother. In school he became more and more seclusive, spending all his time alone and rebuffing all friendly advances. He felt that the other boys spied upon him. He used profane words, did a lot of day-dreaming; he only whispered when he spoke and said that he was a homosexual. He became more and more detached; he tried to run away. Then paranoid ideas about his father and homosexuals developed. He heard voices, developed ideas of reference and would do nothing but stay in his darkened room, listening to the radio. He only wore women's clothes now. Subsequently he went into a catatonic stupor.

In spite of shock treatment and an attempt at psychotherapy, the boy did not respond at all. His prognosis had to be regarded as bad.

Case Y

Age: 17 years

The next patient was a girl whose childhood and early life was one of disturbance at every level. Her mother had had a difficult delivery. The baby cried throughout infancy. Until she was four months old, she was breast-fed and suffered from an unusual amount of colic. She took better to the bottle than to the breast and was weaned easily at eight months. She sucked her thumb until she was seven months of age, when thumb guards were put on. Though bladder training was tried at two to three months, it was never successful until she was fifteen years of age. She stopped soiling at one year. She walked early but was very slow in talking. Her mother described her as being independent very early, but insatiable for kindness. Since she did not learn from punishment, she would always repeat what she had been punished for.

She did not get along with other children; when they took her things away, she could not hold her own. She hit her brother and sisters. She suffered from many nightmares. Her unsuccessful bladder training was very embarrassing to her.

In school she made no progress. If she liked a teacher, she would work, otherwise not. Generally she disliked the teachers. Her parents described her as dishonest, lacking in the sense of the value of money, very disorderly, and without friends.

At sixteen years she ran away from a party where she felt herself unsuccessful. Upon her return home she began having hallucinations. She had ideas of being poisoned by her mother. Gradually she became more and more withdrawn and developed a hebephrenic symptom complex. She did not respond to shock treatment or psychotherapy.

Case Z

Age: 19 years

Z had been a source of concern since birth. A premature baby, he was breast-fed for several weeks and then put on the bottle without difficulty. He cried a great deal during infancy and was restless in his sleep. From the beginning he had poor coordination. He walked and talked at twenty months of age. Bowel training had been tried right after birth and was completed at one year. Bedwetting did not cease until he was six years old.

When he was three, he was noted for his irritability, nervousness, restlessness and "general weakness". Until he was six years old, he sucked his thumb. He was always full of physical complaints, unhappy, secretive, difficult to approach and different from other children. At the slightest frustration he had severe temper tantrums which grew increasingly violent as he grew older. He would pick up the handiest object, even a knife, and attack his opponent. His cruelty to animals was often extreme. He never had a normal childhood interest and never made a friend.

At school he was unhappy and did no work. Because of his bad adjustment he was sent from one school to another without any success.

He invented minor illnesses to avoid tasks and expressed a feeling of inadequacy in every field. He was sly and untruthful. Once at camp he threw rifle bullets into the fire; afterwards he denied having done so. At ten he set fire to a stateroom on board ship.

Immediately before his overt breakdown at nineteen years of age he made three dramatic attempts at suicide. Then he became more and more confused. He was diagnosed as schizophrenic.

It is noteworthy that of the nine cases described only one is that of a girl. A tentative explanation is offered. It may be that mental disorder of this kind manifests itself in boys in aggressive behavior, whereas in girls it is expressed by quietness, shyness and withdrawal, aggressive behavior and temper tantrums occurring less frequently. Therefore the girls are less disturbing to the environment, and hence are not brought so frequently to the attention of physicians and educators. But this should be verified by careful statistics.

Discussion

In observing cases A through F, we are struck by one common feature in spite of the varied overt behavior. All the children show a disturbed past from an early age in addition to the severe symptoms at the time of examination, a combination which should make the observer aware of the severe condition. When we compare the behavior of these children with the emotional life and the reactions of children less than three years of age, it becomes more intelligible.

During the last part of the first year of life the normal child has just begun to realize that he cannot possess his mother completely. (By "mother" is meant the person who takes most care of the child and on whom he is emotionally completely dependent; the person who provides food and shelter, who comforts him in his moments of distress, who loves him and cuddles him; in short, the person from whom he receives gratification and security.)

Modern investigators of child development are becoming increasingly aware of the importance of this early mother-child relationship (13). In the normal situation the child feels well and happy when his mother is about. This situation seems to enable him to grow up emotionally and to make his first attempts at becoming independent, such as learning to talk, to walk and to explore the world around him. Although this development is a maturational[3] one, recent investigation (24, 26) has shown that this process can be greatly influenced by con-

3. For the use of this term see Hartmann-Kris-Loewenstein, *this Annual*, II.

ditions in the environment. Analysis of these conditions shows that it is mainly the presence of warmth, affection and love which furthers development, and their absence which retards development. Interruption through circumstances due either to illness, departure or death of the mother, or illness of the child with subsequent hospitalization, brings about a regression in the child to an earlier stage of behavior. The child seems temporarily to have lost his achievements. The child may suddenly not be able to walk or talk and in many cases bowel and bladder training, if it has been achieved, breaks down. The child seems more dependent on his mother than before. He seems to need her attention as when he was much younger. He cries more and seems to want to be cuddled and held all the time. After such an experience some children tend to reject the mother, which is the result of their great disappointment in her (13).

One of the decisive traumas in the development of the growing child is the discovery that his mother has other interests beside himself. He reacts to this with great jealousy. However, in a situation where the child is adequately loved, the discovery will be compensated for by the mother's feelings for him as expressed by her attitudes (13). This situation tends to increase the child's natural drive to grow away from his great dependence on his mother. In his development toward greater independence, it is very reassuring to him to know that if the need arises his mother will be there to take care of him again, to protect, help, and love him. The somewhat older child seems to begin to erect the image of this loving mother in his fantasy, which in her absence he uses to comfort himself. Freud (14) explains the hide-and-seek game of a young child whose mother is absent in this way. This fact may well be of the greatest importance for the development of the ego and superego of the growing child and seems to be part of the processes of introjection of and identification with the parental images.[4]

Beside feeling jealous the young child will also feel frustrated in other respects in his relationship to his mother. He will have to learn that he cannot have his way all the time, that his mother is not always there when he wants her to be, that he has to refrain from many instinctual pleasures. He reacts to these frustrations with hostility, negativism, periods of stubbornness, breakdown of toilet habits,

4. This concept needs further clarification in relation to the concepts of narcissism and object relationship as well as to problems of ego strength and superego formation.

eating disturbances, fears or temper tantrums. Temper tantrums at an early age are to be regarded as a normal manifestation. It is only when they persist or are too frequent or too violent that they have to be regarded as pathological.

All the children described in this paper can be understood as never having outgrown this early mother relationship. They all functioned well in the company of one adult alone. They were well-behaved, extremely loving, and very good company. The adult may at times be inclined to prefer these children to the more normal ones who seem to have many more interests and who soon become bored with adult company. These abnormal children will become much more violent whenever they cannot have their way or when the adult has to divide his attention between the child and another person. Some of the children mentioned above were described as being very independent. (See cases D, E, Y.) However, close observation has shown that this independence was a reaction to their feelings of great dependence. These children felt so disappointed that they would no longer even show their need to be loved. This factor also explains the bad relationship which all these children had with their mothers. In some cases, even her presence counteracted all psychotherapeutic efforts. This can be compared with Freud and Burlingham's (12, 13) description of young children who, after separation, did not recognize their mothers or refused them; they longed for the mothers when the mothers were absent, and received them with hostility when they returned.

When these seemingly independent children were offered a relationship with one adult, they became just as dependent upon the new person. As has been described in the paper on temper tantrums (15), the best way to stop the tantrum is for the person whom the child loves and trusts to come, put his arm around the child and assure him of his love. The younger child, especially, will then cuddle up in her arms like a baby and sobbingly relate all the wrongs people have done to him in his life. This response is an example again that the children are on the emotional level of the very young child. The young child whose tantrums express a state of great unhappiness and frustration also needs reassurance and love. The author does not want to convey the idea that one should yield to young children if their outburst is a reaction to a necessary frustration. But for a satisfactory later development they need reassurance and love in addition to the amount of discipline adequate for their age. The same holds true for the disturbed child. It is not wise to yield to him. He has to be taught to live up to the minimal standards that are set for him. But in the attempt to live up to them he needs the constant assurance of the educator's love and affection for him.

It is easy to understand that it is scarcely possible for these children to do well in school. A child under two is hardly able to join or hold his own in a group. The most he can do is to play for a short while with one other child. In this play he shows clearly that all will go well as long as he can play with the toys he wants to play with, and as long as the other child does not interfere with his wishes. If another child receives the attention of an adult, then he too may claim this attention. He frequently accomplishes this by aggressive behavior toward the rival. The same seems to happen to the disturbed children. In the school situation they have to share the attention of the teacher with many other children. This arouses all their conflicts. One of two reactions then occurs: either they become unmanageable as reflected in their hostility and disobedience to the teacher and aggressiveness toward other children, or they withdraw into their fantasy life. The hostility to the teacher is comparable to the hostility to the mother out of jealousy. The other children in the class are the rivals for the teacher's attention.

Daydreaming and seclusiveness become more and more apparent the older the child becomes. It is very possible that this may be understood as a retained reaction of the much younger child. The young child spends a great deal of his time playing fantasy games with his toys or listening to stories. One expects that the child in the latency period spends most of his time playing and learning in groups. The abnormal child has never been able to fit into groups and continues his earlier pursuits of playing alone. When he becomes somewhat older, he leaves the toys and then is lost in his fantasies, which offer him great satisfaction. From analytic experience the author has learned that many of these fantasies are of an omnipotent nature. These omnipotent fantasies prevent the child from entering activities alone as well as in groups. The child wants to know everything at once without failure and he wants his performance to be the best. He fears the disappointment of not being able to accomplish this although his potentialities might even, in some instances, make it possible. This fear of failure reinforces his withdrawal into his fantasy life. In the fantasy he can continue to believe that he is the best. In several cases the disability in learning could also be explained by his need for omnipotence. So the teaching situation is intolerable because, as a pupil, the child is not in control of the situation; as several children expressed it: "I have to have control about everything and therefore I cannot do what the teacher says."

The cruelty of these children is like that seen in many young children who have not yet developed any reaction-formation. Also, in the relationship to the animal these children can live out many of their omnipotent fantasies. On the other hand, there are certain animals they love deeply. Some of the children never could treat those cruelly. The love for these animals is stronger than that felt for any playmate. The analysis of one child seemed to indicate that he had a close identification with the animal. Case B, who killed his toad after speaking to it endearingly, seems to contradict this. But this may well have been a projected suicide. From his analysis it was clear that the other animals he killed were substitutes for his brother whom he hated.

As long as these children feel satisfied, that is, when they feel loved by one adult and that adult is present, they are bright, alert and interested. When this relationship is interfered with, they react with an outbreak of rage in which they are completely out of contact with reality. They express paranoid ideas and they have lost all sense of what is dangerous and what is not. To the observer they seem to be more and more overcome by their emotions; they become dangerously violent towards others and themselves; they react like adult psychotics. The less sick child in his temper tantrum is never overcome by his emotions and always retains enough contact with reality to be aware of what he is doing and to control it if he would take the effort.

It is obvious to the observer that the children described also lose contact with reality of everyday life as soon as they are left to themselves. It seems that they need an actual relationship, that is, the *presence* of an adult who loves them, in order to maintain their hold on reality. In the relationship with the adult it is the child's dependence upon the adult and the child's belief in his own omnipotence in this relationship which keeps his hold on reality intact.

In this connection the author would like to suggest the term *reality span,* by which is meant the measurement of the ability to remain in contact with reality. The reality span in all the cases described was extremely small, and dependent upon the presence of the adult. It seems that in the normal child the fantasies of omnipotence gradually are given up because the child tests them in reality. Probably in the later period of infancy the child already begins to learn how small, dependent and incapable he is. It is possible that at this point he will resort to erecting the mother in his fantasy during her absence. It may be that this process is possible only when he gives up the fantasy of his own omnipotence, although temporarily he has transferred the omnipotence to her (and the other adults in the environment). It seems to the author that this is a decisive step in the development of the ego and that it is accomplished by a correct perception of the self in relation to the environment. It is the child's first step toward achieving emotional independence from the mother, the first step toward the development of a mature ego. If the mother relation is maintained during her absence, he can tolerate the absence and gradually he can become less dependent on her presence in order to feel secure as well as to do what is expected of him. Further reality testing will gradually diminish the belief in the mother's omnipotence and that of other adults.

The children described in this paper have been able to estalish this relationship to only a very small extent. The omnipotence fantasies seem to hold the greatest satisfaction for them, more than reality has to offer. They therefore withdraw into their fantasies as soon as the relationship with the adult with whom they actually lived out this fantasy, ceases. Interruption of these fantasies again evokes violent tantrums on the part of the child.

The author believes that the inability to give up the fantasy of omnipotence is a failure in the reality testing of the child. This may be the decisive factor in the development of the psychosis, perhaps in the development of all functional psychoses. The fact remains that the reality span in all psychotic patients is very small, verging towards nil.

In treatment the psychotic patient often regains his hold on reality through the extremely indulgent and tolerant attitude of the psychotherapist, but cannot sustain it in the absence of the psychotherapist. This is comparable to the relationship between abnormal children and adults in their environment; which again is similar to the relationship of the mother to the young child (9, 11, 23).

Along with the small reality span is also found an only slightly developed ability to test reality. This explains why all of them got into dangerous situations, especially during tantrums, and why so few learned through experience.

One also finds, as indicated above, that these children were much less able to learn to control their instinctual drives than others. Their bowel and bladder training in many cases was harder to establish, and also broke down more easily (B, C, D, F, Y). They masturbated more openly or indulged in sexual and anal activities at an age where the more normal child had long since outgrown them (A, B, and C).

Much of the behavior of these children can be understood in terms of their being unable to control an impulse as well as their lacking the reasoning and ability to foresee consequences or to identify with their victims (cruelty to animals, setting fire to buildings, etc.), as would be expected from their high intelligence and their age. It is striking to observe how the impulse gets an increasingly strong hold on them. Needless to say, these children are tormented by many fears and nightmares. As all fantasy life, as compared with their sense of reality, seems to have such strong hold on them, so their anticipations and fears also seem to have more reality value for them.

The younger the child the less one expects from him the ability to handle his impulses and to be independent. One grants him a great amount of fantasying. When these children become older, they have at their disposal only the ways of handling and controlling their emotions and fantasy life that they had early infancy and childhood. However, their impulses have developed far beyond the stage of infancy. These children are faced with the threatening situation of lacking the normal means of handling their impulses. Naturally, the older the child gets, the more alarming is the psychological picture. At puberty acute schizophrenia develops. It is possible that more careful investigation of cases of schizophrenia in adolescence will show that the outbreak is not so acute but has been preceded by a history comparable to the cases described here. Cases X, Y and Z may prove this contention (10).

In the publications of Bradley (2), Eickhoff (8), Potter (21), Greblaskaja (16), Tramer (25), children have been described who were diagnosed as psychotic or schizophrenic. The symptomatology of these children is, in general, characterized by extreme withdrawal up to catatonic stupor mannerisms, bizarre behavior, explosive outbursts and paranoid ideas. It is the experience of the author that when these children are also treated with the method described above, namely, by giving them the opportunity to establish a completely dependent relationship on one adult who will treat them with as much indulgence as possible, these psychotic children respond quite favorably. Especially when this beloved adult is present, they become less withdrawn, they are able to learn something and they may have fewer explosive outbursts.[4] However, as far as the author's experience goes, the improvement is only a matter of degree.[5] In many cases the picture does not change fundamentally and the children remain psychotic.

Some of the children described by the author have improved under the regime of a love relationship with one adult combined with child analysis. In the beginning of the treatment the child was given as much freedom as possible. The standards of behavior were heightened gradually with improvement, and were at all times adapted to the child's emotional immaturity. Their adjustment has been such that although they are still disturbed in their behavior, they have been able to make a better adjustment at home and at school. By the regime of one adult is meant that one or two adults only deal with the child and that for a long period of time he participates in a group situation only in the company of one of these adults and is also tutored by one of them. The period of observation has been too short to warrant any definite pronouncements as to treatment methods and their results.

Summary

This paper has described cases of children whose overt symptomatology was that met in children with extreme behavior disorders. Close observation showed that the emotional development of the children was retarded and that their behavior could be understood when it was compared with the feelings and reactions of very young children. Three cases were described whose earlier symptomatology had been similar to that of the previous cases, and who in adolescence developed schizophrenia. It is possible that the difference between the

4. Erik H. Erikson, in a personal communication, has described a similar experience.

5. Bradley (2), Cottington (4), Creak (5), and Lourie, et al (20) have a more optimistic point of view on the cases they have described.

cases described and those which have the classical diagnosis of schizophrenia in childhood is only one of degree.

It is suggested that the difference between normal or neurotic
development and that of the child who will become psychotic
lies in an early disturbance of the ego development. The normal
child is able to erect an image of his mother within his ego which
enables him to be contented in her absence and which seems to be the
core of his development to a mature and independent individual.
The psychotic child functions only in the presence of a mother-
substitute (seldom his own mother). Disappointment in her or her
absence suffices to throw him into a state of withdrawal or incites
a temper outburst in which he breaks away from reality and develops
paranoid ideas.

The therapy of individual attention and modified psychoanalysis
has been successful in a few cases. However, the duration of observation is too short and the number of cases treated too small to make
any definite statements as to prognosis or to recommend any definite
treatment. But for these children, as well as for the normal and neurotic
children with whom they mingle and who suffer through them, early
recognition of the underlying disorder is essential.

BIBLIOGRAPHY

1. Bender, L. *The Nervous Child*, 1, 1942.
2. Blank, R., Smith, O. C., Bruch, H., "Schizophrenia in a Four-year-old-
    Boy", *J. Psychiatry*, 100, 1944.
3. Bradley, C. *Schizophrenia in Childhood*, New York, 1941. See also
    "Psychoses in Children", *Modern Trends in Child Psychiatry*, New
    York, 1945.
4. Cottington, F. "Treatment of Schizophrenia of Childhood", *The Nervous
    Child*, 1, 1942.
5. Creak, M. "Psychoses in Childhood", *Proc. Royal Soc. Med.* 31, 1938.
6. Despert, L. "Schizophrenia in Children", *Psychiatric Quarterly*, XV, 1941.
7. Despert, L. "Prophylactic Aspect of Schizophrenia in Childhood", *The
    Nervous Child*, 1, 1942.
8. Eickhoff, L. "Acute Schizophrenia in Childhood", *Edinburgh Med. J.*,
    51, 1944.
9. Federn, P. "Psychoanalysis of Psychoses, I-III", *Psychiatric Quarterly*,
    XVII, 1943.
10. Freud, A. and Burlingham, D. T. *Monthly Reports of the Hampstead
    Nurseries*, Foster Parents Plan, 1941-1946.
11. Freud, A. and Burlingham, D. T. *War and Children*, Internat. Univ.
    Press, 1943.

12. Freud, S. *Beyond the Pleasure Principle,* Hogarth, 1922.
13. Friedlander, D. "Personality Development of Twenty-seven Children who Later in Life Became Psychotic", *J. Abnorm. Soc. Psychol.,* 40, 1945.
14. Fromm-Reichmann, F. "Psychoanalytic Psychotherapy with Psychotics", *Psychiatry,* VI, 1943.
15. Geleerd, E. R. "Some Observations on Temper Tantrums in Children", *Amer. J. Orthopsychiatry,* XV, 1945.
16. Greblaskaja, A. "Zur Klinik der Schizophrenie des frühen Kindesalters", *Schweizer Arch. Neurol. und Psychiatrie,* 34, 1934, 1935, 1936.
17. Harms, E. "Childhood Schizophrenia and Childhood Hysteria", *Psychiatric Quarterly,* XIX, 1945.
18. Kanner, L. *Child Psychiatry.* Springfield, 1937.
19. Kasanin, J. "Developmental Roots of Schizophrenia", *Amer. J. Psychiatry,* 101, 1945.
20. Lourie, R. S., Pacella, B. L., Piotrowski, Z. A. "Studies in Prognosis in Schizophrenic-like Psychoses in Children", *Amer. J. Psychiatry,* 99, 1943.
21. Potter, "Schizophrenia in Children", *Amer. J. of Psychiatry,* 12, 1933.
22. Rapaport, D. *Diagnostic Psychological Testing,* Chicago, 1945.
23. Schwing, G. *Ein Weg zur Seele des Geisteskranken,* Zürich, 1930.
24. Spitz, R. A. "Hospitalism", *this Annual,* I.
25. Tramer, M. "Tagebuch über ein geisteskrankes Kind", *Zeit. f. Kinderpsychiatrie,* 1934, 1935.
26. Wolf, K. and Durfee, H. "Anstaltspflege und Entwicklung im ersten Lebensjahr", *Zeit. f. Kinderforschung,* 42/3, 1933.

DIARIES OF ADOLESCENT
SCHIZOPHRENICS (HEBEPHRENICS)

By WILLIE HOFFER, M.D., Ph.D., L.R.C.P. (London)

Psychoanalytic investigations of the schizophrenic psychoses have been focused almost entirely on those manifestations which Fenichel (4) grouped under the productive, restitutive signs, namely on delusions and hallucinations. In hebephrenia, a variety of schizophrenia which manifests itself earlier and which is more characteristic of adolescence than the catatonic or paranoid form of schizophrenia, delusions and hallucinations are "inconsiderable" (8). While the psychotic with delusions and hallucinations may display a rich inner life, the delusions sometimes being highly systematized, the content of the hebephrenic's mental processes appears to be fluctuating and incoherent and is difficult to define. It has so far been impossible to find motives for typical hebephrenic activities such as blind rage, inappropriate laughter and silly behavior, as the psychiatric description in terms such as "inappropriate" or "silly" suggests. To what psychic content or aim they may be related can only be a subject for speculation; Mayer-Gross (9) considers them a discharge of surplus impulse. Why a surplus of impulse expresses itself in these typical hebephrenic activities is a problem which has so far remained unsolved. Psychoanalysts may be inclined to compare these activities with compulsive neuroses; but here compulsive acting occurs within an organized personality which one is reluctant to attribute to the hebephrenic psychotic whose ego is more dissimilar than similar to that of the obsessional.

While then the hebephrenic's personality or what is left of it still remains obscure one cannot hope to throw much light on it by studying the fully developed cases encountered in the psychiatric wards. The necessity for an early study has been repeatedly stressed, but Mayer-Gross says that the early stages are rarely seen by psychiatrists. Katan (7) has recently emphasized the necessity for a close study of the very first onset of schizophrenic delusions and this also applies to hebephrenic manifestations.

Objections have been raised to the use of the psychoanalytic interview for such a purpose. For the interview necessarily leads to an increase of self-observation which according to Schilder (13) interferes with the usual course of the schizophrenic mental activity. Analytic treatment of incipient hebephrenia for instance may have a precipitating effect; this none will deny. Psychoanalytic insight into the morbid changes in personality will probably show that the hebephrenic adolescents rapidly develop a pseudo-transference in which the analyst is used as a refuge against the distressing changes the sufferer feels but which he finds increasingly difficult and finally impossible to express in words or gestures. I can confirm this fact from some cases I had in earlier years. I am speaking here of the hebephrenic psychosis only. The difference between the interview with a neurotic and that with a hebephrenic is that the former aims at communicating his thoughts whereas the latter tries to restore a disintegrating personality by talking. As far as I could observe from a few cases, the failure to restore the personality by talking is followed by an increase of motor activities, exhausting exercises, running about, climbing on roofs, and so on. In the initial stages the hebephrenic also suffers from intense anxiety and it seemed to me that speech and actions were used—however ineffectually—to combat this anxiety concerning the loss of object relationships and the sense of his own identity. But this, of course, is hypothesis.

Is hebephrenia the purely regressive type of schizophrenia?

Fenichel (4) expresses the opinion that in hebephrenia "the ego undertakes no activity for the purpose of defending itself but, beset by conflicts, 'lets itself go'. If the present is unpleasant, the ego drops back to the past; if newer types of adaptation fail, it takes refuge in older ones, in the infantile ones of passive receptivity and even perhaps in intrauterine ones. If a more differentiated type of living becomes too difficult, it is given up in favor of a more or less merely vegetative existence; Campbell called it schizophrenic surrender." The impression of surrender can however only be supported by observing the hospitalized patient. While the regressive nature of the schizophrenic process has long ago been stressed (Freud, Jung, Storch) clinical observation and the patient's own introspection during the very early stage do not support the surrender theory and that of the *purely* regressive nature of the hebephrenic process.

Fenichel points out that the loss of object relationship is often a very gradual one; this suggests that defensive processes have been at work but have failed and resulted in exhaustion of the powers of defense and in the disintegration of personality. The slow and gradual change from a tolerably or well adapted adolescent to a creature which is almost emptied of emotions, unable to feed or clean itself, abruptly laughing or raging or occasionally subject to hallucinations, must be accompanied by mental processes. It certainly justifies the questions: What is going on in the hebephrenic's mind before it succumbs? Why should no attempts at restitution be made? The concept of restitution coined by Freud in connection with Schreber's autobiography has in itself no bearing on the final result of the schizophrenic process. While making attempts at restitution the schizophrenic does not follow rational lines, he attempts to restore the world, the vanishing object relations, and the change of ego cathexis by resorting to delusions and hallucinations, which he conceives to be real. In hebephrenia communication by words is gradually lost and restitution is attempted by doglike adherence to leaders, school-fellows and persons of the other sex. Magic gestures support these attempts. Hypochondriasis which so frequently appears as an outstanding initial symptom is used to obtain attention, reassurance and epidermic stimulation; it manifests itself in a desire to be medically examined (*Arztsüchtigkeit*) (8). We have also to keep in mind that the characteristics which make us think of surrender are not confined to hebephrenia but apply to psychoses in general, especially to "terminal dementia" (affective hebetude). Any conclusion as to the mental processes leading to this result has therefore to be postponed until the demands of the "genetic approach" have been fulfilled.

Diaries as a means of studying the hebephrenic process.

Psychotics not infrequently enjoy elaborating their mental activities in writing; in psychoanalysis the classical example is the case of Schreber. Muncie (10) also quoted some pages from the notebook of one of his cases and illustrations of this kind are no rarity, particularly if one deliberately looks for them. Especially in adolescence the tendency to solitude and isolation (2) evokes a need for recording experiences of any kind, but keeping a diary cannot be understood merely as a method of recording; it is a more complicated process and serves many purposes. Charlotte Bühler (2) went so far as to say that 50 per cent of students in Vienna, Athens and New York begin to keep diaries. In his outstanding monograph Bernfeld (8) has shown that this is a literary usage bound up with tradition and culture and almost as old as the invention of writing itself. According to C. Bühler adolescents begin to keep diaries at the age of fourteen to eighteen and stop between seventeen and twenty-one, twice as many writing only for a half to one year compared with those who continue to write for two to three years. There is therefore a probability that diaries could be used to elucidate the initial stages of psychotic processes just as for any other psychopathological state in adolescence. This would be especially desirable where the nature of the mental illness makes verbal communication difficult or impossible (e.g., mutism).

The two diaries discussed here have been kept for more than twenty years because of the relative completeness of the case histories and because I am still in contact with one of the writers; the other died in a mental hospital two years after entering it. They were written by two male adolescents between fifteen and seventeen-and-a-half. They were second cousins but lived in different places and had never met. There were other psychotics in the family, but the parents and grandparents were well adapted people.

I shall call the writers Richard and George, and shall discuss the restitutional function of their diaries separately, preceding each by a short life history.

The Case of Richard

Richard was the younger of two children. His sister who was three years older played the most important role in his emotional life. She was, from early childhood on, a self-assertive, active person, who after a violent spell of jealousy poured out all her desires for motherhood, leadership and supervision on her brother from his birth till his death at the age of twenty. He became her doll, her pupil and adorer. An early photograph of a group of children clearly shows a difference in the facial expression of the two children. She had a happy expression, energetic, shrewd, he at the age of two looks gloomy and spiteful, and each hand firmly grasps a stick. ("I have nothing to hold on to" became a frequent complaint in his diary.) The sister later modified her possessiveness towards her brother under the influence of his active drives and yielded to his need for self-assertion. When he was ten she took him to a club where the activities of the junior members were confined to hiking on Sundays. She admired his liking for books and philosophical reflections when he was adolescent, but worried about his seclusiveness and taciturnity. After her brother's death she married an old friend, a member of the club, whose Christian name was the same as her brother's, but she proved completely frigid and divorced her husband. She later became a Nursery School teacher and finally refused to part from a group of children she had looked after for more than two years in a concentration camp for Jews and went with them to Auschwitz, an extermination camp.

Richard was a quiet boy from early childhood on, always a "shut-in personality". Anything he had to learn in order to acquire proper habits and manners he learned with ease, being perfect at the kindergarten and at school. His voice was reputed to be soft; he was no fighter and had to be protected against aggressive children. From about the age of four onwards he was considered a thinker. He was sociable, but rather passive and easily overlooked. When entering adolescence he became still more interested in books, and soon his reading of philosophy and literature threatened his progress at his secondary school. He was a good student at first. When he was fifteen his quarterly school report deteriorated, though he succeeded in putting things right. He had changed to the senior group in the club, where debating, and planning emigration to Palestine were the main activities.

Shortly before his sixteenth birthday he started to keep a diary (in shorthand, very clearly and neatly) and did so for 16 months, until co-ordinated activity became impossible for him. This happened when he had entered the highest form and faced the burden of preparation for his final examination. His slow deterioration had of course been noticed by his family and was attributed to overwork and reading until late at night. It is important to note that during the critical year preceding the complete breakdown his sister lived away from her family, and one of the letters Richard wrote her just about the middle of the period of diary writing reads as follows: "Dear sister, When I write you I feel happy because when I meet you in my imagination I feel myself a complete unity and therefore I can give you a clear, unified picture of myself. In writing to you just now I give way to a momentary impulse and I have to control myself continually so as not to write too much nonsense. I am completely overwhelmed by my feelings. I can really give way to feeling. My relations with reality are childish, I can hardly grasp material things. You must not take my letter literally, I write phrases which are just reproduced from memory. I have to stop now, my thoughts have become unbridled and I shall try to continue later when reason returns . . ." Continuing: "I shall try to give you an idea of the position here, naturally in quite a subjective way, as far as I can see it. Family life is at the moment cold. Father behaves with tact, he has, so to speak, an expectant attitude towards me and mother, I appreciate this really as far as I can, considering my weak personality. Mother is unable to add anything of value to the family atmosphere. Although she cannot fulfill such expectations she seems to be content with herself and is able to devote herself to work she likes. This is certainly a noble characteristic. I thought so today when I looked at the street from the window and saw mother coming home from the shop. It is Saturday today and she was certainly very tired as she had worked the whole day in the shop. She walked slowly step by step. Her eyes did not wander like those of other people in the street. She walked quietly and as if she were proud of herself. She has a strong personality.

I will not suggest that you should take things I write too seriously, there may be an error here and there when I write to you, and that is due to the fact that I cannot be measured by common standards. Naturally father and mother expect me to make conversation, but that has always been my weak spot, that I cannot chatter, I have always been like this since childhood. But I believe that when my mind grows stronger this intrinsic deficiency will be compensated. My reason must help me, otherwise if I still remain a stupid day-dreamer I shall never achieve anything in life—as a materialist. I should be quite capable of creating a world of my own, but that is utopia."

It is also important that during the period when he was keeping the diary he succeeded in controlling his masturbation which up till then had overshadowed his life from about eleven onwards.

When it was obvious that he had to leave school, he was sent to a psychiatrist who diagnosed the case as dementia praecox. Richard soon became very restless, ran about in the streets, grimaced, held his head stretched forward, stopped talking completely and finally became dirty. He had to be moved into a mental hospital where he died two years later from fulminant tuberculosis.

Impoverishment of the social self.

As Buxbaum (3), Redl (12) and others have shown, the social activities of adolescents are instigated by their need to "seek satisfaction which the family normally refuses to give". This is a universal method of dealing with frustrations of the sexual and aggressive instincts at the peak of sexual desires (Buxbaum). Naturally, social satisfaction cannot be achieved all at once and varying degrees of anxiety have to be dealt with during these processes. Group life is the source not only of many satisfactions, but of frustrations as well, and the psychotically disposed adolescent should be expected to react differently from the normal one. His capacity for adaptation to changing social conditions is usually limited, although this may not easily become apparent; withdrawal from and repression of unpleasant experiences may not be different from the non-psychotic when considered from outside. According to Freud (6) detachment of the libido from objects occurs in every act of repression. Normally the detached libido retains its mobility, and can become reinvested in object cathexes after the anxiety which caused repression and libido detachment has been warded off by defense mechanisms. In psychoses the process is different. In paranoia for instance the withdrawn libido is assumed to have become fixed to the ego and is used for its aggrandizement.

The withdrawal of libido thus leads in the psychotic to a regression into a more narcissistic stage of ego organization. Richard's type of reaction when considered from outside appears as the slow retreat of a constantly frustrated social life. In fact social activities cease only gradually, after attempts at maintaining them have failed. These are at first of a defensive nature and aim at a real contact in spite of the fear of losing social relationships, but later they change into an unrealistic restitution of the social self, until all social drive has ceased to exist. Where restitutional attempts are mingled with aggression, social isolation is hastened by the group's withdrawal in self defense.

Though Richard cannot be called "asocial", he showed from early childhood onward almost no ability to make and keep active social contact. He began to read early and read many books, and he excelled in his knowledge. Between the age of seven and ten he learned to play the piano without being taught. And still in the pre-psychotic phase his psychological conflicts concerning his inability to feel any real attachment to a group are in the foreground and the main defensive and restitutional attempts centre round this problem. This is remarkable as one would expect such attempts to be made in a sphere where previous experience and skill have paved the way for success.

One of the focal points of Richard's disturbed social relations was his feeling about his parents, with whom he thought he had many reasons to be dissatisfied. His mother especially had never behaved to him as a mother should; the facts he gives in the diary tend to point to this conclusion. "I confess I should now be quite another boy if my mother had been different. But my mother does not understand this. I always try to keep away from my mother because in her I see myself at my worst. How much my mother could have given me in the past! Not only is my nature similar to my mother's, but I also physically resemble her (I resist that with all my strength) . . . If I become like my mother I lose all power to face the struggle for life." But he made a similar remark about resembling his father's relatives. The truth as regards these complaints seems to be that from early childhood he had little emotional and actual contact with his parents and spent most of his time alone with a maid. His sister went to school when he was three, his father travelled for his shop while the mother ran it, spending only part of the time with her son in the morning and in the evening. Though it cannot be proved, it seems that his oedipal relationship was comparatively weak from the onset and the only attachment he succeeded in forming was one to his sister. Considering the role of the street and also of distance and separation in his life, speculation tends to lead to the assumption that he always felt a longing for something which was still outside him and of which he had never been able to take possession: a proper object relationship based on his experiences with the objects of early childhood.

When still a pre-school child he had opportunities for enjoying normal pleasures with his parents, who were simple people but not without a high degree of responsibility towards their children. However, he thought of them only reproachfully. "I have been spoiled. With every spoonful of soup she

put into my mouth she took me on her lap. Father scolded us and I cried
and felt that Father wanted me to be different . . . Mother said I should run
about in the street. I said I would only if I had a hoop. I got it but did
not run about."

His home life seems always to have been determined by this early
conflict in his feelings. From childhood on he spent hours looking through
the window into the street where in earlier days the mother must have been
frequently pointed out to him by the maid when she was returning home.
In adolescence this leaning on the window sill became a compulsion. He
used to think and read in this position.

His own inner wishes and the opportunities offered by school life brought
him into contact with boys of his own age. He was a typical "follower"
(*Mitläufer*): "I think with great satisfaction of the time when I ran about
on the market place with V. and K. and when we shared a salted herring
on the stairs of our house. And when I played at horses and wore the
harness with little bells on it near the theatre, while F. played the
driver." According to his diary he first became fully aware of his social
self when he was eleven: "When I spent my first holiday with Czech people
I awakened and my struggles started. For there I had company and I think
for the first time I felt the difference between life at home and with other
people, but I do not think I realized this up till now. How obviously inferior
my home was, even compared with this place. Since then my youth has been
a restless hunting, a striving to get on with my arms stretched forward." Here
again I draw attention to his emphasis on the need for something to hold
on to.

Afterwards he became, to some extent, a leader in the club which he
had joined because his advanced philosophical interests and knowledge made
him attractive to his fellows there. He was also an excellent school-boy, but
from all this he gained little satisfaction, because inwardly he did not feel
attached to any group. He was never interested in the organization or
running of the club but only in its ideals, in its literary and artistic pursuits.

One of the first symptoms from which he suffered was a change in
his relation to the club. He began to realize the difference between his social
nature and that of his friends. In searching for possible causes of that
change a similar change of his interest in his sister has also to be considered.
He was now approaching puberty and his sexual feelings towards his sister
became reawakened. A conflict arose between two feelings, tenderness for
his sister and sexual feelings which had been latent since childhood and
now complicated his life still further. His increased though painful interest
in his social relations and the reactions to this interest cannot be understood
without evaluating his relations with boys and girls (homo- and heterosexual
striving); the diary offers some material for this.

During the whole period when he was keeping the diary he was most
painfully aware of moving in a vicious circle. He blamed his inability to talk
and his increasing difficulty in thinking clearly and formulating his thoughts

as the causes of his social inferiority, but felt he needed the club and school as a forum from which to express his social self. He developed two methods of temporarily overcoming a feeling of terror of losing his identity which he compared to being like a piece of wood or a dog; he developed defensive methods which brought him nearer to his leaders and fellows at first, and later, after these methods had been exhausted, his diary indicates that he fought a delusion in which he felt superior to the others, great, omnipotent and unified.

Neurotic defense and psychotic restitution.

In the following paragraph fantasies and activities concerning Richard's social contacts will be viewed from two current psycho-analytic aspects—defense and restitution. By defense of the social self, I refer to an unconscious mental activity which aims at warding off anxiety arising from social experiences. Repression plays a large part in every mental activity aiming at defense against anxiety, but apart from repression adaptive measures are taken by the ego, and these measures manifest themselves in the character and in the symptoms; their all-important function in puberty has been shown by Anna Freud (5). In the pre-psychotic phase no clear-cut distinction can be made between "defense" on the one hand and "restitution" on the other.—Restitution means a mental activity by which a psychotic person attempts to restore the feeling of contact with the world of objects and this is mainly brought about by delusions and hallucinations.

The obvious defense against social frustration of any kind is a retreat into fantasies. Like most adolescents Richard made use of fantasies which centered round three subjects: a hiking tour during the summer holidays which was combined with a general gathering of clubs from different towns; life in Palestine with other boys who felt like himself, and finally the idea of impressing his teachers and schoolfellows with his high conception of life and other ideals. But reality proved again and again that actual contact with the group inevitably led to frustration. Instead of admitting anxiety he tried to explain his failure by imagining himself to be stupid or lacking in understanding, or unable to share the predominant feeling and activities of the group—friendship, discussions or gaiety. He looked for the culprit and easily found it in himself whom he accused and scolded with a severity which sometimes approaches psychotic self-accusation. There appears to be no doubt that the diary shows a functioning of the superego almost to the end.

Attempts to defend himself against the unpleasant feelings of a frustrated social self were made in several ways and were varied like those of normal adolescents, but with a smaller range and with less confidence in his success. His interest in the leaders, who were a little older than himself, increased. He made an effort to concentrate on them, he hung on their lips and listened carefully for words, which would evoke emotions in him. When he succeeded he felt elated, but this never lasted long, though in his imagination he was able to enjoy it all retrospectively.

He then tried to feign understanding of their speeches by accompanying them with a "lively facial expression". He had not yet started to grimace, but in his case the lively facial expression may be considered a prodrome to grimacing. Preconsciously it had a double function: to prove to himself that he had grasped what they said and approved, and to show them his devotion.

But that helped him only while he listened to them. His self-contempt was less painful when he considered that not only he himself but his whole group compared unfavorably with members and groups of other towns, whom he found more serious and advanced than his own. But he felt an outsider again when he realized that his own friends were gay, though also, as he thought, superficial and incapable of behaving as they should because of their inferiority.

He therefore turned towards those whose inferiority was unquestionable: the younger ones on the one hand and the dull ones on the other. When hiking he joined the younger boys, and on several occasions he mentions remorsefully that he feels strongly attracted by them, for in them of course he tries to see himself. He preferred to feel like the younger ones instead of feeling different. Later he mentions that he invites only the bad chess players to play chess with him.

Sometimes his silence during discussions gave him satisfaction because he believed that the other boys would take his silence, as an admission of his inferiority, but would not believe in it and his non-existent self-respect would thus be restored. The psychoanalyst quite rightly sees in these self-observations the proof of a competitive, active homosexual striving. It was latent until he approached puberty. Richard's lack of any active aggressive feeling or open competition had been observed by his sister and parents from his early childhood on. The diary makes very little mention of the father except that the boy fears his comments on his (the boy's) silence and lack of progress at school.

In the later stages of the pre-psychotic phase, in which his misery grows and it becomes increasingly difficult to defend himself against it he seems to be inclined to adopt a still more passive attitude towards social stimulation from outside and as he can do very little to prevent it he feels it as a danger: "It seems that I cannot face the struggle of life. The milieu has a terrible influence on me. My most difficult problem is: How can I succeed in expressing my individuality?" The well known struggle between individuality and sociability in adolescence becomes a danger in the pre-psychotic phase. The integrating power of the ego has shrunk to such a degree that social stimulation from outside and the inner drive towards social relations can only be dealt with through a delusional increase in the ego-feeling. In other words, an attempt has to be made to throw the whole cathexis of the ego into the struggle for social contact: "I often feel in doubt whether I should sacrifice my own ego when other people exert an influence over me or whether I should preserve myself," and he continues, exposing a delusion of grandeur: "I feel myself as something Holy. I feel that what is in me must develop freely and will later show itself through my own individuality in its full light." His belief in his own holiness is only one of several ideas of grandeur in which he approximates most closely to a system of delusions. However they were not openly expressed except in the diary: "A will which overflows, mighty and strong. As if I raise the level of the school class. I feel restless. I think too realistically (previously he had complained for a long time that he felt unrealistically in contrast to his fellows and teachers, now his own reality has become the only one.) Like today when I felt as if I were drunk. It can't go on. Suddenly I see myself in the centre of the club and of the class. I get so agitated, it annoys other people, so I wanted to get away from the class today. Weakness: too strong a will, (unnatural) vanity, I spiritualise everything. Today I have not spoken ten words and still think, God knows what about myself (sic!).[1] To be alone, no contact with people. I do annoy them! It seems that I have grown out of high school. I believe that my schoolfellows do not experience so much, have not seen so much social misery except K. Miserable fanatic. Some forms of good manners are still lacking. As I am now I am unable to meet people. At the dancing lesson tomorrow I shall have to prove whether I am a proper human being or not. I am still very stupid. I went too far in my vanity. I do not know what to say but with my mental activity I excite everybody."

When he had reached this stage of social abulia certain changes in his physical appearance had taken place which brought criticism and ostracism from his schoolfellows. "It is alarming that when I talk to anybody my facial expression is disturbingly vivid. It bears no relation to what I think and that's wrong. It shows a lack of self-control. I have the face of a monkey and my schoolfellows stare at me."

The hebephrenic phase proper had now been approached. Social activities had ceased although he still attended school for a short time. Diffusion of instincts (Freud, Nunberg and others) seemed to come to the fore. Detachment of libido had gone very far, he took little notice of his parents, and of his sister who had been called home. She established verbal contact only for very short periods; speech had almost completely ceased, but he still kept clean and took food and water. Aggressive drives became manifest in motor activities, in running, grimaces and laughter. These, however, may have an archaic social meaning. But he still complied with simple orders. At this stage entries in the diary naturally ceased.

The Case of George

George who is now nearly forty years old, and in a civilian occupation, has so far suffered from three schizophrenic episodes. The first broke out

---

1. This shows self-irony.

when he was seventeen-and-a-half, just at the end of a two-year period of diary keeping. The morbid states closely resembled the main features of hebephrenia as described by Kahlbaum and Hecker in 1871. Confusional states changed into more manic and depressive ones, a definite character trend which he was known to have had since childhood, came more and more to the fore: precocious and pert behavior, talkativeness and the use of bombastic words. He spent some weeks in a demented state from which he finally made a more or less complete recovery which enabled him to take up skilled work in factories, and later the position of a clerk in an office. He has since been earning his living except for two further episodes lasting about a year each. Twice he succeeded in taking up a quasi-marital relationship with motherly women, which obviously greatly contributed to a healthier contact with reality. He still invests considerable mental activity in ambitious plans and causes some trouble in his social relationships. Some people are frightened of him because of his aggressive outbursts when frustrated.

He is the only child of parents who, soon after marriage, broke off marital relations altogether, although they did not part. The alienation of the parents became known to George early in his childhood. He lived at home and was very well looked after. His home was in a small town in Czechoslovakia. He was a sociable child but precocious, competitive, ambitious, envious, jealous and touchy. This sounds very inconsistent, but he succeeded in blending these qualities in his personality from childhood on. At school his only difficulty was his forward manner. When he was eleven, he moved to relatives in a nearby town but came home frequently; this did not constitute a separation from his mother. Attachment between him and his mother was extremely strong. He attended secondary school very satisfactorily, and was excellent at mathematics and languages, the teachers complaining only of his lack of discipline; at home he had never been asked to achieve the high standard of discipline required at his secondary school. When he was twelve he joined a club and made lasting friendships there. He got on well with people who knew a great deal and had achieved much, but his ideals were figures of historical, literary and political importance. He began to read the newspapers at an early age. School life and club activities fascinated him, judging from his diary, because they gave him ample scope for ambition and competitiveness.

His life changed completely when he left his secondary school at the age of fourteen and became a lodger in a distant town in order to attend a technical school. There was no club and there were no admiring relatives but only dull people and a cousin in the same form who proved much too superior and at the same time not ambitious enough to make competition attractive. This made him feel depressed and furious. As a form of escape he began to keep a diary and restored his self-esteem by retreating into fantasies of being a poet and a writer. He spent a great deal of time in reading, but he read only superficially.

Reading and the wish to write poetry appear in his diary as reactions against a strong feeling of mental poverty, shallowness and helplessness. He tried to ward these off by literary ambitions and preparations for creative work. This system worked as long as he got on fairly well at school. When he began to realize that his school work was deteriorating, he restrained his literary ambition and imposed a very strict compulsive regime on himself, successfully controlled his conduct and did in fact succeed in keeping up with the other students. He was aware that he did this because he did not want to disappoint his mother who had made great financial sacrifices on his account. The masochistic denial of his ambitions lasted for about eight months after which he wanted once more to return to his secondary school and to prepare for University entrance. The content of the diary now changed to a review of his life. In his fantasy he maintained the necessity of becoming great. The technical school gradually compelled him to face a world of precision and mathematical accuracy which he could master only in his fantasy or in his demands on himself, but never in actual fact. After the third year of technical school he had to spend a few weeks in a factory as a technical apprentice and there the breakdown occurred. The fourth and last chapter of his diary consists of about fifteen pages with only one sentence of bombastic but most revealing content on each page.

Creative fantasies in hebephrenia.

There are roughly three groups of adolescents involved in some form of creative mental activity: adolescents who succeed in expressing thoughts and feelings which they consider creative, those who indulge in fantasies of being creative but under the influence of their reality sense restrict themselves to the realm of fantasy and day-dreams, and those adolescents who delude themselves into thinking they are creative. They do not show the products of their activities, but they are moved to tears or elated by their creative feelings. They may move their lips as they think, or if unobserved may pose to recite their poems and even mention them to their friends, but never or rarely produce anything at all.

George clearly belonged to the third group. So far as I know he never wrote or recited one of his poems or his essays. He was swamped in fantasies, but behaved as if he were a great writer. Here are the titles his diary gives for the essays he contemplated: "On foreign words" (in the diary he reproached himself for his growing addiction to foreign words, a symptom of hebephrenia mentioned by Hecker), "Concerning the form and content of prose" and "Natural philosophy".[2] He also contemplated writing historical works on Sallust and Catilina and intended for more than a year to write on Caesar. He accumulated a great number of books from public libraries to

2. The adolescent characteristic of composing title pages, which may or may not be followed by the actual composition to a paper was noted by Freud (1896) when he wrote about himself to a friend: "I have today, as adolescent poets enjoy doing, written out a title page:

VORLESUNGEN UEBER DIE GROSSEN NEUROSEN
Neur. Angst, Hysterie, Zwangsneurose."

prepare these works, always encouraging himself to read diligently. While he was at the technical school he mentioned that he was about to read the whole of the Roman classics, Schopenhauer, whose aphorisms he imitated, Abraham a Santa Clara, Lichtenberg, Goethe, Schiller, Hermann Hesse, Sven Hedin, Spinoza, Otto Braun, Hans Blueher, and Winckelmann. Under the influence of the poet Storm he wrote "less poetry and came nearer to being a critic". He wrote that he was studying the history of the Renaissance and stated: "I now understand the history of the Renaissance up to myself much better." (This was twenty months before he fell ill.) "Once I walked along a railway track with a friend, X. I thought a great deal. But I wondered why those who walk in the inner circle of a curve slow down. Suddenly I realized it was centrifugal force. I transferred my thoughts to history. I intended at first to form a theory of physics and then to demonstrate how physical laws can be applied to history. In this way I approached the study of physics, and did all this in order to understand the present better. Subconsciously this was the statesman in me." (Four months before complete loss of contact with reality.) He was angry when he bought a medieval biography and found that it had been translated into Modern German, as he wanted to read it in the original tongue. He produced his poems when walking in a park or wood, he recited them to himself or simply moved his lips. He frequently asked himself whether he was a poet or not.

Megalomanic as these fantasies and statements are, they are not so far in themselves pathognonomic; any adolescent might cling to them for a while. George himself produced many reasons for believing himself to be and attempting to become a poet. Being a poet raised his self-esteem, and he also wanted to impress his language teacher who appreciated his wide reading and his command of the language. But the pathognonomic feature lies in overshooting the target. His teacher would have been only too pleased with some modest achievement instead of this imaginary knowledge of world literature. The interest his teacher took in his ambitions acted as an initial stimulus, which however caused reactions of fantastic dimensions. The teacher's praise then no longer mattered to him; he saw himself as the greatest poet and linguist of all time. Another motive for producing poems was to satisfy the expectations of a club friend who wrote to him frequently and enclosed some of his poems in his letters. George could not send any poems, nevertheless his belief in his own superiority grew immensely and he belittled his friend in his diary. Creative activities served to solve the problem of masturbation; "washing away the dirt" George called it. Such attempts on his part were bound to fail; his problem was not to substitute the one for the other, but to raise his self-esteem by using each of them alternatively. The need for an increase of ego feeling was insatiable; once a withdrawal of cathexis from an object occurred (as with the poet friend) it was a continuous withdrawal. In his creative activities he wanted to build up a world of his own, but in the attempt he lost contact with the real world and did not succeed in getting any echo. He felt criticized if people did not share his opinion of himself. This "criticism" was unbearable to him as it meant a denial of his existence (confirmation of his fear). Genetically this fear is derived from the earliest of the anxieties, namely, object-loss. Ernest

Jones introduced into our nomenclature the term "aphanasis" for the fear of total extinction in cases of progressive ego disintegration.

The one link with reality was still his mother, who in his world of greatness was the only object which mattered to him. Allegorically speaking, she called him back from psychotic reality and made him a little child. When he thought of her he could not claim to be a poet, when he went home for a school holiday all creative thoughts and reading ceased. He asked himself what he was. "I am so poor, how poor I am! Not one science, that would give me an insight into my poverty. This again is nonsense and my only endeavor is to be a success. The reason is that I am wretched. I do so many futile things and I therefore become futile myself . . . I thought of the bird Nerops who started to fly towards heaven but could not turn away his eyes from the earth . . . I have nothing inside me, I am empty . . . For the time being an ingenious madness, more madness than genius . . . Eloquence conceals emptiness . . . I can't get rid of doubts about myself. My future is dark. I can't see it."

The obsessional episode.

While his thoughts and feelings were vacillating between greatness and emptiness he felt he was menaced by a bad school report and by ill-feeling between himself and his mother. He succeeded in warding it off by imposing on himself a very strict regime which for short periods stopped his indulging in delusions of greatness and· moral masochism. This caused many social difficulties. He became very·irritable and impatient and demanded praise. He wrote: "I see that I have two grave faults: one being irritability and restlessness and the other snobbishness.

"I shall try to avoid the former by compelling myself to be regular in everything. This is only possible when at the technical school, not when at home on holiday. Punctually at seven I must get up, meals must be punctual, breakfast at 7:45, lunch at 12:45, supper 7:15. Monday and Tuesday at 8:30. Of course they must not do any housework when I am in. Moreover the table must be cleared at once and any other jobs must be done immediately after meals. I must be very strict about this. I must be punctual myself, but I must also insist on punctuality from others. Unfortunately I cannot yet go for regular walks, but I must try. During lunchtime I must do some homework, later on Tuesdays, possibly also on Mondays technology, Tuesday technology and mechanics. Wednesday chemistry, Thursday technology, Friday history and chemistry. Nothing special before supper. Relax, put down my expenses in the cash book if I stay at home, prepare my work if I have to go out. During meals I shall not think at all if possible. Just concentrate on eating properly and nicely. Fussiness will not be allowed nor brooding over the cooking. If I feel like doing some work after a meal I shall get on with it so long as I enjoy it. If I am not in a very good mood I shall study the 'Letters on concentration'. If necessary do some school work, math, later Czech and English. I read as little as possible, but only good books. Newspapers at present as seldom as possible, not even in the lavatory. At 10 I shall stop working, at 10:30

I'll go to bed. Before that I shall go through the events of the day. For the moment I shall answer letters during the week. If I am at home over the weekend on Saturday and Sunday. I search for peace everywhere. While I try to face every possible situation and resist all restlessness and irritation I renounce them finally and try to stop them. As regards snobbishness: I shall try to do as the school requires. I shall banish Jewish vanity and boasting of my disgusting cleverness. I shall castigate myself in the diary. Clumsiness I shall try to avoid by being constantly on the alert and by means of exercises."

His aims in this compulsive regime however went beyond the benefits to be gained from obsessional mechanisms. They kept him in contact with his mother's ideal of him, he once more became a good student, but this did not bridge the gulf in himself. His solution had little stability. He took up a former fantasy of returning to secondary school and preparing for the University where he thought he would study law and history. His mother was deeply moved and admitted that the technical school was not the right place for him but told him with tears that she had not enough money to afford a long course of study. The final decision was postponed and in his diary he entered into a lengthy account of his life, which shows much insight into himself and into the nature of his conflicts.

Restitution through an autobiography.

"How far am I dissatisfied with life? I changed over to the technical school without any desire to do so. Perhaps they would have let me stay on at the secondary school if I had been less of a scamp and more adaptable. It was partly vanity but still more boredom that caused it. If I had then known myself better, perhaps things would have turned out differently. At any rate, I must be careful that my vanity does not land me in similar mishaps. However, it was quite a good thing that I left the secondary school. I should have remained a prig, should have become a greater fool than ever. Dogmatism and obstinacy are my chief faults. At that time I knew nothing about myself. Even more than today, I had no idea what to strive for. It is true I had plans—but they vanished. And I regretted that, but it did not help. It only depressed me. Remorse should always exhort us but never oppress us. Then of course there was masturbation as well. I learnt it from K. then I satisfied myself a little or much. Eventually I met Sch., that was the climax; afterwards I gave it up. At any rate one should be careful in sexual matters as regards speech and action. One should only use sex to learn to know people. However this must not be exaggerated. One should only yield if one is truly in love. I tried to find help in work. I became mad with ambition. One must not work from despair; one should search for the causes of one's unhappiness and try to put it right by natural means . . . Two years ago an idea of my true vocation began to dawn on me. But since then I have not got much further. Half-thought-out plans filled my mind and have again been neglected. Why is it? I could not think about myself, I could not shed any light upon my mind. I was moody, all right. I waited until irritability should be followed by some pleasure in work. I lived a dream life . . . Onanism made a hermit of me. It made me unsociable. For a while work satisfied me, I gave up masturbation for a short time. But I gained no more influence in spite of everything. Was it surprising that I stretched my arms backwards to where love and friendship were waiting? I felt much more affectionately towards my home. I exchanged letters with the members of the club. I was still ambitious but remained a child because I got so much satisfaction from the rear . . . I was in conflict with my surroundings. I looked around in order to alter my situation. I changed into the opposite. I began to produce poetry. I did not seek consolation in my poems nor did I curse my suffering in them. I do not know whether I started before A. sent me his first poems. But he certainly stimulated me as well as my teacher N. But my poetry was unnatural. I searched for a diversion from my misery. Except for A. nobody knew about it.

"During the Easter holiday I saw so clearly the differences between my parents. I did not think of changing them but only tried to keep aloof. I stood on my own feet. I felt much better when I saw I was alone and had to get satisfaction from myself. I saw, or rather felt that my future lay in something different from what I had aimed at so far. I felt I should return to secondary school. My thoughts about prose lacked the natural foundations and I felt the lack of knowledge. One of my plans was a draft for 'Caesar'. My aims did not go beyond thoughts and plans. I thought words would master everything, but I had not even enough courage for words. The only way I could bring about a change was to have a good school report and then to ask for a transfer from school. It should be the need for change, not lack of knowledge which brought it about."

These are only some examples of a lengthy description of his adolescent life. It must have been a great effort for him to achieve even for a few weeks a synthesis between contrasting emotions and to restrain his ambition and moral masochism. The practical result of this period was that he passed his examination at school. The change of school did not materialize and he planned a hiking tour at the end of the holiday after having spent a few weeks in a factory far away from his home. It was there that the first episode occurred which led to his confinement in a mental hospital.

A restitution attempt by means of aphorisms.

The psychological process active in a person formulating or writing an aphorism has not yet to my knowledge been psycho-analytically studied. Both wit and aphorism have in common the fact that the length and extent of preconscious elaboration is out of proportion to the condensed conscious material. Both devices save expenditure of energy; their function is in the first instance economic. While a multitude of thought and feeling is put into the form of an aphorism all mental activity is concentrated on a few words and mastery over internal reality is gained for a short time.

In George's case it seems that during the onset of the final crisis he maintained in his aphorisms contact with the world for an unknown period of time, though this mastery was very precarious and hung by a thread. "Anyone who is able to believe in me should believe in me." This apparently means: As I am alone here in Slovakia where nobody believes in me and I am unable to do my work properly there will still be somebody somewhere who believes in me. Other examples are these:

"There will be a great time, a time full of storm and sunshine."
"And afterwards there will be a fine time, full of rest and shadow."
"He who grows too quickly, perishes."
"Everything great is crazy."
"Restlessness within rest is a miracle."
"I am not God, I am only God's servant."[3]
"I kill—but I was also killed."
"Blessed be he who has come to me, cursed be he who fled from me."

"I have suffered the earth's painful agony, I have not redeemed you, you must redeem yourself,
Fear nothing, I was afraid,
and therefore I died.
You need have no cares
You will be cared for
He who envies to him will come . . ."

All that can now be said about these sentences is that they show a realization of instinctual diffusion (Freud, Nunberg) in which death is likened to the loss of self. The diary ends with three letters which are illegible and adorned with flourishes.

In the factory George attracted attention by developing peculiar mannerisms, aggressive behavior and suspiciousness, and one day he went to a nearby river where he put his forehead in the water and remained with legs stretched out, leaning forward. He was then taken away to an observation ward.

Conclusions.

Diaries of adolescents, rare or difficult to obtain as they may be, offer an opportunity for studying the pre-psychotic phase of schizophrenia from an unconventional viewpoint. While such studies can only complement organized personality studies, begun at birth, these two adolescent diaries show clearly that during the gradual and insidious onset of the variety of schizophrenia known as hebephrenia, the adolescent struggles with conflicts which are neither so frequent

3. According to Kris and Pappenheim (11) two types of an artist's relationship to God can be distinguished: one in which the artist is God's rival and the other in which he is his tool.

nor so outspoken in neuroses. The underlying conflicts are partly of a neurotic nature, commonly operative in the non-psychotic adolescent as well, being intimately blended with conflicts of purely psychotic nature. Fear of losing contact with the self and the world of objects is predominant and is the mainspring of defense actions and the attempts at restitution of the self and objects. The causes of the psychotic loss of contact with the objective world according to Freud's theory must be sought in the earliest phase of ego development which coincides with the oral phase of libido organization. Attempts at restitution are not restricted to this period but may be made on any level of development; we come to this conclusion when we evaluate the psychotic patient's behavior in acting out his fantasies. The diary of a psychotic should be considered in the light of the restitution process and the temptation to interpret it like a neurotic's diary should be resisted. While the psychotic's restitution may closely resemble neurotic defense in the pre-psychotic state the underlying disturbance of the ego is different. In the neurotic's childhood, anxiety was aroused in connection with an instinctual drive, and the drive was subjected to repression. As far as repression of a drive involves the ego itself, the ego becomes mutilated, but its functioning may only become restricted, not totally paralyzed, in later life. In psychotics, for reasons unknown and at present merely speculative, there is a fundamental impairment of certain ego functions which manifest themselves for instance in the separation of concrete and verbal manifestation. Words lose much of or even all their objective content and are used as if they were things in themselves.

In the two diaries two different methods of attempting restitution could be shown. Each adolescent followed the line for which he had fewest gifts. The thinker and hermit longed for social contact, the jester and would-be leader wanted to become a poet, to create something original. Following the assumption that the symptom contains both the breach and the reparation, this would mean that the traumas in childhood interfered with the feeling of contact with the mother in the first case, and with the control of the mother by thoughts and words in the second.

Whether or not experiences like these occur in early childhood it is impossible to say—but there must be careful exploration of such possibilities in the future.

Diaries are documents of adolescent thought processes. Their value as regards any direct revelations may be slight, but great if one thinks of the gaps they reveal in our knowledge of the psychotic's childhood.

BIBLIOGRAPHY

1. Bernfeld, S. *Trieb und Tradition im Jugendalter*, Leipzig, 1931.
2. Bühler, C. *Kindheit und Jugend*, Leipzig, 1931.
3. Buxbaum, E. "Transference and Group Formation and the Treatment of Juvenile Delinquents", *this Annual*, I.
4. Fenichel, O. *The Psychoanalytic Theory of Neurosis*, Norton, 1945.
5. Freud, A. *The Ego, and the Mechanisms of Defence*, Hogarth, 1937.
6. Freud, S. "Psychoanalytic Notes upon an Autobiographical Account of a Case of Paranoia (dementia paranoides)", *Coll. Papers*, III.
7. Katan, M. *De Grondbeginselen van de Waanvorming*, Leiden, 1946.
8. Mapother and Lewis: "Psychological Medicine", in Price, *Practice of Medicine*, London, 1942.
9. Mayer-Gross, M. "Schizophrenie", in Bumke, *Handbuch der Geisteskrankheiten*, V.
10. Muncie, W. *Psychobiology and Psychiatry*, London, 1939.
11. Pappenheim, E. and Kris, E. "The Functions of Drawings and the Meaning of the 'Creative Spell' in a Schizophrenic Artist", *Psa. Quarterly*, XV, 1946.
12. Redl, F. "The Psychology of Gang Formation and the Treatment of Juvenile Delinquents", *this Annual*, I.
13. Schilder, P. See 2, for quotation.

ANACLITIC DEPRESSION

An Inquiry into the Genesis of Psychiatric Conditions in Early Childhood, II.[1]

By RENÉ A. SPITZ, M.D. (New York)

with the assistance of KATHERINE M. WOLF, Ph.D. (New York)

I. *Observation*

A. A circumscribed psychiatric syndrome.

In the course of a long term study of infant behavior in a nursery[2] where we observed 123 unselected infants, each for a period of twelve to eighteen months, we encountered a striking syndrome. In the second half of the first year, a few of these infants developed a weepy behavior that was in marked contrast to their previously happy and outgoing behavior. After a time this weepiness gave way to withdrawal. The children in question would lie in their cots with averted faces, refusing to take part in the life of their surroundings. When we approached them we were ignored. Some of these children would watch us with a searching expression. If we were insistent enough, weeping would ensue and, in some cases, screaming. The sex of the approaching experimenter made no difference in the reaction in the majority of cases. Such behavior would persist for two to three months. During this period some of these children lost weight instead of gaining; the nursing personnel reported that some suffered from insomnia, which in one case led to segregation of the child. All showed a greater susceptibility to intercurrent colds or eczema. A gradual decline in the developmental quotient was observed in these cases.

---

1. This is the second of a series of articles presenting findings of the Psychoanalytic Research project on Problems of Infancy. The first was published under the title, "Hospitalism", *this Annual*, I.

2. For detailed description of the conditions prevailing in this institution, *loc. cit*, pp. 60-65.

This behavior syndrome lasted three months. Then the weepiness subsided, and stronger provocation became necessary to provoke it. A sort of frozen rigidity of expression appeared instead. These children would lie or sit with wide-open, expressionless eyes, frozen immobile face, and a faraway expression as if in a daze, apparently not perceiving what went on in their environment. This behavior was in some cases accompanied by autoerotic activies in the oral, anal, and genital zones. Contact with children who arrived at this stage became increasingly difficult and finally impossible. At best, screaming was elicited.

Among the 123 unselected children observed during the whole of the first year of their life we found this clear-cut syndrome in 19 cases. The gross picture of these cases showed many, if not all, of these traits. Individual differences were partly quantitative: i.e., one or the other trait, as for instance weeping, would for a period dominate the picture, and thus would impress the casual observer as the only one present; and partly qualitative: i.e., there was an attitude of complete withdrawal in some cases, as against others in which, when we succeeded in breaking through the rejection of any approach, we found a desperate clinging to the grown-up. But apart from such individual differences the clinical picture was so distinctive that once we had called attention to it, it was easily recognizable by even untrained observers. It led us to assume that we were confronted with a psychiatric syndrome, which we illustrate in the three case histories following:

B.   Case histories.

Case 1.

Colored female. No significant events or behavior during the first half year. She is a particularly friendly child who smiles brilliantly at the approach of the experimenter.

When she was 7½ months old we noticed that her radiant smiling behavior had ceased. During the following two weeks it was impossible to approach her, as she slept heavily during the total of 12 hours we were there. After this period a change of behavior took place, which was protocolled as follows:

"She lay immobile in her crib. When approached she did not lift her shoulders, barely her head, to look at the experimenter with an expression of profound suffering sometimes seen in sick animals. With this expression she examined the observer. As soon as the observer started to speak to her or to touch her she began to weep. This was not the usual crying of babies which is always accompanied by a certain amount of vocalization going into screaming. It was a soundless weeping, tears running down her face. Speaking to her in soft comforting tones only resulted in the weeping becoming more intense, intermingled with moans and sobs, shaking her whole body.

"In the course of a two months' observation it was found that this reaction deepened. It was more and more difficult to make contact with the child. In our protocols there is a note seven weeks later to the effect that it took us almost an hour to achieve contact with her. In this period she lost weight and developed a serious feeding disturbance, having great difficulties in taking any food and in keeping it down."

After two months a certain measure was taken. The syndrome disappeared.

Case 2.

White female. Intelligent, friendly child who smiles easily and ecstatically at the approaching observer. No notable event in the course of the first 7 months. At this time a change occurred in the child. The observers got the feeling that the child was apprehensive. A week or two later the change was accentuated. The temper of the child had become unequal. She still was mostly friendly to the observer, but as often as not broke out crying when the observer approached closer. After another two weeks she could no longer be approached. No amount of persuasion helped. Whenever approached she sat up and wailed. Two weeks later, she would lie on her face, indifferent to the outside world, not interested in the other children living in the same room. Only strong stimulation could get her out of her apathy. She would then sit up and stare at the observer wide-eyed, a tragic expression on her face, silent. She would not accept toys, in fact she withdrew from them into the farthest corner of her bed. If the approach was pressed she would break into tears. This went on until the child was 9 months old.

At this point a certain measure was taken. The syndrome disappeared.

Case 3.

White female. This is a moderately intelligent, unusually beautiful child with enormously big blue eyes and golden curls. At the end of the eleventh month the child, who never had been very active, began to lose interest in playing with the experimenter, so that testing became difficult. In the following two weeks this behavior was more marked. The child was not only passive, but refused to touch any toys offered to her. She sat in a sort of daze, by the hour, staring silently into space. She did not even show the apprehensiveness in the presence of the approaching observer that was shown by other children. If a toy was put into contact with her she would withdraw into the farthest corner of her bed and there sit wide-eyed, absent, and without contact, with an immobile rigid expression on her beautiful face. When the toys were left with her she did not touch them until the experimenter had left the room. Then she immediately threw them out of her bed, where one would find them five or ten minutes later, forming a half-circle around the child, who would be sitting again in the same posture as before, or lying on her face. At 11 months 25 days (O; 11+25) she was observed to alternate playing with her feces, with genital masturbation, still in the same position described above. The fecal play would consist in her pulling a small pellet of feces the size of a very small pea out of her soiled diaper. With the same rigid immobile expression and rigid immobile body, she would roll this pellet on the sheet, pick it up, roll it between thumb and forefinger without looking at it, lose it from her fingers, and eagerly seek it again on the sheet. The time when she was seeking it on the sheet was the only moment when the rigid expression disappeared: and a near smile appeared when she had found it again. Alternately, she would rub her genitals.

As in the other cases, a certain measure was taken, in this case when the child was eleven months thirty days (0; 11+30). The syndrome disappeared.

In all three cases the measure taken was the restitution of the mother, from whom the child had been separated approximately three to four months earlier.

II. *Discussion of the Syndrome*

In the three case histories the principal symptoms composing the syndrome are manifest. These symptoms fall into several categories; within each category we have grouped them on a scale of increasing severity. They are not all necessarily present at the same time, but most of them show up at one point or another in the clinical picture. They are:

Apprehension, sadness, weepiness.

Lack of contact, rejection of environment, withdrawal.

Retardation of development, retardation of reaction to stimuli, slowness of movement, dejection, stupor.

Loss of appetite, refusal to eat, loss of weight.

Insomnia.

To this symptomatology should be added the physiognomic expression in these cases, which is difficult to describe. This expression would in an adult be described as depression.

A. Etiology.

1) General environment.

The following table shows the sex and race distribution of our sample.

Table 1.

	White	Colored	Totals
Male	37	24	61
Female	40	22	62
Totals	77	46	123

These 123 infants stayed in the nursery from their fourteenth day to the end of their first year and in a few cases up to their eighteenth month. No selection was made in the infants observed. We invariably tested and followed each child admitted to the nursery up to the day when it left. The observations took place at weekly intervals, and totalled approximately 400 hours for each child. All these infants shared the same environment, the same care, food, and hygiene.

An apparently milder form of the syndrome presented in our three case histories, with a similar drop in developmental quotient, was observed in 26 cases.

We shall now proceed to investigate the factors in the background and in the environment of these cases in order to isolate those that are etiologically significant.

2) Factors without demonstrable influence on the causation of the syndrome.

a. Race and Sex.

The following two tables show the distribution of the different degrees of depression according to color and sex.

Table 2. (Distribution according to race)

	White	Colored	Totals
Severe depression	7	12	19
Mild depression	17	9	26
No depression	32	18	50
No diagnosis[3]	21	7	28
Totals	77	46	123

Table 3. (Distribution according to sex)

	Male	Female	Totals
Severe depression	9	10	19
Mild depression	13	13	26
No depression	26	24	50
No diagnosis	13	15	28
Totals	61	62	123

The factors of color and of sex do not appear to exert demonstrable influence on the incidence of the syndrome.

b.   Chronological age.

The youngest age at which the syndrome was manifested in our series was around the turn of the sixth month; the oldest was the

3. As in any psychiatric study, no exact diagnosis could be made in a certain number of cases. We include them in our tables for the purpose of showing the proportion of such undiagnosed cases within unselected total of observed children.

eleventh month. The syndrome therefore seems to be independent of chronological age, within certain limits.

c. Developmental and intellectual level.

It might be objected that in early childhood the developmental age is more significant than the chronological age. A hypothesis might state that a certain level of intelligence is prerequisite for any psychiatric syndrome. However, we have found the syndrome in question in children whose development was advanced by two months beyond their chronological age, just as well as in children whose development was one month retarded, as compared to their chronological age: the developmental quotients of the children affected would vary from 91 to 133; nor did the syndrome appear earlier in the children with the higher developmental quotient. So it would seem that within reasonable limits these factors play no significant role in the formation of the syndrome. The following table shows the average of the developmental quotients of the children with no disturbance, with mild disturbance, and with severe disturbance.

Table 4.

	Average developmental quotient
Severe depression	110
Mild depression	109
Others	109

3) An etiologically significant factor.

There is one factor which all cases that developed the syndrome had in common. In all of them the mother was removed from the child somewhere between the sixth and eighth month for a practically unbroken period of three months, during which the child either did not see its mother at all, or at best once a week. This removal took place for unavoidable external reasons. Before the separation the mother had the full care of the infant, and as a result of special circumstances spent more time with the child than is usual in a private home. In each case a striking change in the child's behavior could be observed in the course of the four to six weeks following the mother's removal. The syndrome described above would then develop. *No* child developed the syndrome in question whose mother was *not* removed. Our proposition is that the syndrome observed developed only in children who were deprived of their love object for an appreciable period of time during their first year of life.

On the other hand, not all children whose mothers were removed developed the same syndrome. Hence, mother separation is a necessary, but not a sufficient cause for the development of the syndrome. The additional etiological factors which are required to make it effective in producing a depression will be touched upon in a later part of this paper, and discussed at length in a paper in preparation.

4) Reactions to the loss of the love object.

The syndrome in question is extremely similar to that which is familiar to us from Abraham's (1) and Freud's (6) classical descriptions of mourning, pathological mourning, and melancholia. The factor which appears to be of decisive etiological significance in our cases is the loss of the love object; this brings the syndrome closer to the consequences of the loss of the love object, as described by these authors. In melancholia there is added the feeling of being unloved, along with an incapacity to love, self-reproach, and suicidal tendencies. The absence of these symptoms in the child can be attributed to two reasons:

1) the child's fewer resources,
2) the difference in psychic structure between adult and infant.

As regards the greater resources of the adult: an adult suffering from melancholia is capable of expressing verbally that he feels unloved and that he is incapable of feeling love for anybody. We suspect that a child who up to a certain point was outgoing and friendly, but who now withdraws from every friendly approach, is expressing the same thing with the equipment at his disposal. We have of course no way of verifying this suspicion, just as we have no way of knowing whether anything like self-reproach can exist in a ten-month-old baby, even though it deprives itself of its usual enjoyment of toys or food. Nor can the infant enact a suicide; but it is striking that these cases one and all show a great susceptibility to intercurrent sickness.[4]

4. This is strongly borne out in another series of cases observed in another institution. These were of a more severe nature—the resulting mortality among the children involved took on the aspect of a major catastrophe. See "Hospitalism", (20).

The difference in psychic structure between child and adult is far-reaching in its consequences. In the adult we have a well established organization consisting of id, ego, and superego. Particularly the manifestations of the superego are conspicuous in melancholia.

In the infant, during the first year, only an id and a still weak— one might nearly say nascent — ego are available. The weakness of the ego makes it especially vulnerable to such a trauma as the loss of the love object is to the adult. On the other hand, we may expect that just because the infantile ego is not yet well-knit nor firmly established, it may be more amenable than that of the adult in accepting a substitute love object. Severe traumata in the case of the adult impinge on a solid, complete ego organization, and force it into a regression to an earlier fixation point. Not so in the case of the infant. Here the injury will be manifested in the form of a disturbance of the ego development. This can take the form of a retardation, or a deformation, or even of a destructive paralysis of ego development, dependent on the severity and the duration of the trauma.

Accordingly, clinical pictures vary in severity from temporary developmental arrest to loss or inhibition of already acquired functions (one of the children observed by us was already able to stand alone when he lost his mother; for the following three months he stayed supine or at best stay in his cot), and in extreme cases result in irreversible progressive personality distortion. On the other hand, since the infant's ego organization is in the process of development, recovery from damage that is not irreparable is swifter, more dramatic than in the case of the adult.

The clinical picture of the consequences of the loss of the love object will be as varied in the infant as in the adult. In the adult we encounter mourning, pathological mourning, depression, melancholia. We cannot yet distinguish the phenomena observed in infants in such detail. For the time being and for the purposes of the present paper, we discuss that form of the clinical picture which in our belief comes closest to what Fenichel described as "simple depression", in his elaboration of the earlier findings on pre-oedipal infantile depression, called by Abraham "primal parathymia" (1). In view of the etiological factors which appeared in our findings, we prefer to follow a suggestion of R. M. Kaufman and to call the picture observed by us "anaclitic depression".

B.   The concept of early depression in the literature.

The psychoanalytic significance of the clinical symptomatology of melancholia was described by Abraham and Freud (1, 2, 3, 6). Both emphasized its similarity to cases of mourning, a psychic manifestation belonging to the field of normalcy. In all publications on the subject it was stressed that both melancholia and normal mourning originate from the same kind of trauma, i.e., a loss of the love object, the difference between normal mourning and pathological mourning being in the existence in the latter of fixation points on the oral-sadistic level. The primal parathymia observed by Abraham is placed in the years immediately preceding the oedipal conflict, and the examples given are typical of precursors of oedipal experiences.

These suggestions of Abraham of course do not exclude the existence of a depression in the first year of life. Accordingly, Fenichel (5, p. 405) states:

"The formulation can now be made that the disposition for the development of depressions consists in oral fixations which determine the reaction to narcissistic shocks. The experiences that cause the oral fixations may occur long before the decisive narcissistic shocks; or the narcissistic injury may create a depressive disposition because it occurs early enough to still be met by an orally oriented ego. It may also occur that certain narcissistic shocks, because they are connected with death (and the reaction to death is always oral introjection of the dead person), create the decisive oral fixation.

"Regarding the factors that create oral fixations in the first place, the same holds true as for other fixations; the determinants are extraordinary satisfactions, extraordinary frustrations, or combinations of both, especially combinations of oral satisfaction with some reassuring guarantee of security; actually traumatic experiences in the nursing period can be found more often in subsequent manic-depressive patients than in schizophrenics."

On the basis of our findings on 19 severe and 26 mild cases we believe that we are now in the position to offer clinical evidence for Fenichel's assumption that the equivalent of the primal parathymias described by Abraham can be observed during the first year of life.

In order to avoid the assumption that we are here speaking of what Melanie Klein (12) calls "the depressive position" in infancy we now discuss her theoretical views.

In psychoanalytic theory depression is an abnormal psychic manifestation, expressly considered the result of a specific environmental constellation. In the Kleinian system, depression is not only different in principle, but is also of primary significance as the cornerstone of the whole system. Melanie Klein (12, 13, 14, 15) considers depression the *fons et origo* of all human psychic development. She and her school (Heimann, Isaacs, Rickman, Riviere (17), Rosenfeld, Scott, Winnicott) postulate the presence of a so-called "depressive position" in infancy. This, in their opinions, is the fundamental mechanism of the infant's psyche, disposing of powerfully operating instruments of introjection and projection, upon which all further psychic development is based.

Our findings do not represent a confirmation of the view of Melanie Klein and her school. She states (12):

"The infantile depressive position arises when the infant perceives and introjects the mother as a whole person (between three and five months) . . . the assumption seems justified that the seeds of depressive feelings, in so far as the experience of birth gives rise to a feeling of loss, are there from the beginning of life. I suggest that the 'depressive position' in infancy is a universal phenomenon.

"The coordination of functions and movements is bound with a defense mechanism which I take to be one of the fundamental processes in early development, namely the manic defense. This defense is closely linked with the 'depressive position'."

In other words: Melanie Klein (12) posits a "depressive position" as an immutable stage in infantile psychic development, appearing between three and five months, irrespective of the child's individual history, experience, and environmental circumstances. She views the "depressive position" as part of the congenital equipment of every human being.

We are accustomed to consider our anatomical and physiological equipment as congenital. Of recent years, the tendency has been to restrict which psychic functions are to be considered inherited or congenital. Nonetheless, such endowments as: neural patterns based on anatomic and physiological premises, as well as on developmental sequences; perceptive modes as expressed in the principles of Gestalt; perhaps even certain basic reactions as described in the Watsonian triad of Love, Fear, and Rage,—are generally accepted as congenital and universal.

But the psychic element posited by Melanie Klein (12) is of a very different nature from all of these. It is hard to conceive of the "depressive position" as a universal keystone of personality. We have become familiar with depression from the study of mental disease (of melancholia) in grown-ups. Psychoanalytic research, specifically that of Freud and of Abraham, demonstrated that it is a result of a regression to the oral-sadistic level of ego development. It would seem as if this finding had provoked a misinterpretation on the part of Melanie Klein. She appears to have concluded that since melancholia was a regression to the oral-sadistic level of the libido, the infant on progressing to this oral-sadistic level would have to develop melancholia. This of course is circular reasoning. Melancholia is the consequence of several factors, *one* of which is a fixation point at the oral-sadistic level of development. That fact in itself, however, is insufficient for the emergence of melancholia. Without the concurrence of certain experiential events dependent on environmental constellations, no melancholia will occur. The experiential events in question are of a severely frustrating nature and they presuppose the existence of some part of the ego organization which is to be frustrated. If these specific experiential events do not take place, or if they take place in a modified form, a completely different mental disease or perhaps even only a special character formation will emerge.

Melanie Klein, on the other hand, assumes that human beings are born with a finished and complete psychic structure. Here she falls into the same category as do other modifiers of psychoanalytic theory, like Adler, Jung, Rank (16), and Reich. Mostly they had an axe to grind, whether that was for the purpose of eliminating the problems of infantile sexuality from psychoanalytic theory, or of satisfying the postulates of an ideological allegiance. Thus, with the help of the trauma of birth, Rank saddled heredity plus the experience of birth with the responsibility for the etiology of neurosis; and reduced the role of infantile sexuality, oedipal experience, and environmental influence to insignificance.

In contrast to Melanie Klein (12) and her group, when we speak of anaclitic depression in infants, we do not consider depression as *the* typical or as *a* typical mechanism of infantile psychic development. We do not consider depression as an integral element of the infantile psyche. To state that all human psychic development is determined by a "depressive position" in infancy makes as little sense as to state that erect human locomotion is determined by fracture or luxation in infancy—though some infants' gait at the outset may be vaguely reminiscent of a fractured or luxated limb. We speak of depression as a specific disease in infants arising under specific environmental conditions.

III. *Diagnosis and Prognosis of the Syndrom?*

A. Diagnosis.

The problem of diagnosis of psychiatric disturbance in early infancy, during the preverbal stage, is difficult. In the first place, the question arises whether in this stage anything in the nature of psychosis can exist. Psychosis is by definition a disturbance in the relations between the different spheres of the personality. It would therefore look as if the formation of a superego or, at the very least, those abstractive functions of the unconscious parts of the ego that ensure conceptual thinking, would have to be present to enable us to speak of psychosis in the infant. For if anything is certain, then it is that the infant is not ruled by a superego, nor does it dispose of abstractive functions in any way demonstrable before the age of approximately eighteen months. Therefore that part of the psychotic destruction in the personality that involves the higher functions of the ego will not be manifested.

However, psychosis is characterized not only by delusion, disturbance of thought processes, abnormal thought production and mental confusion (memory defect, confabulation, impairment of apperception and attention, disorientation, ideational disorders, suspicion, etc.). It also involves modification of motility, grossly expressed by hypermotility, specific motor phenomena, or by hypomotility (catatonia, cataplexia, etc.) ; and it is more subtly manifested in the form of postural changes and pathognomonic expression. And finally, the most outstanding changes in the psychotic personality are those manifested in the affects. The changes in motility and the affective disorders are manifestations that do not require the presence of a fully organized ego capable of conceptual thinking, let alone the presence of a superego. Disturbance in these two fields presupposes an elementary organization of the ego, enabling it to perform the function of a coordinating center for elementary perception and apperception, for elementary volitional coordination of motility, as well as a capacity for such elementary differentiation of affect as is involved in the capacity to produce distinctly discernible positive or negative affective reactions on appropriate stimulation. This stage is reached when the child arrives at the second half of the first year of life (9, 21).

At this stage the child is capable, as we have stated above, of reacting to environmental experience by demonstrable affective disorders. We will show further on that gross disorders of motility are also manifested. The more subtle disorders can be detected in the dejected pathognomonic expression and posture of these infants. They show an obvious distaste for assuming an erect position or performing locomotion. It is in such behavioral changes that we have to seek the evidence of the pathological process.

Manifest evidence of this process is unmistakable to the practised eye. The poverty of the symptomatology reflects the exiguousness of the modes of expression and the number of activities available to children of this age. As a consequence of the pathological process even this small number of expressions and actions is reduced—or expressions and activities achieved in the normal course of development by the one-year-old do not materialize. Such a reduction in the performance, emotional and otherwise, of the infant are apt to impress the psychiatrist as an arrest in development rather than as a personality disorder. We believe—and we will bring proof of this in the further development of our case histories—that to consider the phenomena in question as an arrest in development only is to take a superficial view. The inadequacy of our means of communication with the infant is of course a severe handicap for diagnostic recognition of possible psychiatric disorders at this age. We are limited to the observation of behavior and its deviations; to the interpretation of visible manifestations of emotions; to the taking of a detailed anamnesis with the help of our own observation and that of the persons living with the child; and finally, to the quantifiable results of testing procedure. Thus the diagnostic signs and symptoms fall into the groups of static ones, genetic ones, and quantitative ones.

1)   The static signs and symptoms.

The static signs and symptoms are those observable phenomena that we are able to ascertain in the course of one or several observations of the infant in question. We have mentioned them in Part II of our study. One of the outstanding signs is the physiognomic expression of such patients. The observer at once notices an apprehensive or sad or depressed expression on the child's face, which often impels him to ask whether the child is sick. It is characteristic, at this stage, that the child makes an active attempt to catch the observer's attention and to involve him in a game. However, this outgoing introduction usually is not followed by particularly active play on the part of the child. In the main it is acted out in the form of clinging to the observer and in sorrowful disappointment at the observer's withdrawal.

In the next stage the apprehensiveness deepens. The observer's approach provokes crying or screaming, and the observer's departure does not evoke as universal a disappointment as previously. Many of the cases observed by us fall into the period of what has been described as "eight months anxiety" (4, 9, 11, 18).

The so-called "eight months anxiety" begins somewhere between the sixth and eighth month and is a product of the infant's increasing capacity for diacritic discrimination (19) between friend and stranger. As a result of this the approaching stranger is received either by what has been described as "coy" or "bashful" behavior, or by the child's turning away, hanging its head, crying, and even screaming in the presence of a stranger, and refusing to play with him or to accept toys. The difference between this behavior and the behavior in anaclitic depression is a quantitative one. While in anaclitic depression, notwithstanding every effort, it takes upwards of an hour to achieve contact with the child and to get it to play, in the eight months anxiety this contact can be achieved with the help of appropriate behavior in a span of time ranging from one to ten minutes. The appropriate behavior is very simple: it consists in sitting down next to the cot of the child with one's back turned to him and without paying any attention to him. After the above mentioned period of one to ten minutes the child will take the initiative, grab the observer's gown or hand—and with this the contact is established, and any experienced child psychologist can lead from this into playing with the child's active and happy participation. In the anaclitic depression nothing of the sort occurs. The child does not touch the observer, the approach has to be moderately active on the observer's part, and consists mostly in patient waiting, untiringly repeated attempts at cuddling or petting the child, and incessant offers of constantly varied toys. The latter must be offered with a capacity to understand the nature of the child's refusal. Some toys create anxiety in some children and have an opposite effect on others; for example, some children are attracted by bright colors but are immediately made panicky if a noise such as drumming is provoked in connection with this brightly colored toy. Others may be attracted by the rhythmic noise. Some are delighted by dolls, others go into a panic and can be reassured by no method at the sight of a doll. Some who are delighted by a spinning top will break into tears when it stops spinning and falls over, and every further attempt to spin it will evoke renewed protest.

When finally contact is made the pathognomonic expression does not brighten; after having accepted the observer the child plays without any expression of happiness. He does not play actively and is severely retarded in all his behavior manifestations. The only signs of his having achieved contact is, on the one hand, his acceptance of toys; and on the other, his expression of grief and his crying when left by the observer. That this qualitative distinction is not an arbitrary one can be seen from the fact that in a certain number of the cases in which the anaclitic depression was manifested late, we could observe the eight months anxiety as well as the anaclitic depression at periods distinct from each other. In one case, for instance, the eight months anxiety actually appeared at 0;7+14 and had already completely subsided and disappeared when the anaclitic depression was manifested at 0;11+2.

In the next stage the outward appearance of the child is that of complete withdrawal, dejection, and turning away from the environment. In the case of these children even the lay person with good empathy for children has no difficulty in making the diagnosis, and will tell the observer that the child is grieving for his mother.

2)   The genetic signs.

The genetic signs can be disclosed with the help of a longitudinal investigation of the infant's development. A careful anamnesis reveals that before the above described attitude set in, the child was a pleasant, smiling, friendly baby. If the observer is lucky he may ascertain whether the child is already past the eight months anxiety, that it has come and gone. If the nursing staff reports a sudden development of changed behavior in the child without demonstrable organic disease and if this can be correlated to a separation from the child's mother or mother substitute, our suspicion as to the presence of anaclitic depression will be confirmed. It should not be overlooked that when we speak of the mother we are using a term which should really cover a wider field. "Love object" would be the more correct expression and we should say that these children suffer a loss of their love object.

3)   Quantitative signs.

Quantitative signs can be detected by consecutive developmental tests which, if compared to each other, will at the beginning of the anaclitic depression show a gradual drop of the developmental quotient; this drop progresses with the progression of the disorder.

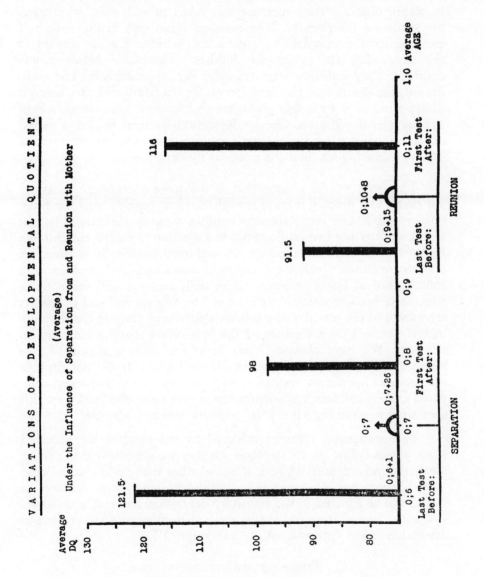

VARIATIONS OF DEVELOPMENTAL QUOTIENT

Under the Influence of Separation from and Reunion with Mother
(Average)

B. Prognosis: with intervention.

In the three case histories given by us in the beginning we ended by stating that a certain measure was taken in each case, whereupon the syndrome disappeared. The measure taken was in the nature of environmental manipulation. It consisted in returning the mother to the child. The change in the children's observable behavior was dramatic. They suddenly were friendly, gay, approachable. The withdrawal, the disinterest, the rejection of the outside world, the sadness, disappeared as if by magic. But over and beyond these changes most striking was the jump in the developmental quotient, within a period of twelve hours after the mother's return; in some cases, as much as 36.6 per cent higher than the previous measurement.

Thus one would assume that if adequate therapeutic measures are taken, the process is curable with extreme rapidity and the prognosis is good. The last statement requires some qualification. To our regret we have not been and are not in a position to follow the children in question beyond a maximum of eighteen months. It is therefore open to question whether the psychic trauma sustained by them as a consequence of being separated from their mothers will leave traces which will become visible only later in life. We are inclined to suspect something of the sort. For the sudden astonishing jump in the developmental quotient on the return of the love object is not maintained in all cases. We have observed cases in which, after a period of two weeks, the developmental quotient dropped again. It did not drop to the previous low levels reached during the depression. However, compared to these children's pre-depression performance, the level on which they were functioning after their recovery was not adequate.

The spectacular recovery achieved by the children we observed again places before us the question whether we are justified in calling the syndrome a depression and, if so, whether it should be considered as a phenomenon of more than transitory importance, whether it should not be equated to the transitory depression observable in adults —whether indeed it should not be equated to mourning rather than to depression. (See appendix, A. 1, paragraph 2.)

C. Prognosis: without intervention.

The main reason why, apart from all physiognomic, behavioral and other traits, we feel justified in speaking of an anaclitic depression going far beyond mourning and even beyond pathological mourning is that we have observed a number of cases in which no intervention occurred and where it became only too evident that the process was in no way self-limiting. These cases were the ones observed in Foundling Home.[5] In that institution, where medical, hygienic, and nutritional standards were comparable to those obtaining in Nursery, the separation from the mother took place beginning after the third month, but prevalently in the sixth month. However, whereas in Nursery the separation was temporary and the love object was restored after approximately three months of absence, in Foundling Home the love object was not restored. The picture of depression was as clear-cut as in Nursery, with some additional developments: for the picture of children in advanced extreme cases varied from stuporous deteriorated catatonia to agitated idiocy.

If we compare the pictures of the two institutions we are confronted with a syndrome of a progressive nature which after having reached a critical point of development appears to become irreversible. It is this characteristic which causes us to call the picture depression and not mourning. And beyond this, in Foundling Home we encounter a phenomenon more grave than melancholia. Notwithstanding the satisfactory hygiene and asepsis, the rate of mortality of the infants reared there was inordinately high. In the course of two years 34 of the 91 children observed died of diseases varying from respiratory and intestinal infections to measles and otitis media. In some cases the cause of death was in the nature of cachexia. This phenomenon savors of psychosomatic involvement.

No intervention was effective in the case of the longer lasting separation in Foundling Home. This finding is one of the reasons why we spoke of three months as a critical period. The second reason is that in Nursery we observed towards the end of the three months the appearance of that kind of frozen, affect-impoverished expression which had strongly impressed us in Foundling Home. Furthermore, a curious reluctance to touch objects was manifested, combined with certain unusual postures of hands and fingers which seemed to us the precursors of the extremely bizarre hand and finger movements composing the total activity in those infants of Foundling Home whom we described as presenting a picture of stuporous catatonia.

5. Described in earlier paper (20). As there, to facilitate distinction between the two institutions, we call the one in which cases described up to now were cared for, *Nursery,* and the one we are about to describe, *Foundling Home.*

After their recovery in the course of their further development, which to our regret could not be followed beyond one-and-a-half years, the children in Nursery did not show any spectacular changes. As indicated above it, it is therefore impossible at this point to state whether this early depression left any visible traces. One would be inclined to expect it. One would be inclined to expect some fixation.

IV. *The Therapy: Dynamic and Structural Considerations*

A. The rudimentary ego.

1) As in melancholia (5, p. 402; 8) there occur in anaclitic depression more or less successful attempts to regain the lost objective world. The term "attempts at restitution" has been reserved by Freud for certain phenomena in schizophrenia. The attempts to regain the lost objective world in melancholia and also in anaclitic depression take the form of finding a substitute object (3; 5, p. 404; 10). We will therefore call this trend "attempts at substitution". These attempts form part of recuperative trends which become visible in anaclitic depression as they do in any other disease. We will encounter them in the course of our further discussion.

During the depressive stage of melancholia when the superego intolerably oppresses the ego, the outcome can only be a complete destruction of the individual, as in suicide. Against these demands of the superego we have the reaction of the id drives. This reaction, however, is unsuccessful because the superego produces anxiety, forcing the id drives along the path dictated by the pleasure-pain principle; thus one part of the id drives is put into the service of the destructive superego demands. This part is represented by the desexualized id drive.

In case of a favorable outcome, however, the aggressive id drive is not completely desexualized. The sex-fused portion of the aggressive drive then may remain available to the ego. If such is the case it may be used in the interest of those self-curative tendencies which every living organization will manifest both in organic and psychic sickness. In its attempts to comply with the superego's demands the sex-fused id drive is used in the establishment of a compulsive system. Through the compulsive neurotic behavior and its rigid adherence to arbitrarily established rules, the superego can be at least temporarily satisfied that, with great sacrifices, its demands are being complied with. With this a remission (in the picture of an obsessional neurosis with compulsive ritual) begins, and thus interrupts the progress of melancholia.

2)   Another outcome is possible if the ego does not succeed in putting the sex-fused id drives in the service of the appeasement of the superego, but the superego on the other hand does not succeed either in putting the defused drives into the service of its own destructive tendencies. In this case the id drives, aggressive and sexual, are shunted into an ego reinforcement. This then enables the ego to overpower, as it were, the superego, and to incorporate it into itself. As in the depressive phase the imago of the love object is introjected, whereupon the fury of the superego is unleashed against it, so in the manic phase the superego, which in itself is the recipient of the archaic imagines of the original love objects, is now incorporated in the ego. The result is that the limits between the systems are abolished, and the manic picture develops.

Both outcomes of the manic-depressive process center around the ego and can be considered as representing attempts of the ego to escape annihilation, and it is in view of this that we consider them recuperative trends even when they are unsuccessful.

Such trends presuppose, however, the presence of the three systerms, id, ego, and superego. In the infant the superego is absent, so that it is impossible to assume destructive hostility of the superego. However, the loss of the love object in itself is equivalent to a hostile deprivation for the infant. The organization with which the infant can react to this deprivation is its ego, inadequate as it is at this period. As Freud established, the ego at this early age is mainly a body ego. The organizations of which the ego disposes are 1) a very rudimentary ideational organization, barely adequate for diffuse hallucinatory processes, and 2) a rapidly developing locomotor system.

B.   Recuperative trends versus institutional care.

At this same period the id drive in regard to the object is patterned on the anaclitic model. All locomotion will therefore be put in the service of an attempt to get gratification of the drive for anaclitic social relations.

The demand for social relations is subject to development in the course of the first year of life. Up to the sixth month these demands can be and are expressed only in a passive manner, since the infant has not achieved locomotion yet. Therefore the social demands of the infant are initiated not so much by the infant's activities as by the adult's activity.

From six to twelve months, however, its social demands are expressed actively, as shown in the results of the Hetzer-Wolf tests. At the age level of seven months, one of the test items consists of observing whether the infant already creates contact actively. At the level of nine months, the test consists in observing whether without intervention of the examiner the infant will grasp the hand or the coat of the averted adult.

One might also formulate this by saying that before the sixth month the passivity of the social demand is expressed in the fact that it is only manifested in the pathognomonic reaction of the infant to the adult. Before the sixth month the social contact manifestation is initiated by the adult and the child follows him; whereas after six months the infant takes the initiative and seeks for the adult.

In a certain percentage of our cases of anaclitic depression we have found that the infants did not show the anxious attitude immediately after being deprived of their love object. We were informed by the staff that these children were disturbed by the absence of their mothers. Nevertheless they seemed to turn with eagerness to the observer. We might interpret this behavior as an attempt at substitution of the lost object along the anaclitic mode.

However, if active attempts at substitution are to be initiated through social contact, locomotion is a necessary prerequisite for such an attempt. In institutionalized children both the opportunity to reestablish anaclitic object relations through social contact, and the opportunity for locomotion, are severely handicapped.

From the dynamic point of view locomotion and motility in general fulfills the important task of offering a necessary channel of release for the aggressive drive. When motor activity is inhibited in infancy, all normal outlets of the aggressive drive are blocked. In this case only one alternative remains for dealing with the aggressive drive: that is, to direct it against the self. The resulting dynamic picture is identical to the one we have previously described for melancholia. The only difference is that whereas in melancholia it was the superego which made use of the aggressive drive against the ego, in the case of inhibited motor activity in infancy the intervention of the superego is unnecessary.

Actually the difference between the dynamics in melancholia and those in anaclitic depression are not as great as might appear from a theoretical point of view. The hostile ego-oppressive authority in melancholia is the superego. In anaclitic depression the restriction of motility and the deprivation of the love object is imposed by the surrounding grown-up world. This world of grown-ups which forms the immediate environment of the infant is the identical one from which in the oedipal stage the imagines will be taken for the purpose of forming the superego. In other words, both in melancholia and in anaclitic depression the sadism which threatens the patient with extinction originates from the same source: except that in melancholia the source is an intrapsychic representation, while in anaclitic depression the source is the living original of the later intrapsychic representation.

An objection might be raised at this point: if anaclitic depression is provoked by inhibiting the locomotion of infants separated from their love object, why is it that a significant number of the infants observed by us in Nursery, the majority in fact, remained unharmed? And what is the reason for the severe nature of one group of infantile depression, for the milder course of the others?

The answer is that in both cases the outcome depends on the measure of success achieved in this institution in providing the infant with a substitute love object. The separation of the infants from their mothers takes place in Nursery between the sixth and the ninth month. Another of the inmates is then assigned to the care of the motherless child. The substitute mother thus cares for her own child and for a stranger. Though the enlightened management of Nursery exerts the greatest care, their selection is limited by the available number of inmates. Also it is hardly to be expected that a group of delinquent girls, as these were, will furnish very high grade mother substitutes.

We suggest that when the mother substitute is a good one, depression does not develop. Where the mother substitute turns out to be an aggressive, unloving personality, the parallel to adult melancholia is enacted in real life. Just as in melancholia the ego is oppressed by a sadistic superego, here the body ego of the infant is oppressed by a sadistic love object substitute.

Inhibited in its motor release, the pent-up aggressive drive is turned against the ego. The ego then is caught between a hostile love object substitute and its own aggressive drive. Bereft of locomotion, it cannot actively seek replacement for the lost love object among the other grown-ups in the institution.

An indirect confirmation of this view is contained in the following table, which refers to the original mother-child relationship. In it we tabulate the number of children and the nature of their depression, on the one hand, the nature of the relations between the child and its mother, on the other. The mother-child relation was established by our observation of the way the mother behaved to her child. For the purpose of corroboration these observations then were compared with the information gathered for this purpose from the unusually able head-matron of Nursery. This somewhat complicated procedure made it impossible to procure reliable data on all the 95 children in question; but we did get them on 64, appearing in the table below.

Table 6.

Mother-Child Relation

	Good			Bad		
	Intense	Moderate	Weak	Intense	Moderate	Weak
Severe Depression	6	11	—	—	—	—
Mild Depression	4	—	3	7	—	4
No Depression	—	—	2	11	2	14

The figures speak for themselves. Evidently it is more difficult to replace a satisfactory love object than an unsatisfactory one. Accordingly depression is much more frequent and much more severe in the cases of good mother-child relationship. In bad mother-child relationship not a single severe depression occurs. It seems that any substitute is at least as good as the real mother in these cases.

In institutions motor activity is inhibited for organizational reasons: lack of adequate nursing staff requires that the children be mostly confined to their cots, and move freely on the floor only for very restricted periods, if at all. The ego therefore is impoverished by being deprived of the release of motor activity. The aggressive drive is pent up and directed against the ego.

This restriction, however, also precludes the children's actively seeking replacement for the lost object among the grown-ups present in the institution or through contact with other children. Thus institutional routine will jeopardize the chances of substitutive attempts of the ego both in the motor and in the emotional sector.

C.   Facilitation of recuperative trends in institutions.

The theoretical considerations elaborated above on the parallelity of the roles played by the superego in melancholia on the one hand, and on the other by the originals of the later imagines in an anaclitic depression, hold promise of a much more successful and effective therapy in the latter. Changing the superego in melancholia or assuaging it is a laborious, time-consuming, and all-in-all not very hopeful task. Providing a mother substitute (if restoring the mother is precluded) for a child suffering from a not too advanced anaclitic depression, refraining from inhibiting its motility, should be matters for an efficient and adequate environmental manipulation. The correctness of the latter statement is borne out by our observations on the prompt results after restoration of the love object to the deprived infants. It is also borne out by the favorable results of liberating motility and providing an adequate mother substitute for those infants for whom the original love object could not be restored.

It is easy to visualize that these elements in the picture of infantile depression will be subject to a wide scale of variations, depending on the rapidly developing changes in personality that take place during the first year of infancy; and on the wide gamut of environmental facilitations offered by the different types of institutions.

As regards the first, the changes in personality, it is self-evident that no imaginable motor activity exists in the first six months of life which could conceivably be used for attempts at substitution of the lost object. During this period, routine care of the infant, at least during the first three months, covers a large part of its social requirements. This picture changes completely in the second half of the first year of life. Locomotion develops rapidly and the demand for love switches from previous passivity to activity.

Institutional confinement of infants to their cots after the sixth month thwarts their use of locomotion in attempts at substitution. The infant's active attempts to make contact with other infants or adults in the environment are blocked. The infant is at the mercy of the compliance of its environment, and of the ability of the institution to provide an adequate substitute object.

Hence we will find clinical pictures of increasing severity according to the capacity of the institution in question to afford children deprived of their love objects an outlet in the form of free locomotion and substitute love objects. This is the reason why the results of child care in the worst foster homes surpass (with a few exceptions) those of the best institutions.

In the case of the infants observed by us in Nursery, we found that in so far as the object was not restored, or an adequate substitute object not supplied, the depression progressed rapidly. Beginning with sadness and weeping, it continued into withdrawal, loss of appetite, loss of interest in the outside world, dejection, retardation, and finally, a condition which could only be described as stuporous.

D.   The actual therapeutic measure.

Our dynamic and structural model of the anaclitic depression suggests the obvious therapeutic measures. It is gratifying to find that for once in psychiatry they appear to be really effective where they can be applied. They fall into three classes:

1) prophylaxis,
2) restitution,
3) substitution.

1)   Prophylaxis: deprivation of infants, during the first year, of love objects for a prolonged period, should be strenuously avoided. Under no circumstances should they be deprived for over three months of love objects, during the second half of their first year.

2)   Restitution: if infants have been deprived of their love objects during their first year for a prolonged period, restitution of the love objects within a period of maximally three months will enable them to recover, at least partially, from the damage inflicted.

3)   Substitution: where neither prophylaxis nor restitution is possible, the substitution of the love object by another one is advisable.

Particular attention should be given to the facilitation of the infant's locomotor drives in the largest measure possible, and to the supporting of its tendencies to choose actively its own substitutes for the love object of which it has been deprived.

V. *Summary*

A.   A psychiatric syndrome of a depressive nature is observed in a series of infants and classified as anaclitic depression.

B.   Its etiology is related to a loss of the love object, combined with a total inhibition of attempts at restitution through the help of the body ego acting on anaclitic lines.

C.   Prophylaxis and treatment is suggested on the basis of these structural and dynamic findings.

D.   Some of the results of such treatment are reported.

E.   Theoretical assumptions concerning melancholia are discussed.

APPENDIX

A.   Various observations with theoretical implications.

In the course of this study a number of observations were made which we have not cared to include in our general conclusions for several reasons. Some of these observations appear to us to lead to conclusions which are still of too speculative a nature for the purposes of the present study. Others again are too scattered and irregular to represent satisfactory findings for the purpose of establishing or confirming any theory. We therefore bring them here in order to call the attention of other investigators to these phenomena, in the hope that they may be utilized in later work.

1.   The variations of the DQ (developmental quotient) in the course of anaclitic depression.

In all our cases without exception a gradual decline of the DQ began when the infant was deprived of its love object. This decline paralleled the increasing severity of the developing symptoms. This is a welcome confirmation of our observations; an unexpectedly surprising and dramatic change in the DQ occurs when the love object is returned. We had the opportunity to test such cases immediately after the return of the love object, i.e., within twelve hours. DQs would jump as much as 36.6 per cent in this brief period. The developmental age of the children would take a jump from 0;11+0 to 1;4+0; or from 0;9+0 to 1;1+0. This in itself is surprising enough, but it is still more surprising that in the case of a child whose developmental age had jumped within three days from 0;11+0 to 1;3+28, it receded again, and for the following two months moved between 1;1+21 and 1;1+24.

It is an extremely striking finding that faculties already acquired should be lost in the course of the anaclitic depression, that when the love object returns they should be regained suddenly in a manner far surpassing the actual age of the child, but that after a short while the level of achievement should settle back again more closely to the performances to be expected according to the child's actual age. In view of our discussion of the fact that the ego at this period is mainly a body ego, that on the other hand the tests applied to establish the DQ require a good deal of body activity, one gets the impression of a sudden ego expansion having taken place on the return of the love object. This ego expansion is out of proportion to the age-adequate capacities of the child, and sinks back to a more normal proportion if no further disturbances intervene. The curious phenomenon of this sudden ego expansion which on the return of the love object replaces the depression makes us inclined to speculate whether there may be any analogy between this manifestation and the replacement of a depression by a manic episode.

2. Some considerations in regard to assumptions of psychoanalytic theory and their verification.

The predominant role of oral eroticism in melancholia has always been stressed in psychoanalytic literature (3). It is assumed that a regression to the oral biting phase takes place, with fantasies of introjection. Anal-sadistic trends appear enormously increased. Therefore we would expect to find striking oral biting and anal-sadistic phenomena in our depressed infants. Such was not the case, at least not in that measure which one would expect in view of the comparatively simple, elementary structure of early infantile psychic patterns.

a. Oral biting manifestations.

The one oral symptom common to all of the children was loss of appetite; on the other hand, we observed a greater tendency of the depressed children to stuff everything—hands, clothes, toys—into their mouths, and to keep them there. Prior to the depression these children were not noticeably prone to finger-sucking. During the depression finger-sucking increased conspicuously. We encountered biting phenomena in some of the depressed children, but not in all. In those cases in which we could observe them, they had not been present prior to the depression. It is an outstanding fact that the biting activities *never* were in evidence *during* the depression; they appeared after the depression had lifted. Interesting manifestations will be found in the following quotation from the protocol of one of our cases.

Aethelberta, white female:
"From the beginning far advanced in her development, friendly, well liked. At 0;7+16 slightly depressive expression in the face noted, simultaneously with a decrease of the DQ. Inquiry elicits that she had been separated from her mother ten days before. In the following weeks she becomes weepy; by the time she is nine months old the nursing staff observes that

the child is getting thinner and suffering from insomnia; she seems to be watching everything and allegedly cannot go to sleep for this reason. She finally is isolated for the purpose of overcoming her insomnia. Approaching her becomes difficult; she is mostly sitting in her bed, her dress in her mouth, or sucking her hand. In the following weeks she refuses to touch toys and lies dejected on her bed, face averted from the experimenter. Films taken by us during these weeks show a pathetic picture of sorrow, help-lessness, and demand for assistance. The DQ drops further. The child, up to this point vigorously healthy, develops a stubbornly persisting cold. At 0;10+22 a mother substitute is delegated with instructions to be particularly loving to the child. The effect of this measure becomes immediately visible, though the child is by no means cured. She now accepts contact with other children in an aggressive form. At 0;10.29 she is biting, scratching, and pinching other children to the point of drawing blood. By 0;11+5 she tries for a prolonged period to bite the observer's nose, chin, neck, and hand. During these attacks she reaches out with her hands and vocalizes different incoherent sounds, among which the word 'ma-ma' returns several times. At 0;11+19 the mother is returned. Simultaneously she has become friendly and positive, and her DQ has suddenly risen 29.28 per cent."

There are many traits in this picture which could be used to confirm psychoanalytic theory and we have quoted it for this reason. We do not at this point feel justified, however, in drawing conclusions because similar phenomena are manifested only by a minority of our cases.

b.   Anal-sadistic manifestations.

Anal activities showed a somewhat different pattern. Like oral biting phenomena they were very striking in some cases and absent in others. However, in those cases where they were present they could be observed both during the depression and after the depression had lifted. The phenomena observed in these children were: playing with feces, with or without accom-panying genital masturbation, and in some cases, coprophagia. Fecal games and oral biting manifestations appeared frequently, although not necessarily, in the same children. In the case of Aethelberta, for instance, as well as in that of another child, the games consisted in rolling fecal pellets, which seemed to be the only toy these children enjoyed. Aethelberta continued the fecal games after the depression had lifted, in the form of social games, trying to feed her play partner with the pellets. In another case in which biting and fecal games were simultaneously present, the pellets were used for covering the bed with a layer of feces and for throwing out through the bars of the cot, so that the surroundings of the bed were also completely covered with feces. Genital masturbation, which at this age is not particularly frequent in infants, was observed in nearly all of the children in whom fecal games were observed.

BIBLIOGRAPHY

1. Abraham, K. "Notes on the Psychoanalytical Investigation and Treatment of Manic-Depressive Insanity and Allied Conditions", *Selected Papers*, Hogarth, 1927. (Originally 1912.)
2. Abraham, K. "The First Pregenital Stage of the Libido", *ibid.* (Originally, 1916.)
3. Abraham, K. "A Short Study of the Development of the Libido", *ibid.*
4. Bühler, Ch. *Kindheit und Jugend*, Leipzig, 1931.
5. Fenichel, O. *The Psychoanalytic Theory of Neurosis*, Norton, 1945.
6. Freud, S. "Mourning and Melancholia", *Coll. Papers*, IV. (Originally, 1917.)
7. Glover, E. "Examination of The Klein System of Child Psychology", *this Annual*, I, 1945.
8. Harnik, J. "Introjection and Projection in the Mechanism of Depression", *Int. J. Psa.* XIII, 1932.
9. Hetzer, H. and Wolf, K. M. "Baby Tests", *Zeit. f. Psychol.*, 107, 1928.
10. Jacobson, E. "Depression; the Oedipus Conflict in the Development of Depressive Mechanisms", *Psa. Quarterly*, XII, 1943.
11. Jersild, A. T. and Holmes, F. B. "Children's Fear", *Child Dev. Mon.*, 20, 1935.
12. Klein, M. "Emotional Life and Ego Development of the Infant, with Special Reference to the Depressive Position", Controversial Series of the London Psychoanalytic Society, IV, *Discussion*, March 1944.
13. Klein, M. *The Psycho-Analysis of Children*, London, 1932.
14. Klein, M. "Mourning and Its Relation to Manic-Depressive States", *Int. J. Psa.*, XXI, 1940.
15. Klein, M. "The Oedipus Complex in the Light of Early Anxieties", *ibid.*, XXVI, 1945.
16. Rank, O. *Das Trauma der Geburt und seine Bedeutung für die Psycho-analyse*, Int. Psa. Verlag, Wien, 1924.
17. Riviere, J. "Original Papers on the Genesis of Psychical Conflict in Earliest Infancy", *Int. J. Psa.*, XVII, 1936.
18. Shirley, M. M. *The First Two Years, A Study of Twenty-Five Babies*, Vol. II, Minnesota Press, Minneapolis, 1933.
19. Spitz, R. A. and Wolf, K. M. "The Smiling Response: A Contribution to the Ontogenesis of Social Relations", *Gen. Psychol. Mon.*, XXXIV, 1, 1946.
20. Spitz, R. A. "Hospitalism; An Inquiry into the Genesis of Psychiatric Conditions in Early Childhood", *this Annual*, I, 1945.
21. Spitz, R. A. and Wolf, K. M. "Diacritic and Coenesthetic Organizations", *Psa. Rev.*, 32, April, 1945.
22. Watson, J. B. *Psychology from the Standpoint of a Behaviorist*, Lippincott, 1919.

PSYCHOANALYTIC ORIENTATION IN CHILD GUIDANCE WORK IN GREAT BRITAIN[1]

By KATE FRIEDLANDER, M.D. (London)

The purpose of this short communication is to record the theoretical background of the establishment of a child guidance service which allows of the application of psychoanalytical theory and experience to the problems of child guidance work to a larger extent than is usually possible.

Although I am aware that most of the ideas set forth in this paper are not in themselves original, I have not found any stress laid in the literature on the manner in which a service is established in relation to the scientific, more especially psychoanalytical work which can be accomplished within its limits. It therefore seems justifiable to describe the theoretical principles which led to the establishment of this service, although the experiment is too new to prove its value by the results achieved.

From the study of the literature and from my own experience in various child guidance clinics I have come to the conclusion that the most unsatisfactory aspect of child guidance work is the psychotherapeutic treatment of the child. Either there is an indication for child analysis(1), in which case weekly interviews can at best achieve a cessation of symptoms without real change in the libido position and Ego- and Super-Ego distortions; or the disturbance is a more superficial one and it is doubtful whether environmental changes including treatment of the mother or of both parents would not in themselves be sufficient to allow of a more normal development. This dissatisfaction will be felt especially strongly by psychoanalysts who are accustomed to understanding the genetic basis of a disturbance and who ask about the reasons for the disappearance of symptoms and about other changes which may occur.

---

1. This paper is included in order to permit comparison of one aspect of the present state of child guidance work in Great Britain and in America.

The treatment of the individual child has never been considered as the sole function of a child guidance clinic. The idea behind child guidance work has always been that the child should be understood in its relationship to its family setting and that handling of the mother and, in many cases, treatment of the mother are of equal importance. The work with mothers has been studied very carefully, especially by psychiatric social workers, and techniques of treatment have been worked out. The relationship between mother and child when both are undergoing treatment and the effect of the one upon the other have also received ample attention. But not much stress is laid on the fact that a change in the child's symptoms may perhaps be due solely to a changed attitude on the mother's part and not to its own attendance at the clinic.

I do not wish to imply that the questions raised above are not in the minds of many workers in child guidance clinics. To solve these questions takes time and personnel for scientific research. In America, some child guidance clinics, notably those of Healy, the Jewish Board of Guardians, the Philadelphia Clinic and others are in a position to achieve this end. In Britain, the pressure of work, lack of personnel and suitable premises, and lack of financial aid have severely curtailed any such attempt.

Supposing methods of psychotherapy for children could be worked out satisfactorily and were to gain general validity, would the treatment of individual children, lasting for months or even years, solve the problem of the large number of disturbances met with in the child population of a community? I think not. In a clinic staffed by a full time psychiatric social worker, a part-time psychologist, and a psychiatrist not more than six to eight children can be under treatment at weekly interviews at the same time. If we allow as average treatment time three months, which is an under-estimate, not more than twenty-four to thirty-two children can be treated at one such clinic during the space of a year. Although I cannot give exact figures, the number of children who need treatment in a child population of about 10,000 served by such a clinic is much higher. This fact is borne out by the long waiting lists in nearly every clinic, at least in Britain.

The development of group therapy and of more adequate facilities for the training of personnel may somewhat alter these figures, but will still not solve the problem entirely.

The function of a child guidance clinic as opposed to the function of treatment of individual children in private psychiatric or psychoanalytic practice and in out-patient departments is to deal with the problem of the emotionally disturbed child in a community as a whole, to investigate the social and preventive aspect as well as the psychological and psychiatric one: to fulfill this task satisfactorily it will furthermore be necessary in such a clinic to devise methods of treatment which are not short-cuts of intensive individual treatment—such short-cuts are always unsatisfactory—but new methods adapted to this special task.

I do not believe that psychoanalytical treatment introduced as such into child guidance clinics would mitigate the difficulties. It is not the function of a child guidance clinic to cure a few children at the expense of the others for whom no time would be left. But I do believe that the application of psychoanalytical theory and experience to the various problems of child guidance work can contribute substantially to their satisfactory solution.

It is not my intention in this paper to outline this possible contribution in all its various aspects and details. I shall stress certain points only in their relation to their practical application.

1) *Psychoanalytical Approach to the Problem of Prevention in a Child Guidance Clinic.*

It is implied in psychoanalytical theory that a certain percentage of neurotic and character disturbances of adults could be prevented if the child were to live within an environment allowing of a normal development up to the age of six to seven years. There are of course cases in which constitutional factors seem to prevail in the causation of the disturbance over environmental ones. No statistics are available, but it is safe to say that these cases are in the minority if we consider the child population as a whole and not only the clientele of a clinic. There has recently been some controversy about the preventive aspect of child guidance work. But this is concerned more with the question whether treatment given to already disturbed children prevents neurotic illness in later life. Healy's recent statistics (2) are the first attempt at an assessment of results in carefully investigated cases in relationship to the treatment each case received and they seem to point towards a positive answer. I do not think that the facts at present at our disposal warrant a denial of the assumption that an unfavorable environment promotes the development of mental disturbances. The reverse assumption that a favorable environment prevents the establishment of neurotic disturbances has as yet to be proved. An indication of its correctness can be found in Anna Freud's work in the war time nurseries.

Starting from this assumption, it will be necessary to discuss what kind of environment we consider favorable for mental and emotional development in early childhood, and in what way a community can be educated to provide such an environment insofar as psychological implications are concerned; as regards social implications we are not in a position to create a direct influence.

Hoffer (3) has recently made a historical survey of psychoanalytical education, which indicates that during the development of the psychoanalytical theory our notions about the ideal environment for the growing child have undergone considerable changes. Although it is certainly true that many questions cannot as yet be fully answered, there are certain outlines and certain details for whose general application we can press.

Generally speaking we know how important is an undisturbed mother-child relationship during the first six years; we know that it is of importance for achieving later mental equilibrium that the three phases of libidinal development should be run through without the arrest of libido during any phase with the establishment of a fixation point. We know that too much frustration or too much gratification or an alternation of the two during any one phase are favorable conditions for the establishment of a fixation point. Mainly owing to Anna Freud's work we have become aware that education working with the fear of loss of love rather than with direct restriction of instinctive urges is more likely to avoid this danger; giving sufficient time and scope for sublimation of pregenital drives will further the slow development of a strong and healthy Ego. Given an environment favoring these factors during the first three years there is a very good chance that the conflicts of the oedipal phase can be resolved instead of being repressed and a Super-Ego will emerge which leads towards social adaptation but allows sufficient instinct gratification.

On the basis of these theoretical conceptions practical advice can be given to mothers during the first year on how to avoid feeding disturbances with all their implications, how to achieve the training for cleanliness so as to guarantee the most positive character development, and how to deal with disturbances arising during the oedipal phase. We can advise mothers on the basis of our knowledge how to achieve obedience which is due not to fear and submissiveness, but to the establishment of an independent Super-Ego. This last factor, though it plays an important role even in early infancy will be most important in education during latency and puberty

As stated above, many details, especially as regards the practical application of our theoretical knowledge, still remain to be worked out. But at present the general public is so far removed from our ideals of education that there is ample scope for our preliminary work.

The question arises in what way a child guidance clinic can educate the general public in providing a background for the growing child which will promote normal development.

Attempts at such education have been made ever since psychoanalysis was discovered, and that they have not always been successful is due to the resistance of the individual to the acceptance of infantile sexuality with all its implications. But when we compare the situation of today with that of twenty years ago it is evident that such resistance is waning, and that there is a growing awareness of the complicated and conflictful development during childhood and of the helplessness of the untrained person to deal with the problems arising out of it. There is a desire expressed by the majority of people who deal with children in a professional capacity to gain more insight into the working of the child's mind and to be given some interpretation of the puzzling phenomena presented to them. At the present stage we are therefore justified in attempting the education of a community as a whole and not to be satisfied with the individual training of a few workers.

Ideally speaking, such education should start with the professional workers of a community before being applied to the public in general. When starting our education with the mother, we should wish that advice which she gets from other sources, such as the doctor of the health center or the district nurse, should coincide with our advice, especially if in a certain situation she has to act against her own unconscious desires. But in practice, a child guidance clinic will always be in direct contact with mothers whose children are already disturbed. Education with individual mothers starts therefore at the same time as education with professional workers.

The professional workers of a community could at first be offered courses of lectures giving the theoretical background of our ideas of early education. In lectures attended by eighty to one hundred people not much more will be achieved than a statement of our approach. But arising out of such lectures discussion groups can be formed, attended by ten to twelve people, in which with the aid of practical examples a deeper knowledge can be conveyed. Progress will probably be slow, much opposition will have to be overcome, and not everyone will benefit equally from the ideas and practical suggestions offered. But seen over a period of years, such a systematic effort for the education of professional workers, such as teachers, social workers, health visitors, probation officers and so on has a chance to succeed, especially as the workers themselves can constantly apply their new knowledge and observe the results in their own work.

The work with individual mothers at the clinic has as its primary object an alteration of the environment that has caused the child's disturbance. With undisturbed mothers the work will be first and foremost education. Emphasis should be laid on giving the mother as full a picture of the child's emotional development as is possible within her intellectual and cultural limits. This is of value because it will make it unnecessary to give the mother advice for individual situations; if she understands the child's needs, she will automatically adapt her attitude to it. Having in mind the education of the community, we should not be satisfied with helping a mother over the one difficulty for which she has sought advice; we should always bear in mind that she will need help for later situations unless we make her acquainted with the further development. The contact with the individual mothers at the clinic should even at this point be used for our educational purposes.

Such mothers could be educated in groups once their primary difficulties have been resolved. It is very rarely that the mother's faulty handling of her child is due solely to lack of knowledge: there is always an interaction between this and the mother's own problems. In group discussions resistances and anxieties can be dealt with more quickly and effectively than in individual interviews.

If the education of the professional workers of a community has gone on for some time and shows some effect plans can be put into action for a more systematic education of parents, mothers first of all.

As the working capacity of a child guidance clinic is limited, only certain sections of the community can be approached. The most promising starting point will be work with mothers who attend maternity and antenatal clinics. Young mothers and expectant mothers will be most eager to get help in bringing up their children. Groups of such mothers should be carefully collected: the aim of such group discussion should again be, not to give them standardized advice on how to behave in the feeding situation or how to handle the training for cleanliness, but rather to explain the child's needs and to let the parents develop their own ideas on the basis of such knowledge. Even neurotic mothers will be able to benefit to a certain extent by such discussions.

A wider section of the public can be included in this educational program by giving lectures on child development within the school syllabus to boys and girls between the ages of fifteen and seventeen. Because of their own conflicts of adolescence the detailed study of early childhood will be of fascinating interest to young boys and girls, and they will have no difficulties during this period in accepting the dynamic conceptions of our teachings. The interesting work by Reichenberg-Hackett (4) confirms this assumption.

2) *The Psychoanalytical Approach to Treatment in a Child Guidance Clinic.*

It is not justifiable to separate the educational aspect of child guidance work from its treatment aspect, as probably the most potent factor in the treatment of children and their parents is of an educational nature. The distinction is rather one between the education in general and the handling of individual cases in the clinic.

As in general medicine, treatment of an emotional disturbance can be successful only if based on a correct diagnosis. It is in the field of diagnosis that psychoanalysis can contribute most substantially to the problems of treatment. From the point of view of the psychoanalyst, diagnosis of mental disturbances in children does not mean that categories must be found into which each case can be fitted as is possible to a certain extent with adult mental disturbances. Anna Freud (1) has recently indicated that diagnosis in childhood entails an assessment of the disturbances of instinct-, Ego-, and Super-Ego development together with an assessment of the child's activities.

The correct psychoanalytical diagnosis of a disturbance will allow us to draw conclusions as to its origin and the possibilities for its cure. Unfortunately we are not far enough advanced yet to be able to diagnose each disturbance met with in the work at a child guidance clinic in one or even several interviews. But it is well worth while to spend enough time on this very important problem. Those cases which according to Anna Freud need child analysis cannot be treated satisfactorily in any other way. But they are only a small minority amongst the clientele of a child guidance clinic.

Generally speaking our psychoanalytical approach will lead us in disturbances of children under the age of five to work through the mother rather than to treat the child directly. The attendance of the child may be necessary for a number of interviews during which he will reveal to us his phantasies in his general behavior and play activities. This knowledge will be used in our work with the mother. During the latency period, direct methods of treatment with the child will have to be used. It will be a task for the future to work out such methods in detail and to base them on a theoretical background. In puberty the therapeutic approach to boys and girls is often again of a more educational nature.

It is not my intention to go into details of treatment within the limits of this paper. I merely seek to point out the value of the application of psychoanalytical knowledge to the problem in general.

If a child guidance clinic is to serve the functions outlined above it must have freedom of action so far as access to the public is concerned. It cannot work under an authority with different aims; its caseload must be determined by the capacity of the clinic and not by other interests, its professional workers must be trained in the same theoretical background. Considering the fact that many of the ideas outlined above are theoretical deductions which have not yet been put into practice systematically, the clinic ought to have facilities for research. In order to assess the value of educating the public, a secluded community is preferable to a center in a capital town. In order to assess the value of psychological treatment, a community where the disturbances are not due solely to social and economic factors is to be preferred.

I formed these ideas on the function of a child guidance clinic when working at long established clinics whose administrative leaders were unaware of the wider problems involved. I came to the conclusion that the work outlined above can be carried out only if the establishment of the service is already based on the indicated theoretical background.

During the last two years an opportunity offered itself to put these ideas into practice. It may be of interest to describe the beginnings of a scheme which seems to allow of the application of psycho-analytical knowledge to child guidance work in its widest sense.

In October, 1944, the County of West Sussex wished to establish a Child Guidance Service. The county is a small one, with a child population of 20,000, and is rather independent from the neighboring counties by reason of its history. There had never previously been a child guidance service in the county, and there was as yet no propaganda concerned with the problems of mental health. It is mainly a rural area, with little industry, and a middle class population with very little real poverty. The most promising aspect of the intended scheme was the proposal by the Local Authority that the child guidance service should act under a sub-committee of the County Council, in Education Department. Members of all social services were represented in cooperation with but not under the authority of either the Health or the the child guidance committee.

I agreed to take over the organization of the service, and the year 1945 was used to work out details of the scheme, to select and appoint a staff, and to do some preliminary propaganda work in the County.

There are three urban centers in the three corners of the County, in each of which it was planned to open a clinic. Two of the clinics, one in C— and one in H—, were opened in January, 1946; the third center, in W—, will not be opened until October, 1946, because of housing difficulties, but some work is already being carried out by the staff appointed to this center. One or another of the three centers can be reached from every point in the County in at the most an hour's time by bus or train, but the average distances are much shorter, and the greater part of the population lives in the urban centers. Each clinic is staffed by a full time psychiatric social worker, a part time psychologist, and a part time psychiatrist.

The clinics are ordinary family houses with six to eight rooms, redecorated and furnished adequately for their purpose. It has already become obvious that the friendly atmosphere created by this environment helps us considerably with our propaganda work.

The clinics are open to every child up to the age of eighteen living in West Sussex. No fees are charged, whether chlidren attend infant welfare centers and county schools or not. A certain routine has to be observed in the manner of referral, but in principal children of all social strata have easy access to the clinics.

The three clinics work in all important aspects as a unit. In a weekly meeting, attended by all the members of the staffs of the three clinics, administrative and especially scientific questions concerned with the education of the public and the treatment of parents and children are discussed, so that each worker is kept fully informed of the progress of work in the other centers.

The selection of staff is of course one of the most important factors in the establishment of such a scheme. Ideally only analytically trained personnel can fulfill the requirements of such a service. We have succeeded in securing a staff approaching this ideal as closely as is possible under the existing circumstances, when analytical training for other than practising analysts is not functioning. During the year from the first conception of the scheme to its establishment in practice, members of staff were appointed and started a theoretical seminar some months before the work began. This has proved very fruitful, as cooperation between the members of the staff was already established when they started their practical work.

Each clinic has a full time secretary. Records are kept of each interview, and copies of treatment interviews are available so that each member of staff can read case histories other than their own. The case file gives the full story of what has been done—insofar as that is possible even with the best method of recording. The case discussions in the general staff meetings will in time allow of a uniform method of recording.

The Committee has agreed to give the staff freedom as regards the acceptance of cases, decision on which rests with the psychiatrists, and to the number of cases seen per week. Frequent contact with members of the Committee during the period of preparation has fully convinced them that with too great a caseload, the quality of the work suffers and they have in principle agreed to an increase of staff in order to avoid accumulation of cases and waiting lists; they have furthermore accepted the importance of educational work outside the clinics, and realize that this takes up time which would otherwise be spent on clinical work. It is due to the intelligent and progressive attitude of the chairman and some members of the Committee that our proposals have been accepted.

So far as can be judged from the short time of its actual operation, the setting of this child guidance scheme permits of the putting into practice of the ideas set out in the beginning. It makes possible an experiment in educating over a term of years the population of a county with no interference other than that arising from the resistance of the people themselves. It is of course doubtful whether the results of this education can ever be objectively assessed, but we are certainly given the opportunity for working out methods of research in that direction. There is well-trained personnel and enough time is available for research to be undertaken in the clinical field, from the educational as well as the psychotherapeutic angle.

I should like to record briefly some of the practical experiences during the first four months of our work.

A) *Education of the Public.*

During the year preceding the opening of the clinics I gave a course of six lectures to an audience of teachers, social workers, health visitors and so on in C—, in which I described the phases of the maturation of the libido together with the Ego and Super-Ego development up to the beginning of the latency period. While avoiding technical terms, I did not fail to lay full stress on the importance of infantile sexuality. The audience was enthusiastic, and their own observations brought forward during the discussion showed that at least a number of them had understood the implications. The attitude of these professional workers living in the County was one of eagerness to learn and of readiness to believe what I explained to them so long as it coincided with their own experience and was of some practical value to them. They found that Freudian psychology did offer them what they wanted. As already stated, I did not expect an audience of sixty to eighty people to learn very much from such a course; these lectures were really intended to arouse interest in the subject and to produce a common basis for later discussion groups. Nearly all those who attended wished to take part in the future in such discussion groups and when asked again half a year later their interest had not flagged.

I gave a similar course of lectures in H—, when the clinic there was already open. In H—, which is nearer to London, the response, while still satisfactory, was not so whole-hearted as in C—. A sufficient number of people wanted to partake in discussion groups, and these have already started.

Insofar as one is able to assess results, I believe that the fact that the cases referred to the clinics are most suitable material and that the attitude of professional workers towards the clinics is most friendly may be connected with this preliminary propaganda. A more tangible result is the active cooperation of some health visitors with the clinic in H—. Having been made aware of the importance of early recognition of disturbances, they refer to us children under the age of five and are cooperating with us in the most positive manner. Encouraged by our interest in their problems, they have arranged for our psychiatric social worker to interview mothers at the Infant and Maternity Center so that she may decide for herself which cases should be referred to the clinic. This has already given us the opportunity to start a small educational group with mothers whose children are educational problems only.

Another promising outcome of these initial lectures was the proposal by the headmistress of a large secondary school for girls that members of the staff of the clinic should give a course of lectures on the emotional development of the child within the ordinary school syllabus. The proposal came spontaneously as the result of a question put after a lecture on how mothers could best be educated to bring up their children more normally.

We have also had repeated requests to give single lectures to parent-teacher associations in various villages and to a mothers' association of a nursery school. The content of such lectures is discussed beforehand so as to fit into our general educational program. We are careful not to go too quickly and to encourage the audience to express their doubts rather than to overrule them.

The initial successes of our educational program do not make us blind to the resistance which must necessarily be present against the acceptance of the psychoanalytical doctrine, especially among the older generation. Those professional workers who are in constant contact with small children have little difficulty in accepting our explanation of their behavior—especially if they are young. In dealing with this natural resistance in future there are some factors which we believe may help us to cope with it in a positive way. During the preparatory period we had to fight for our independence and our very appropriate housing. We won this fight and thus gained a position of authority within the community which would have taken us years to establish if we had been judged by the results of our work. We often heard it said that we must be very powerful people if we succeeded in getting such beautiful houses and nice modern furniture from the County Council. The professional workers and the general public identified themselves with us in our rebellion against the parent-figures and respect us now because we were successful.

If a child guidance clinic is in a position of authority in a community, the resistance of some people to the teachings of the clinic·

cannot immediately affect the work as referrals come from many sources. There is time to wait and see whether the pressure from those parts of the community which accept our teachings will not slowly influence those who are resisting.

B) *The Clinical Work.*

I will give two examples of the types of cases referred and our methods of dealing with them.

P. is a very attractive, active and lively child of eighteen months, who for the last ten months is said to have had severe feeding disturbances. The mother was worried because it seemed to her that the child had altogether lost interest in food. As the child appeared quite well nourished it seemed that the mother's anxiety caused her to exaggerate the severity of the disturbance. The child was seen only once but the mother came weekly and later fortnightly for an hour's interview. She was a stable, intelligent woman, and was devoted to this her first child. The history revealed that the disturbance was probably due to two factors: the mother's over-anxiousness to feed the child well, which caused her constantly to interpose herself between the child and its hunger, and a too quick training in cleanliness, so that the child carried over her disgust for feces to certain kinds of food.

The mother was given some understanding of the problems involved on the basis of which she could accept our advice to let the child eat on her own, not to force her and not to object if she became messy with her food. We also advised her to give the child some freedom of choice and not to mix various foods together.

This mother was able to act on the advice given and told us after a fortnight that the child's interest in food had returned. Within the space of three months, with various ups and downs, the feeding disturbance had completely disappeared. The mother has a very positive relationship to the clinic and we shall continue to see her for some time, in a group with other mothers whose problems have also been alleviated. We shall discuss with them the next step in their children's development, how to meet difficulties arising out of this development, and we shall observe their reactions to the knowledge we impart to them. This group will continue for some months at weekly intervals.

J., four years, six months, was referred to the clinic for eating difficulties which had existed since she was two years of age, temper tantrums, refusal to speak to strangers and the urge to have certain phrases repeated to her by her mother over and over again. All the latter symptoms appeared after the birth of a brother, a year ago.[2]

Although the mother was a stable, intelligent person, her handling of the child was very unwise and was complicated by the presence of the grand-parents in the house. Many of the child's symptoms could be explained by these bad environmental influences, but the observation of the child at the psychiatric interview showed definite aberrations from the norm: the child did not speak at all, handled the toys in an obsessional way and at times made compulsive movements with her hands and feet.

Though there were definite indications that the child was suffering from obsessional symptoms and possibly from an obsessional neurosis, the picture was by no means clear. The mother was seen alone at weekly intervals for a period of six weeks, during which time the picture of the child's disturbance completely changed: the eating difficulties, the shyness with strangers, and the temper tantrums disappeared, and what was left were the obsessional symptoms: a bed ritual which the mother had formerly overlooked, obsessional grunting noises, obsessional movements with her feet and the desire for the repetition of certan phrases. At this stage the child was seen again, and now came at weekly intervals to the clinic, mainly for the purpose of observation. The material which revealed the girl's hatred of her brother and her penis envy was not interpreted but used in order to show the mother the child's conflicts. It took the mother a long time to accept the fact of the girl's hostility to her brother, and until then she was unable to follow our advice in that respect. With this understanding on the mother's part the obsessional symptoms disappeared within a few weeks, and to the outsider the child is completely changed: instead of a disgruntled, whining little girl she is now a happy, pretty child. Her play activities have become normal. We shall soon stop seeing the child but we shall continue to see the mother as one of a group for some time to come.

In both these examples the educational work with the mother proved successful in a short space of time because they were both stable and intelligent women and their attitude to the clinic was positive from the beginning. The problem is much more complicated in cases where the child's disturbance is bound up with the mother's neurosis. But, as Waelder (5) has pointed out, therapeutic work with such neurotic mothers is again educational work which over a long period of time and much more indirectly aims at the same result.

---

2. This case has been dealt with by Miss L. Jacobs and Miss H. Engl and will be published in full detail at a future date.

These examples have been given as illustrations of the statement made above that much of the therapeutic work in a child guidance clinic is educational in nature, and it is with such cases that one can obtain quick and lasting results. The percentage of cases of that type is much higher than that of children who need psychoanalytic treatment. Of one hundred cases seen since the beginning of the work, not more than four children need psychoanalysis, while about half the cases belong to the category described. In children in the latency period educational work with the parents will not undo the already established disturbance. These children are at present treated in child guidance clinics all over the world by various therapeutic methods, with varying results. In a later communication I shall discuss methods of treatment for these cases based on psychoanalytic theory and experience.

BIBLIOGRAPHY

1. Freud, A. "Indications for Child Analysis", this Annual, I.
2. Healy, W. and Bronner, A. "Treatment and What Happens After", Studies of the Judge Baker Child Guidance Center, 1945.
3. Hoffer, W. "Psychoanalytic Education", this Annual, I.
4. Reichenberg-Hackett, W. "Child Care as a Means of Group Therapy", Amer. J. Orthopsychiatry, XV, 1945.
5 Waelder, R. "Contribution to Round Table Conference on Psychoanalytic Orientation in Family Case Work", Amer. J. Orthopsychiatry, XIII, 1943.

EGO DEVELOPMENT AND HISTORICAL CHANGE

Clinical Notes

By ERIK HOMBURGER ERIKSON (San Francisco)

Men who share an ethnic area, an historical era, or an economic pursuit are guided by common images of good and evil. Infinitely varied, these images reflect the elusive nature of historical change; yet in the form of contemporary social models, of compelling proto-types of good and evil, they assume decisive concreteness in every individual's ego development. Psychoanalytic ego psychology has not matched this concreteness with sufficient theoretical specificity. The present collection of notes offers questions, illustrations, and theoretical considerations concerning the relation of the child's ego to the social prototypes of his day.

I. *Group Identity and Ego Identity*

1.

Freud's original formulations concerning the ego and its relation to society necessarily depended on the general trend of his analytic argument at the time and on the sociological formulations of his era. In general, the concept of the ego was first delineated by previous definitions of its better-known opposites, the biological id and the sociological "masses": the ego, the individual center of organized experience and reasonable planning, stood endangered by both the anarchy of the primeval instincts and the lawlessness of the group spirit. One might say that where Kant gave as the coordinates of the moral burgher "the stars above him" and "the moral law within him", the early Freud placed his fearful ego between the id within him and the mob around him.

To take account of this encircled ego's precarious morality Freud instituted within the ego the ego-ideal or superego. The emphasis, at first, was again on the foreign burden which was thus imposed on the ego. The superego, so Freud pointed out, is the internalization of all the restrictions to which the ego must bow. It is forced upon the child ("von aussen aufgenoetigt") by the critical influence of the parents, and later, by that of professional educators, and of what to the early Freud was a vague multitude of fellowmen ("die unbestimmte Menge der Genossen") making up the "milieu" and "public opinion". (8)

Surrounded by such mighty disapproval, the child's original state of naive self-love is said to be compromised. He looks for models by which to measure himself, and seeks happiness in trying to resemble them. Where he succeeds he achieves *self-esteem,* a not too convincing facsimile of his original narcissism and sense of omnipotence.

These early conceptual models have never ceased to determine the trend of discussions and the aims of practice in clinical psychoanalysis.[1] The focus of psychoanalytic research, however, has shifted to a variety of genetic problems. From the study of the ego's dissipation in an amorphous multitude or in a leader-mob, we have turned to the problem of the infantile ego's origin in organized social life. Instead of emphasizing what social organization denies the child, we wish to clarify what it may first grant to the infant, as it keeps him alive and as, in administering to his needs in a specific way, it seduces him to its particular life style. Instead of accepting the oedipus trinity as an irreducible schema for man's irrational conduct, we are striving for greater specificity within this scheme, by exploring the way in which social organization predetermines the structure of the family; for, as Freud said toward the end of his life (9), ". . . what is operating (in the superego) is not only the personal qualities of these parents but also everything that produces a determining effect upon themselves, the tastes and standards of the social class in which they live and the characteristics and traditions of the race from which they spring."

2.

Freud showed that sexuality begins with birth; he has also given us the tools for the demonstration of the fact that social life begins with each individual's beginnings.

Some of us have applied these tools at first to the study of so-called primitive societies where child training is integrated with a

---

1. In Fenichel's comprehensive volume on the theory of neuroses (5) the subject of social prototypes is only introduced toward the end of the chapter on mental development, and then in the form of a negation: "Neither a belief in 'ideal models' nor a certain degree of 'social fear' is necessarily pathological." The problem of the superego's origin in society is not discussed until page 463, in the chapter on character disorders.

well-defined economic system and a small and static inventory of social prototypes.[2] Child training in such groups, so we concluded, is the method by which a group's basic ways of organizing experience (its group identity, as we called it) is transmitted to the infant's early bodily experiences and, through them, to the beginnings of his ego.

Let me first illustrate the concept of group identity by a brief reference to anthropological observations made by Mekeel and myself some years ago. We described how in one segment of the reeducation of the American Indian the Sioux Indians' historical identity of the— now defunct—buffalo hunter, stands counterposed to the occupational and class identity of his reeducator, the American civil service employee. We pointed out that the identities of these groups rest on extreme differences in geographic and historical perspectives (collective ego-space-time) and on radical differences in economic goals and means (collective life plan).

In the remnants of the Sioux Indians' identity, the prehistoric past is a powerful psychological reality. The conquered tribe behaved as if guided by a life plan consisting of passive resistance to the present which does fail to reintegrate the identity remnants of the economic past; and of dreams of restoration, in which the future would lead back into the past, time would again become a-historic, space unlimited, activity boundlessly centrifugal, and the buffalo supply inexhaustible. Their federal educators, on the other hand, preach a life plan with centripetal and localized goals: homestead, fire place, bank account— all of which receive their meaning from a life plan in which the past is overcome, and in which the full measure of fulfillment in the present is sacrificed to an ever higher standard of living in the (ever removed) future. The road to this future is not outer restoration but inner reform.

Obviously every item of human experience as lived by a member of one of these groups, and as shared or debated by members of both groups, must be defined according to its place on the coordinates of these interpenetrating life plans.

Comparisons of erstwhile primitive groups with the remnants of such groups and with subgroups in modern society notoriously attempt to bridge almost unsurmountable systematic differences. A short survey denoting a few of the most obvious contradictions in such comparison, is needed here. Primitive cultures are exclusive. Their image of man-

2. This paper is a sequence to "Childhood and Tradition in Two American Indian Tribes" (3) and overlaps with it in this introductory part.

kind embraces only their own tribe. In modern civilization the image of man is expanding and is ever more inclusive. New syntheses of economic and emotional safety are sought in expansive and ever more inclusive formations of new entities and new identities: regions, nations, classes, races, ideologies. The development of these wider syntheses is accompanied by reactionary spasms, where fear of loss cf privileges arouses archaic fears of extinction and fears of loss of cultural identity.

Primitive tribes have a direct relation to the sources and means of production. Their tools are extensions of the human body. Children in these groups participate in technical and in magic pursuits; to them, body and environment, childhood and culture may be full of dangers, but they are all one world. The inventory of social prototypes is small and static. In our world, machines, far from remaining an extension of the body, destine whole human organizations to be extensions of machinery; magic serves intermediate links only; and childhood becomes a separate segment of life with its own folklore. The expansiveness of civilization, together with its stratification and specialization, force children to base their ego models on shifting, sectional, and contradictory prototypes.

3.

In turning from the consideration of groups to that of individuals, let me postulate that the growing child must derive a vitalizing sense of reality from the awareness that his individual way of mastering experience (his ego synthesis) is a successful variant of a group identity and is in accord with its space-time and life plan.

A child who has just found himself able to walk seems not only driven to repeat and to perfect the act of walking by libidinal pleasure in the sense of Freud's locomotor erotism; or by the need for mastery in the sense of Ives Hendrick's work principle; he also becomes aware of the new status and stature of "he who can walk", with whatever connotation this happens to have in the coordinates of his culture's life plan—be it "he who will go far", or "he who will be upright", or "he who might go too far". To be "one who can walk" becomes one of the many steps in child development which through the coincidence of physical mastery and cultural meaning, of functional pleasure and social recognition, contribute to a more realistic self-esteem. By no means only a narcissistic corroboration of infantile omnipotence (that can be had more cheaply), this self-esteem grows to be a conviction that the ego is learning effective steps toward a tangible collective future, that it is developing into a defined ego within a social reality. This sense I wish to call ego-identity. I shall try to clarify it as a subjective experience and as a dynamic fact, as a group psychological phenomenon and—in the bulk of this paper—as a subject for clinical investigation.

I shall first take recourse to the well-established concept of "personal identity". The conscious feeling of having a personal identity is based on two simultaneous observations: the immediate perception of one's selfsameness and continuity in time; and the simultaneous perception of the fact that others recognize one's sameness and continuity. What I propose to call ego-identity concerns more than the mere fact of existence, as conveyed by personal identity; it is the ego quality of this existence.

Ego-identity, then, in its subjective aspect, is the awareness of the fact that there is a self-sameness and continuity to the ego's synthesizing methods and that these methods are effective in safeguarding the sameness and continuity of one's meaning for others.

4.

Before approaching the subject of ego-identity from our traditional clinical angle, I shall briefly point to a few conceptual dilemmas.

a. When Freud spoke of "the superego or ego-ideal", he tentatively tossed together a dynamic and an ideational concept, one that has force and one that has image. For decades, psychoanalysts have used whichever of these concepts suited their argument or the way their minds worked. Some emphasize that the superego represents a transformation of instinctual energy into moral energy (the original quality breaking through in moralistic sadism). To some, the ego-ideal is more a kind of control board, which gives signs if and when a switch should be thrown which will unloose superego energy against the id and restore the equilibrium of self-esteem. Most workers are concerned only with what happens to the energy; the ideational part is left to social anthropologists. But while it was a step of inestimable import when Freud applied contemporaneous concepts of physical energy to psychology, the resultant theory that instinctual energy is transferred, displaced, transformed in analogy to the preservation of energy in physics no longer suffices to help us manage the data which we have learned to observe.

It is here that ego concepts must close a gap. We must find the nexus of social images and of organismic forces—and this not merely in the sense that here images and forces are, as the saying goes, "interrelated". More than this: the mutual complementation of ethos and ego, of group identity and ego-identity puts a greater common potential at the disposal of both ego synthesis and social organization.

b. When a Sioux Indian—at the height of his religious endeavors—drives little sticks through his breast, ties the sticks to a rope, the rope to a pole, and then (in a peculiar trance) dances backwards until the rope tightens and the sticks split his breast, so that the gushing blood runs freely down his body, we find a meaning in his extreme behavior: he is turning against himself the first provoked, then energetically frustrated infantile impulse to bite his mother's breast, a "fixation" which we found to be of decisive relevance in the Sioux' group identity and in his individual development.[3] This ritual puts "id" and "superego" in clear opposition, as do the abortive rituals of our neurotic patients. It makes similar sense when a Yurok man, having been with a woman, proceeds to heat himself by the fire of the sweathouse until he is supple enough to squeeze through an oval opening in the wall, only to jump into the cold river; whereupon he considers himself again pure and strong enough to net the sacred salmon. Here, obviously, self-esteem and inner security are restored by atonement. The same Indians, when indulging in promiscuous intercourse after having achieved the yearly communal engineering feat of bridging the river with a dam that yields a whole winter's supply of salmon, apparently experience the manic relief of orgiastic excess, which, once a year, throws atonement to the winds. But if we try to define the state of relative equilibrium between these better known extremes; if we ask what characterizes an Indian when he does not do much more than just calmly be an Indian, bent on the daily chores of the year's cycle, our description lacks a fitting frame of reference. We look for small signs of the fact that man, anywhere, anytime, betrays in minute emotional and ideational changes, an ever present conflict manifested in a change of mood from a vague anxious depression through what Freud referred to as "a certain in-between stage" to heightened well-being—and back, ("von einer uebermaessigen Gedruecktheit durch einen gewissen Mittelzustand zu einem erhoehten Wohlbefinden").[4] But is this in-between stage dynamically so unim-

---

3. As explained in detail in this Annual, I (3), such a collective fixation point is a meaningful part of the total instinctive self-regulation of a culture.
4. Quoted from memory.

portant that it can be defined by pointing out what it is not; by stating that neither a manic nor a depressive trend is, at the time, clearly noticeable; that a momentary lull exists on the battlefield of the ego; that the superego is temporarily non-belligerent and that the id has agreed to an armistice?

c. The necessity of defining the relative equilibrium between various "states of mind" became acute in the need to appraise morale in the present war. This writer had an opportunity to make a few observations on one of the more extreme milieus of human endeavor, namely, life on submarines. Here emotional plasticity and social resourcefulness are put to a high test. The heroic expectations and phallic-locomotor fantasies with which an adolescent volunteer approaches life on a submarine are on the whole not verified in the small chores and in the constricted space of his daily experience on board and in the relatively blind, deaf, and dumb role demanded of him in action. The extreme interdependence with the crew and the mutual responsibility for comfort and life under prolonged conditions of extreme hardship soon supersede the original fantasies. Crew and captain establish a symbiosis not governed by official regulations alone. With astonishing tact and native wisdom silent arrangements are made by which the captain becomes sensory system, brains, and conscience for the whole submerged organism of minutely tuned machinery and humanity; and by which the crew members mobilize in themselves compensatory mechanisms (for example, in the collective use of the generously provided food) permitting the crew to stand monotony and yet to be ready for instant action. Such automatic mutual adaptations to extreme milieus make "analytical sense" primarily where a seeming regression to a primal horde, and to a kind of oral lethargy, can be traced. Yet, if we ask why men choose such a life, why they stick to it in spite of incredible monotony and occasional nightmarish danger, and above all why they function in good health and high spirits, we do not have a satisfactory dynamic answer. In discussions we not infrequently end up by suspecting—on the evidence of mere analogies—whole units, crews, and occupational groups of being regressive, or motivated by latent homosexual or psychopathic tendencies.

Yet what the submarine man on the job, the Indian at work and the growing child have in common with all men who feel at one with what they are doing when and where they are doing it, is akin to that "in-between state" which we wish our children would preserve as they grow older; and which we want our patients to gain, when the "synthetic function of the ego" (Nunberg) is restored. We know that when this is achieved, play becomes freer, health radiant, sex more adult, and work more meaningful. Having applied psychoanalytic concepts to group problems we feel that a clearer understanding of the mutual complementation of ego synthesis and social organization, may help us to appraise therapeutically a psychological middle range, the expansion and cultivation of which on ever higher levels of human organization is the aim of all therapeutic endeavor, social and individual.

II. *Ego Pathology and Historical Change*

1.

A boy of five undergoes a change of personality from a "mother's boy" to a violent, stubborn and disobedient child. The most disquieting symptom is an urge to set fires. His parents were separated at the outbreak of the war. The father joined the air forces, the mother moved in with an aunt. These women on the homefront, with clear expressions of their disrespect for the peacetime father, cultivated babyish traits in the boy, while on the front the father proceeded to become a hero. On the occasion of a furlough, the little boy had the experience of seeing him the admired center of the family at large, the neighborhood, and the whole community. The mother announced that she would drop her divorce plans. The father left—and later was killed in action.

After the father's departure the affectionate and dependent boy developed more and more disquieting symptoms of destructiveness and defiance, culminating in fire-setting. He gave the key to the change himself when, protesting his mother's beatings, he pointed to a pile of wood he had set afire and exclaimed, "If this were a Germany city, you would like what I did." He thus indicated that in setting fires he fantasied being a bombardier like the father.

We see here the identification of a son with his father, resulting from a suddenly increased "oedipus" conflict at the very close of the oedipus age. The father, in his new role of an ideal prototype, becomes more of a threat both as a competitor for the mother, and as a potential aggressor against the son; he thus devaluates radically the usefulness of the boy's feminine identifications. In order to save himself from both sexual and social disorientation the boy must, in the shortest time, regroup his identifications; yet his new, masculine trend of identification, is tragically compromised by the fact, that the great competitor is killed. While this fact by no means devaluates the prototype of the hero, it increases the boy's guilt feeling toward the dead man, whom he wanted to replace; it underlines the dangers accompanying the role of the hero; and it makes the aviator-father a less tangible but only the more dangerous potential aggressor from the world above the skies.

A child has quite a number of opportunities to identify himself, more or less experimentally, with real or fictitious people of either sex, with habits, traits, occupations, and ideas. Certain crises force him to make radical selections. However, the historical era in which he lives offers only a limited number of socially meaningful models for workable combinations of identification fragments. Their usefulness depends on the way in which they, simultaneously, meet the requirements of the organism's maturational stage and the ego's habits of synthesis.

To our patient, the role of the bombardier suggested a possible synthesis of his temperament (vigorous), his maturational stage (phallic-urethral-locomotor); his social stage (oedipus) and his social situation (living with women); his capacities (muscular, mechanical); his father's temperament and defenses (counterphobic); and an acute historical prototype (aggressive hero). Where such a synthesis succeeds, a most surprising coagulation of constitutional, temperamental, and learned reactions may produce radiant health and unexpected accomplishment in activities specifically expressive of the new ego-identity. Our patient was observed swooping down a hill on a bicycle, endangering, scaring, and yet deftly circumventing other children. While thus indulging in his aviation fantasy, he learned playful mastery over his muscle systems, over his aggressive wishes, and the mechanics of a bicycle. Reeducation, while protecting the rights of other children must seize upon the forces thus mobilized for playful learning. For should a child feel that the environment tries to deprive him too radically of all the forms of expression which permit him to exercise his new ego-identity, he will resist with the astonishing strength encountered in animals who suddenly are forced to defend their lives. And indeed, in the social jungle of human existence, there is no feeling of being alive without a sense of ego-identity.

The desperate intensity of many a symptom, then, is a defense of a budding ego-identity, which to the child, promises to integrate the rapid changes taking place in all areas of his life. What to the observer looks like an especially powerful manifestation of naked instinct is often only a desperate plea for the permission to synthesize and sublimate in the only way possible. We therefore can expect the young patient to respond only to therapeutic measures which will help him to complete the prerequisites for the successful formation of his original ego-identity. Therapy and guidance may attempt to substitute more desirable identifications for undesirable ones, but the total configuration of the ego-identity remains unalterable.[5]

2.

In another case, the father is not an American soldier, of this war, but an ex-German soldier of the last war. He emigrated to this country because he could not accept Nazism or was unacceptable to it. His little son had hardly time to absorb Nazi indoctrination before he came to this country, where, like most children, he took to Americanization like a duck to water. Gradually, however, he developed a neurotic rebellion against all authority. What he said about the "older generation" and how he said it was clearly taken from Nazi leaves which he had never read; his behavior was an unconscious one-boy-Hitler-youth rebellion. A superficial analysis revealed that the boy in identifying with the slogans of the Hitler youths identified himself with his father's aggressors, according to the oedipus principle.

At this point, the boy's parents decided to send him to a military school. I expected him to rebel violently. Instead, something happened that I have since observed in other refugee children. A marked change came over the boy the moment he was handed a uniform with the promise of gold bars, stars and rank. It was as if these military symbols affected a sudden and decisive change in his inner economy. The boy was now an unconscious Hitler-youth wrapped up in an American prototype: the military school boy. The father, a mere civilian, now was neither dangerous nor important.

Somewhere, however, it had been this same father and related father surrogates who with unconscious gestures (4) (especially when

5. This has certain obvious implications for the "reeducation" of "bad" nations. It can be predicted that no admission of having sinned and no promises to be good will make a nation "democratic" unless the new identity offered can be integrated with previous concepts of strong and weak, masculine and feminine, based on experiences in the geographic-historical matrix of the nation and in the childhood of the individual. Only a victor who demonstrates the historical inescapability of supernational aims and knows how to base them on established regional identities will make new people out of old nations.

speaking of military exploits during the last war) had helped establish in this boy the military prototype which is a part of every European's group identity, and in the German mind has the special significance of being one of the few thoroughly German and highly developed identities. As a historical focus of the family's general trend of identifications the military identity continues to exist unconsciously in those who are excluded from its consummation by political developments.[6]

3.

These are simple and striking examples. The subtler methods by which children are induced to accept historical or actual people as prototypes of good and evil have hardly been studied. Minute displays of emotion such as affection, pride, anger, guilt, anxiety, sexual tension (rather than the words used, the meanings intended, or the philosophy implied), transmit to the human child the outlines of what really counts in his world, i.e., the variables of his group's space-time and the perspectives of its life plan.

Equally undefined are the minute socio-economic and cultural *panics* which involve the family, causing individual regressions to infantile atonements and a reactionary return to more primitive moral codes. As such panics coincide in time and in dynamic quality with one of the child's psycho-sexual crises, they share in the determination of his neurosis: every neurosis is shared panic, isolated anxiety, and somatic tension all at once.

We observe, for instance, that in our guilt-culture, individuals and groups, whenever they perceive that their socio-economic status is in danger, unconsciously behave as if inner dangers (temptations) had really called forth the threatening disaster. As a consequence, not only individual regressions to early guilt feelings and atonements take place, but also a reactionary return to the content and to the form of historically earlier principles of behavior. The implicit moral code becomes more restricted, more magic, more exclusive, more intolerant, etc. What patients persistently describe as their childhood milieu, often

6. In an outstanding document Bruno Bettelheim (2) has described his experiences in a German concentration camp of the early days. He reports the various steps and external manifestations (such as affectations in posture and dress) by which the inmates abandoned their identity as anti-fascists in favor of that of their tormentors. He himself preserved his life and sanity by deliberately and persistently clinging to the historical Jewish identity of invincible, spiritual and intellectual superiority over a physically superior outer-world: he made his tormentors the subject of a silent research project which he safely delivered to the world of free letters.

is the condensation of a few selected periods in which too many simultaneous changes resulted in a panicky atmosphere.

In the case of another five-year-old boy who produced convulsions after a number of coincidental experiences all concerning aggression and death, the idea of violence had received its problematic meaning from the following trends in the family history. The father was an Eastern European Jew whom the mild and meek grandparents had taken as a five-year-old to the New York East Side, where he could survive only by superimposing on his childhood identity that of a guy who hits first. This rule he built into our patient's identity, not without indicating how much it had cost him. Having survived with reasonable economic success, however, he then opened a store on the main street of a small Yankee town and moved into a residential neighborhood where he had to revoke his initial instructions and to impress his now cocky and inquisitive little boy, pleadingly and threateningly, with the fact that a shopkeeper's son should treat the Gentiles gently. This change of identities occurred in the midstream of the boy's phallic-locomotor stage, when he needed clear directions and new opportunities of expression,—and incidentally at an age analogous to that at which the father had been the victim of migration. The family-panic (let's be gentle or else we will lose ground), the individual anxiety (how can I be gentle if all I have learned is to be tough and when I must be tough to feel safe), the oedipus problem of managing and diverting aggression against the father, and the somatic tension caused by undirected rage—these were all specific to one another, causing a short-circuit instead of the mutual regulation which should dominate simultaneous changes in organism, environment, and ego. His epileptic reaction became manifest.

4.

In the analysis of adults the historical prototypes which determined infantile ego-identity crises, appear in specific transferences and in specific resistances.

The following excerpt from the case history of an adult illustrates the relationship of such an infantile crisis to the patient's adult life style.

A dancer, of considerable good looks (although extremely small stature) developed the annoying symptom of having to hold her torso so rigidly upright that dancing became awkward and ungainly.

The analysis proved her hysterical erectness to be a break-through of a penis envy which had been provoked in childhood along with an otherwise well sublimated exhibitionism. The patient was the only daughter of a second-generation German-American, a successful businessman given to a certain exhibitionistic individualism, which included a great pride in his powerful physique. He insisted on an erect posture (probably no longer consciously Prussian) on the part of his blond sons, but did not require the same from his dark-skinned daughter; in fact, he did not seem to see much worth exhibiting in the female body. This contributed to other motivations in the patient's dancing the overpowering wish to exhibit an "improved" posture which resembled the caricature of Prussian ancestors whom she had never seen.

The historical anchoring of such symptoms is clarified by the analysis of the resistances, with which the symptom is defended.

The patient, who in her conscious thoughts as well as in her positive transference drew a parallel between the father's and the analyst's tall and (to her) nordic physiques, to her great dismay found herself dreaming of the analyst as a small, dirty, crumpled-up Jew. With this image of low birth and weak masculinity, she attempted to disqualify him from the right to explore the secret of her symptom, namely the danger to her fragile ego-identity emanating from the association of her sexual conflicts with an unruly pair of historical prototypes, an *ideal* prototype (German, tall, phallic), and an *evil* prototype (Jewish, dwarfish, castrated, female). The patient's ego-identity had attempted to subsume this dangerous alternative in the role of the radically modern dancer: a creative gesture which in its defensive aspects constituted an exhibitionistic protest against the social and sexual inferiority of women. Her symptom betrays the fact that the father's exhibitionism, as well as his prejudices, because they were inculcated into the patient through the sensual testimony of the oedipus complex, had retained a dangerous degree of disturbing power in her unconscious.

It is usual in our culture that the unconscious evil identity (that which the ego is most afraid to resemble) is composed of the images of the violated (castrated) body, the ethnic outgroup and the exploited minority. Although it manifests itself in a great variety of syndromes, this association is all-pervasive, in men and women, in majorities and minorities, and in all classes of a given national or cultural unit. For the ego, in the course of its synthesizing efforts, attempts to subsume the most powerful ideal and evil prototypes (the final contestants, as it were) and with them the whole existing imagery of superior and inferior, good and bad, masculine and feminine, free and slave, potent and impotent, beautiful and ugly, fast and slow, tall and small, in a simple alternative, in order to make one battle and one strategy out of a bewildering number of skirmishes. In this connection, the latent image of the more homogeneous past exerts its reactionary influence in specific resistances; we must study it, so that we may understand the historical basis of the accentuated alternative the patient's ego is searching for.

Unconscious association of ethnic alternatives with moral and sexual ones are a necessary part of any group formation. Psychoanalysis, in studying them, perfects its therapeutic methods in individual cases and, at the same time, contributes to the knowledge of the unconscious concomitants of prejudice.[7]

5.

Therapeutic efforts as well as attempts at social reform verify the sad truth that in any system based on suppression, exclusion and exploitation, the suppressed, excluded and exploited unconsciously believe in the evil image which they are made to represent by those who are dominant.[8]

7. In the inventory of our patients' ideal and evil prototypes we meet face to face with the clinical facts on which Jung based his theory of inherited prototypes ("archetypes"). As for this theory, we may note in passing that the first conceptual controversies in psychoanalysis throw light on the problem of identity in the initial stages of a science. Jung's mind, it seems, could find a sense of identity in psychoanalytic work only by combining with it a juxtaposition of his ancestors' mystical space-time and whatever he sensed in Freud's ancestry. His scientific rebellion thus led to ideological regression and (weakly denied) political reaction. This phenomenon—as similar ones before and after—had its group psychological counterpart in reaction within the psychoanalytic movement: as if in fear of endangering not only common scientific gains but also the group identity based on them, pyschoanalytic observers chose to ignore the facts observed by Jung along with his interpretation.

Certain phenomena underlying such concepts as the "anima" and the "animus" (whom I seem to recognize in my woman patient's erect image) play a dominant role in ego development. The synthesizing function of the ego constantly works on subsuming in fewer and fewer images and personified Gestalten the fragments and loose ends of all the infantile identifications. In doing so it not only uses existing historical prototypes; it also employs individually methods of condensation and of pictorial representation which characterize the products of collective imagery. In Jung's "persona" we see a weak ego sell out to a compelling social prototype. A fake ego-identity is established which suppresses rather than synthesizes those experiences and functions which endanger the "front". A dominant prototype of masculinity, for example, forces a man to exclude from his ego-identity all that which characterizes the evil image of the lesser sex, the castrate. This leaves much of his receptive and maternal faculties dissimulated, undeveloped, and guilt-ridden, and makes a shell of mannishness out of what is left.

8. According to a communication by Gordon McGregor, Sioux mixed-bloods on Pine Ridge Reservation call Sioux full-bloods "niggers", only to be called, in turn "white trash".

I once met a tall, intelligent ranch owner, who was influential in Western agriculture. Nobody but his wife knew that he was born a Jew and raised in a Jewish street in a large city. His life, while outwardly successful, was made uncomfortable by a network of compulsions and phobias which, in analysis, proved to reproduce and to superimpose on his free movements in Western valleys the outline of the neighborhood in which he grew up. His friends and adversaries, his elders and his inferiors, all unknowingly played the roles of the German boys or the Irish gangs who had made the little Jewish boy miserable on his daily walk to school, which led him from an isolated and more-refined Jewish street through the hostile remnants of tenements and gang warfare to the short-lived haven of the democratic classroom. This man's analysis provided a sad commentary on the fact that Streicher's image of an evil Jewish identity does not surpass that harbored by many a Jew who—with paradoxical results—may still try to live it down in an area where in view of what he is, his past would be relatively unimportant.

The patient in question sincerely felt that the only true savior for the Jews would be a plastic surgeon. In the body ego of such cases of morbid ego-identity, those body parts which are supposed to be of strategic importance in the characterization of the race (in the last case, the nose, in that of the dancer, the backbone) play a role similar to that of the afflicted limb in a cripple and that of the genitals in neurotics in general. The body part in question has a different ego-tonus; it is felt to be larger and heavier, or smaller and disembodied; in both cases it seems dissociated from the whole of the body, while seeming to loom dominantly in the center of the attention of others. In cases of morbid ego-identity and in those of cripples, there are dreams where the dreamer unsuccessfully tries to hide the painfully spotlighted body-part, and others where he accidentally loses it.

What may be called an individual's ego space-time thus preserves the social topology of his childhood surroundings as well as the outline of his body image. To study both it is essential to correlate a patient's childhood history with the history of his family's sedentary residence in prototypal areas (East), in "backward" areas (South), or in "forward" areas (Western and Northern frontier), as these areas were gradually incorporated into the American version of the Anglo-Saxon cultural identity; his family's migration from, through, and to areas which, at various periods, may have represented the extreme sedentary or the extreme migratory pole of the developing American character;

the family's religious conversions or diversions, with their class implications; abortive attempts at becoming standardized on a class level
and the loss or abandonment of that level; and most of all that individual or family-segment which, whatever they were doing and
wherever they were doing it, provided the last strong sense of cultural
identity.

6.

Often, when a psychoanalysis seems immovably bogged down, one
encounters in the patient's memories the picture of a proud grandfather,
whether it is a blacksmith of the old world or an engineer of the new
one; an as yet proud Jew or an unreconstructed Southerner. What these
grandfathers have in common is the fact that they were the last representatives of a world as yet more homogeneous in its feudal values,
masterly and cruel with a good conscience, self-restrained and pious
without loss of self-esteem. It is the world that invented the machine,
and still considered it a gigantic plaything, not apt to challenge the
social values of the men who made it. When we are forced to indicate
to the patient how much he fears the future and that his ego must learn
to make the best and the most of its development within fast-changing
concepts of reality, these grandfathers rise from their graves and
challenge us. Their clearer design for living always has stood behind
and above the father's ethnic feebleness and the mother's driving harsh-
ness. In the following I shall sketch this background for a number
of cases from various regions of this country.

a.   A compulsive patient's grandfather, now deceased, was a business man who built a mansion in a downtown district of an eastern
metropolis. His will demands that the mansion should stand and remain
the family's castle even though skyscrapers and apartment houses are
mushrooming all around it. The mansion becomes a somewhat sinister
symbol of conservatism, telling the world that the X's need neither
to move nor to sell, neither to expand nor to rise. The conveniences
of modern travel are accepted only as comfortably insulated pathways
between the mansion and its extensions: the club, the summer home,
the private school, Harvard, etc. The grandfather's picture hangs over
the fireplace, a little bulb eternally lighting the rosiness of the cheeks
in his generally powerful and contented countenance. His "individualistic" ways in business, his almost primeval power over the fate of his
children, are known but not questioned; rather they are over-compen-
sated for by a sensitive show of respect, scrupulousness and thrift.
The grandsons know that in order to find an identity of their own

they have to break out of the mansion, so to speak, and join the mad striving which has engulfed the neighborhood. Some do, not without taking the mansion with them as an internalized pattern, a basic ego-space, which has determined their defense mechanism of proud and pained withdrawal, and their symptoms of obsessiveness and of sexual anesthesia. Their psychoanalyses last inordinately long, partially because the analyst's four walls become the new mansion; the analyst's contemplative silence and his theoretical approach, a new edition of the mansion's ritualistic isolation. Further resistances become plain in dreams and associations. The curative effect of the patient's politely "positive" transference ends where the reticence of the analyst seems to resemble the restrained father rather than the ruthless grandfather. The father image, it appears, (and with it the transference) is split up; the image of the weak and mild father of today is isolated from the oedipal father image, which is fused with that of the powerful grand-father. As the analysis approaches this double image fantasies appear which make plain the grandfather's overwhelming importance for the patient's real ego-identity. They betray the violent sense of power, the fury of superiority which makes it hard for these overtly inhibited people to enter economic competition except on terms of pre-arranged superior privileges. These men, of the once highest strata, join those from the very lowest ones in being the truly disinherited in American life; from where they are there is no admission to free competition. They now resist cure because it implies a change in ego-identity, an ego-resynthesis on the terms of changed economic history.

The only way of breaking through this deep resignation is serious attention to memories which show (what the child knew) that the grandfather really was a simple man, and that he fulfilled his place not by force of some primeval power, but because history favored his capabilities.[9]

b.   For a Western pattern, I refer to a previously published case. (3, p. 349.) Consider a boy whose grandparents came West, "where seldom is heard a discouraging word". The grandfather, a powerful and and powerfully driven man, seeks ever new and challenging engineering tasks in widely separated regions. When the initial challenge is met, he hands the task over to others, and moves on. His wife sees him only for an occasional impregnation. According to a typical family pattern, his sons cannot keep pace with him and are left as respectable

9. This cannot be analyzed, of course, if the analyst prefers to share his patient's economic royalism, rather than to interpret it.

settlers by the wayside. To express their change of life style in fitting slogans, one would have to state that from an existence characterized by the slogan "let's get the hell out of here," they turn to one expressing the determination "let's stay—and keep the bastards out". The grandfather's only daughter (the patient's mother) alone remains identified with him. This very identification, however, does not permit her to take a husband equal to her strong father. She marries a weak man and settles down. She brings her boy up to be God-fearing and industrious. He becomes reckless and shifting at times, depressed at others: somewhat of a juvenile delinquent now, later maybe a more enjoyable Westerner, with alcoholic moods.

What his worried mother does not know is that she herself all through his childhood has belittled the sedentary father; has decried the lack of mobility, geographic and social, of her marital existence; has idealized the grandfather's exploits; but has also reacted with panicky punitiveness to any display of friskiness in the boy, which was apt to disturb the now well-defined neighborhood.

c.   A woman from the Middle West, rather unusually feminine and sensitive, uses a visit with relatives in the West to consult the writer concerning a general feeling of affective constriction and an all-pervasive mild anxiety. During an exploratory analysis she seems almost lifeless. Only after weeks, on rare occasions, is she overcome by a flood of associations, all concerning sudden, horrid impressions of sex or death. Many of these memories emerge not from unconscious depths, but from an isolated corner of her consciousness, where all those matters are boarded off, which on occasion had broken through the orderly factualness of the upper middle class surroundings of her childhood. This mutual isolation of life segments is similar to that met with in compulsive neurotics anywhere; but in some regions it is more; it is a way of life, an ethos, which in our patient had become truly uncomfortable only because at the moment she was being courted by a European and was trying to envisage life in a cosmopolitan atmosphere. She felt attracted, but at the same time inhibited; her imagination was vividly provoked, but restrained by anxiety. Her bowels reflected this ambivalence by an alternation of constipation and diarrhea. One gained the impression of a general inhibition, rather than a basic impoverishment of imagination in matters both sexual and social.

The patient's dreams gradually revealed a hidden source of unemployed vitality. While she seemed pained and lifeless in her free associations, her dream life became humorous and imaginative in an almost autonomous way. She dreamed of entering quiet church congregations in a flaming red dress, and of throwing stones into respectable windows. But her most colorful dreams put her into Civil War days—on the Confederate side. The climax was a dream in which she sat on a toilet, set off by low partitions in the middle of a tremendous ballroom, and waved to elegantly dressed couples of Confederate officers and Southern ladies who swirled around her to the sounds of powerful brass.

These dreams helped unearth an isolated part of her childhood, namely, the gentle warmth awarded her by her grandfather, a Confederate veteran. His world was a fairy tale of the past. But for all its formalism, the grandfather's patriarchal masculinity and gentle affection had been experienced through the child's hungry senses and had proved more immediately reassuring to her searching ego than either the father's or the mother's promises of standardized success. With the grandfather's death the patient's affects went dead because they were part of an abortive ego-identity formation which failed to receive nourishment either in the form of affection or social rewards.

d. The psychoanalytic treatment of women with a prominent ego-identity remnant of the Southern lady (an identity which pervades more than one class or race) seems complicated by special resistances. To be sure, our patients are dislodged Southerners, their ladyhood a defense, almost a symptom. Their wish for treatment finds its limits in three ideas, which are all connected with the particular provisions in Southern culture for safeguarding caste and race identity by imposing the prototype of the lady on the small girl.

There is, first, a pseudo-paranoid suspicion that life is a series of critical tests when vicious gossips attempt to stack up minor weaknesses and blemishes against the Southern woman—toward a final judgment: to be—or not to be—a lady. Second, there is the all-pervading conviction that men, if not restrained by the formalities of a tacitly approved double standard (which sells them lesser and darker sex objects at the price of overt respect for ladies), will prove to be no gentlemen; that they will at the very least try to blacken the lady's name and with it her claim to a socially superior husband, or to the prospect of having her children marry upward. But there is also the equally ambivalent implication that any man who does not proceed to shed his gentleman's exterior when the opportunity offers itself is a weakling who only deserves to be mercilessly provoked. The usual feelings of guilt and inferiority all exist within the coordinates of a life plan which is dominated by the conscious hope for higher social status, and made morbid by its ambivalent counterpart, the hidden hope for the man who will dissolve the woman's need to be a lady in a moment of reckless passion. In all this there is a basic inability to conceive of any area in life where the standards and the words of a man and a woman could in honesty coincide and be lifted above a certain primeval antagonism. Needless to say, such unconscious standards cause severe suffering in sincere and enlightened women. But only the verbalization of these historical trends, concomitantly with the initial analysis of the patient's character resistances, makes psychoanalysis possible.

7.

In these and similar ways, patients of psychoanalysis repeat in their transferences and in their resistances abortive attempts at synchronizing fast changing and sharply contrasting remnants of national, regional, and class identities during critical stages of their childhood. The patient weaves the analyst into his unconscious life plan: he idealizes him (especially if he is European-born) by identifying him with his more homogeneous ancestors; or he subtly resists him as the enemy of a brittle and tentative ego-identity.

The functioning American, as the heir of a history of extreme contrasts and abrupt changes, bases his final ego-identity on some tentative combination of dynamic polarities such as migratory and sedentary, individualistic and standardized, competitive and cooperative, pious and free-thinking, etc.[10] While we see extreme manifestations of one of these poles, analysis always reveals that this very extremeness (of, let us say, rigidity or shiftiness) represents a defense against the always implied, feared, or hoped for, opposite extreme. Psychoanalysts, in their daily work, are consulted by those who cannot stand the tension between polarities, the never-ceasing necessity of remaining tentative in order to be free to take the next step, to turn the next corner. Many patients hope to find in a psychoanalytic "system" a magic refuge from the discontinuities of existence; treatment itself becomes a regression to a better ritualized, more homogeneous, more patriarchal one-to-one relationship. If not understood,

10. Could it be that the two-party system and other balancing mechanisms in public affairs reflect this polarity in that they automatically counteract any permanent commitment toward one of the poles?

this can become the basis for a stubborn resistance against the successful termination of treatment.

Other resistances are based on class identities which in the present notes have been neglected in favor of (prettier) ethnic configurations suggested by the study of "primitives". The successor and heir of the revolutionary citizen, namely the middle class citizen of today, has made a castle of his home and a kingdom of his ego, and is as determined to seek individual salvation in the "adjustment" to this, his privileged estate, as any feudal aristocrat did before him. Bewildered by changing history, he seeks our help only in regard to a selection of the disturbances which threaten his inner comfort, namely, id urge, superego pressure, and somatic tension. In these respects he will often not hesitate to give revealing material; but he will resist the analysis of his ego and its social coordinates.

We should beware of the addition, in contemporary fiction and drama, of the psychoanalytic couch to such furniture as the royal throne, the executive's desk and the diva's bed, which previously symbolized the desperate insistence on individual salvation within an autocratic illusion.

The cured patient has the courage to face the discontinuities of life in this country and the polarities of its struggle for an economic and cultural identity, not as an imposed hostile reality, but as a potential promise for a more universal collective identity. This finds its limits, however, where people are fundamentally impoverished in their childhood sensuality and stalled in their freedom to use opportunities.

III. *Ego Strength and Social Pathology*

1.

Individual psychopathology contributes to the understanding of ego-identity the study of its impairments by constitutional deficiency, early emotional impoverishment, neurotic conflict, and traumatic damage. Before we turn to examples of ego-damaging social pathology we may at least state a question although its answer will have to wait for a more systematic presentation: what factors make for a strong normal ego-identity? In a general way it is plain that everything that makes for a strong ego contributes to its identity.

Freud originally stated (8) that the sources of human self-esteem (and thus an important infantile contribution to an individual's ego-identity) are

1)   the residue of childish narcissism

2)   such infantile omnipotence as experience corroborates (the fulfilment of the ego-ideal)

3)   gratification of object-libido.

Psychoanalysis came to emphasize the individual and regressive rather than the collective-supportive aspects of these statements. It was concerned with only half the story.

For if a residue of infantile narcissism is to survive, the maternal environment must create and sustain it with a love which assures the child that it is good to be alive in the particular social coordinates in which he happens to find himself. Infantile narcissism, which is said to fight so valiantly against the inroads of a frustrating environment, is in fact first built up and nourished by the sensual enrichment and the encouragement provided by this same environment. Widespread severe impoverishment of infantile narcissism (and thus of the basis of a strong ego) is lastly to be considered a breakdown of that collective synthesis which gives every newborn baby and his motherly surroundings a super-individual status as a trust of the community. In the later abandonment or transformation of this narcissism into more mature self-esteem, it is again of decisive importance whether or not the more realistic being can expect an opportunity to employ what he has learned and to acquire a feeling of increased communal meaning.

If experience is to corroborate part of the infantile sense of omnipotence, then child training must know not only how to teach sensual health and progressive mastery, but also how to offer tangible social recognition as the fruits of health and mastery. For unlike the infantile sense of omnipotence which is fed by make-believe and adult deception, the self-esteem attached to the ego-identity is based on the rudiments of skills and social techniques which assure a gradual coincidence of functional pleasure and actual performance, of ego-ideal and social role. The self-esteem attached to the ego-identity contains the recognition of a tangible future.

If "object-libido" is to be satisfied, then genital love and orgastic potency must be assured of a cultural synthesis of economic safety and emotional security; for only such a synthesis gives a unified meaning to the full functional cycle of genitality, which includes conception, child-bearing, and child-rearing. Infatuation may project all the incestuous childhood loves into a present "object"; genital activity may help two individuals to use one another as an anchor against regression; mutual genital love faces toward the future. It works toward a division of labor in that life task which only two of the opposite sex can fulfill together: the synthesis of production, procreation and recreation in the primary social unit of the family. In this sense, then, ego-identity acquires its final strength in the meeting of mates whose ego-identity is complementary in some essential point and can be fused in marriage without the creation either of a dangerous discontinuity of tradition, or of an incestuous sameness—both of which are apt to prejudice the offspring's ego development.

The unconscious "incestuous" choice of a mate who resembles infantile love objects in some decisive feature is not to be considered as necessarily pathogenic, as psychopathological writers seem to infer. Such a choice follows an ethnic mechanism in that it creates a continuity between the family one grew up in and the family one establishes: it thus perpetuates tradition, i.e., the sum of all that had been learned by preceding generations, in analogy to the preservation of the gains of evolution in the mating within the species. Neurotic fixation (and rigid inner defense against it) signifies the failure, not the nature of this mechanism.

However, many of the mechanisms of adjustment which once made for evolutionary adaptation, tribal integration, national or class coherence, are at loose ends in a world of universally expanding identities. Education for an ego-identity which receives strength from changing historical conditions demands a conscious acceptance of historical heterogeneity on the part of adults, combined with an .enlightened effort to provide human childhood anywhere with a new fund of meaningful continuity. For this task, the systematic investigation of the following strategic points seems indicated:

1. The coherence of the body image, and its possible basis in fetal experience, with special reference to the importance of the mother's emotional attitude toward pregnancy.

2. The synchronization of postnatal care with the newborn's temperament, based as it is on his prenatal and his birth experience.

3. The sameness and continuity of the early sensual experience of the mother's body and temperament, which nourishes and preserves a lasting fund of narcissism.

4. The synchronization of the pregenital stages and of the normative steps in child development with a group identity.

5. The immediate promise of tangible social recognition for the abandonment of infantile narcissism and autoerotism and for the acquisition of skills and knowledge during latency.

6. The adequacy of the solution of the oedipus conflict, within the individual's socio-historical setting.

7. The relation of the final adolescent version of the ego-identity to economic opportunities, realizable ideals, and available techniques.

8. The relation of genitality to love objects with complementary ego-identities, and to the communal meaning of procreation.

In the following notes I have to content myself with sketching the connection of three of the points mentioned with manifest problems of social pathology. We ask concretely: what possibility is there for the American Negro's pregenital training to work toward a sense of ego-identity? Do we understand the methods by which the American adolescent derives a sense of ego-identity? What is the role of ego-identity in the so-called war neuroses?

2.

In the experiences of pregenital stages the human infant learns the basic variables of organismic-social existence, before his libido becomes free for its procreative task. Child training, in creating a particular ratio of emphasis on such organismic modes as incorporation, retention assimilation, elimination, intrusion and inclusion, gives the growing being a character basis suited to the main modes of later life tasks; if—indeed—later life tasks and early training are synchronized.

Consider our colored countrymen. Their babies often receive sensual satisfactions of oral and sensory surplus, adequate for a lifetime. It is preserved in the way in which they move, laugh, talk, sing. There forced symbiosis with the feudal South capitalized on this oral-sensory treasure to build up a slave's identity: mild, submissive, dependent, somewhat querulous, but always ready to serve, and with occasional empathy and childlike wisdom. But underneath a dangerous split occurred. The humiliating symbiosis on the one hand and, on the other, the necessity of the master race to protect its identity against sensual and oral temptations, established in both groups an association: light—clean—clever—white; and, dark—dirty—dumb—nigger. The result, especially in those Negroes who have left the poor haven of their Southern homes, is often a violently sudden and cruel cleanliness training. This, in turn, transmits itself to the phallic-locomotor stage, in which the restrictions as to what shade of girl one may dream of and where one may move and act with abandon, interfere at every moment of waking and dreaming with the free transfer of the original narcissistic sensuality to the genital sphere. Three identities are formed: (1) mammy's oral-sensual "honey-child": tender, expressive, rhythmical; (2) the clean anal-compulsive, restrained, friendly, but always sad "white man's Negro"; and (3) the evil identity of the dirty, anal-sadistic, phallic-rapist "nigger".

When faced with so-called opportunities which only offer a newly restricted freedom but fail to provide an integration of the identity fragments mentioned, one of these fragments becomes dominant in the form of a racial caricature; tired of this caricature, the colored individual often retires into hypochondriac invalidism as a condition which represents an analogy to the ego-space-time of defined restriction in the South: a neurotic regression to the ego-identity of the slave.

I know of a colored boy who, like our boys, listens every night to the Lone Ranger. Then he sits up in bed, dreaming that he is the Ranger. But alas, the moment always comes when he sees himself galloping after some masked offenders and suddenly notices that in his image the Lone Ranger is a Negro. He stops his fantasies. While a child, this boy was extremely expressive, both in his pleasure and in his sorrows. Today he is calm and always smiles; his language is soft and blurred; nobody can hurry him, or worry him, or please him. White men like him.

3.

Adolescence is the age of the final establishment of a dominant positive ego-identity; it is then that a future within reach becomes a part of the conscious life plan: but does it fit unconscious anticipations?

Among Americans with well-defined ego-identities there is one type of teen-age boy. The family is Anglo-Saxon, mildly Protestant, white collar class. This boy is tall, thin, muscular in his body build. He is shy, especially with women, and emotionally retentive, as if he saved himself for something. His occasional grin, however, indicates a basic satisfaction with himself. His goals are defined. Before the war he wanted to be an athlete; during the war, an aviator (pilot). The attraction of prototypes attached to the avocations of either baseball or aviation lies in such needs as disciplined locomotion; fair aggression; sublimated phallicism; ascetic restraint; counterphobic defense and the temporary avoidance of women.

This boy has what we would consider "pathogenic" parents: his mother is harsh, loud-voiced, big-boned, punitive, and frigid; his father, while exhibiting customary toughness in business, is shy in intimate relationships and not treated too well at home. It is a picture which in case histories is still noted as a symptom, although it quite clearly is a culture pattern. What it will do to a child depends on variables still to be determined.

As for the mother, who shows a certain contempt for male weakness, her bark is worse than her bite. She has a male ideal, usually derived from her father or grandfather, and she indicates to the son that she believes in his ability to come close to this ideal. She is wise enough (sometimes lazy or indifferent enough) to leave it to him whether he wants to live up to this ideal or not. Most important, she is not over-protective. Unlike mothers who drive on but cannot let go (*they* are the pathogenic ones), she does not overly tie the boy to herself. She gives her teen-age children the freedom of the street, of the playground, and of parties, even into the night. It must be admitted that this mother is sure of how far the boy will go in sexual matters, because she feels she has driven the devil out of him when he was small; she has under-stimulated him sexually and starved him emotionally, within reason or, at any rate, convention.

It would be interesting to speculate on how far a certain determined lack of maternalism in American mothers is historically founded, not only in puritanism but in an adaptation to historical conditions which made it dangerous for a son to believe more in the past than in the future; dangerous to base his identity on the adherence to his childhood home rather than on the migration in pursuit of a better chance; dangerous ever to appear to be a "sissy" or a "sucker" instead of one who has learned to tolerate a certain amount of deprivation and loneliness. We should search in every collective vice—and child training today is full of vices—for out-dated historical virtues; for only if one has appraised their erstwhile value in securing survival and identity, can one hope effectively to advise the individual or the community by suggesting measures which are based on existing fragments of cultural identity—or hold one's peace until history changes.

The boys I have in mind, already in early adolescence, are tall, or taller, than their fathers. Their dreams indicate that their physical prowess as well as their independent identity arouses castration fear in them. It is as if in their development they had to stay on a tight-rope: only if they are stronger than or different from the real father will they live up to their mother's expectations; but only if they somehow document that they are weaker than the primal scene father of their childhood will they be free of castration fear. Thus they become boastful and ruthless in many insignificant regards, but submissive and kind where it counts.

How do the fathers prevent too much oedipal guilt in the sons? First of all, in their relationship the future is emphasized as against the past. The future absolves the past. If the sons in their behavior seem to be organized in the pursuit of one further degree of Americanization, it is the fatherly obligation to let the children proceed in their own way. In fact, because of their greater affinity to the tempo and to the technical problems of the immediate future, the children are in a sense "wiser" than the parents; and, indeed, many children are more mature in their outlook on emotional problems. The father of such boys does not hide his weakness behind a mask of inflated patriarchal claims. If he shares with the son an admiration for an ideal type, be he baseball player or industrial leader, comedian, scientist or rodeo artist, the need to become like the ideal is emphasized without burdening it with a problem of the father's defeat. If the father plays baseball with his son, it is not in order to impress him with the fact that he, the father, comes closer to the perfection of a common ideal type—for he probably does not—but rather that they play together at identifying with that type, and that there is always the chance that the boy may approach the ideal closer than the father did. There is always a chance, and a choice. Thus, fraternal images step, boldly or gingerly, into the gaps left by decaying paternalism, fathers and sons are unconsciously working on the development of a pattern which will forestall the reactionary return of more patriarchal oedipal patterns, without on the other hand leading to a general impoverishment of the father-son relationship, and with it, of the ego-identity.

What has already been said concerning the collective space-time and the life plan of a society, shows the necessity of studying the spontaneous ways in which segments of modern society strive to make a workable continuity out of child training and economic development. For whoever wants to guide, must understand, conceptualize and use spontaneous trends of identity formation. Our clinical histories help in such research, where they avoid being too episodic in type, and where stereotypes, such as "the patient had domineering mother" (which are based on comparisons with a family image implied in classical European psychiatry) are further broken down into historically significant variations. During this war, psychiatric and psychoanalytic attempts at explaining what childhood milieus cause or do not cause a man to break down under military stress, have, on the whole, failed for lack of historical perspective.

4.

In our work with veterans discharged from the Armed Forces as psychoneurotics before the end of hostilities, we have become familiar with the universal symptoms of partial loss of ego synthesis. Many of these men, indeed, regress to the "stage of unlearned function". (10) The boundaries of their ego have lost their shock-absorbing delineation: anxiety and anger are provoked by everything too sudden or too intense, whether it be a sensory impression or a self-reproach, an impulse or a memory. A ceaselessly "startled" sensory system is attacked by stimuli from outside as well as by somatic sensations: heat flashes, palpitation, cutting headaches. Insomnia hinders the nightly restoration of sensory screening by sleep, and that of emotional synthesis by dreaming. Amnesia, neurotic pseudologia, and confusion show the partial loss of time-binding and of spatial orientation. What definable symptoms and remnants of "peacetime neuroses" there are have a fragmentary and false quality, as if the ego could not even accomplish an organized neurosis.

In some cases this ego impairment seems to have its origin in violent events, in others in the gradual grind of a million annoyances. Obviously the men are worn out by too many changes (gradual or sudden) in too many respects at once; somatic tension, social panic and ego-anxiety are always present. Above all, the men "do not know any more who they are": there is a distinct loss of ego-identity. The sense of sameness and of continuity and the belief in one's social role are gone.

The American group identity supports an individual's ego-identity as long as he can preserve a certain element of deliberate tentativeness; as long as he can convince himself that the next step is up to him and that no matter where he is staying or going he always has the choice of leaving or turning in the opposite direction if he chooses to do so. In this country the migrant does not want to be told to move on, nor the sedentary man to stay where he is; for the life style of each contains the opposite element as an alternate which he wishes to consider his most private and individual decision. For many men, then, the restraint and discipline of army life provides few ideal prototypes.[11] To quite a few, it represents instead the intensely evil identity of the sucker; one who lets himself be sidetracked, cooped up, and stalled while others are free to pursue his chance and his girl. But to be a sucker means to be a social and sexual castrate; if you are a sucker, not even a mother's pity will be with you.

In the (often profuse) utterances of psychoneurotic casualties, all those memories and anticipations appear associated that ever threatened or are expected to threaten the freedom of the next step. In their struggle to regain access to the non-reversible escalator of free enterprise, their traumatized ego fights and flees an evil identity which includes elements of the crying baby, the bleeding woman, the submissive nigger, the sexual sissy, the economic sucker, the mental moron—all prototypes the mere allusion to which can bring these men close to homicidal or suicidal rage, ending up in varying degrees of irritability or apathy. Their exaggerated attempt to blame their ego-dilemma on circumstances and individuals gives their childhood history a more sordid character, and themselves the appearance of a worse psychopathy than is justified. Their ego-identity has fallen apart into its bodily, sexual, social, occupational elements, each having to overcome again the danger of its evil prototype. Rehabilitation work can be made more effective and economical if the clinical investigation focuses on the patient's shattered life plan and if advice tends to

11. Notable exceptions are the recipients of promising commissions and members of teams in highly mechanized units. However, men whose ego-identity thrives on military service, sometimes break down after discharge, when it appears that the war provoked them into the usurpation of more ambitious prototypes than their more restricted peacetime identities could afford to sustain.

strengthen the resynthesis of the elements on which the patient's ego-identity was based.

5.

In addition to the several hundred thousand men who lost and only gradually or partially regained their ego-identity in this war and to the thousands whose acute loss of ego-identity was falsely diagnosed and treated as psychopathy, an untold number has experienced to the core the threat of a traumatic loss of ego-identity as a result of radical historical change.

The fact that these men, their physicians, and their contemporaries in increasing numbers turn to the bitter truths of psychoanalytic psychiatry is in itself a historical development which calls for critical appraisal. It expresses an increased acceptance of psychoanalytic insights insofar as they concern the meaning of anxiety and of disease in the individual case history. Yet this partial acceptance of painful unconscious determinants of human behavior has the quality of a concomitant resistance against the infinitely more disquieting awareness of a social symptom and its historical determinants. I mean the subliminal panic which accompanied the large scale testing of the American identity during the most recent period of world history.

Historical change has reached a coercive universality and a global acceleration which is experienced as a threat to the emerging American identity. It seems to devaluate the vigorous conviction that this nation can afford mistakes; that this nation, by definition, is always so far ahead of the rest of the world in inexhaustible reserves, in vision of planning, in freedom of action, and in tempo of progress that there is unlimited space and endless time in which to develop, to test, and to complete her social experiments. The difficulties met in the attempt to integrate this old image of insulated spaciousness with the new image of explosive global closeness are deeply disquieting. They are characteristically met, at first with the application of traditional methods to a new space-time; there is the missionary discovery of "One World", aviation pioneering on a "Trans-World" basis, charity on a global scale, etc. Yet, there also remains a deep consciousness of a lag in economic and political integration, and with it, in emotional and spiritual strength.

The psychotherapist, in disregarding the contribution of this development to neurotic discomfort, is apt not only to miss much of the specific dynamics in contemporary life-cycles; he is apt also to deflect (or to serve those whose business demands that they deflect) individual energy from the collective tasks at hand. A large scale decrease of neurosis can be achieved only by equal clinical attention to cases and to conditions, to the fixation on the past and the emerging design for the future, to the grumbling depth and the unsafe surface.

IV. *Historical Connotations of Psychoanalytic Concepts*

1.

In studying the ego's relation to changing historical reality, psychoanalysis approaches a new phalanx of unconscious resistances. It is implicit in the nature of psychoanalytic investigation, that such resistances must be located and appraised in the observer and in his concepts, before their presence in the observed can be fully understood and effectively handled. When investigating instincts, the psychoanalyst knows that his drive to investigate is partially instinctive in nature; he knows that he responds with a partial counter-transference to the patient's transference, i.e., the ambiguous wish to satisfy infantile strivings in the very therapeutic situation which is to cure them. The analyst acknowledges all this, yet works methodically toward that margin of freedom where the clear delineation of the inevitable makes consuming resistances unnecessary and frees energy for creative planning.

It is, then, a commonplace to state that the psychoanaiyst in training must learn to study the historical determinants of what he himself is like, before he can hope to perfect that human gift: the ability to understand what is different from him. Beyond this, however, there are the historical determinants of psychoanalytic concepts.

If in the field of human motivation, the same terms have been used over a period of half a century (and what a century!) they cannot but reflect the ideologies of their day of origin and absorb the connotations of consequent social changes. Ideological connotation is the inevitable historical equation in the use of conceptual tools which concern the ego, man's organ of reality testing. The conceptualizations of man's self-same core and of reality itself are by necessity a function of historical change. Yet, here too, our search is for a margin of freedom, our method, radical analysis of resistances to insight and to planning.

In these concluding notes I wish to suggest various ways in which the changing usage of ego concepts reflects contemporary historical dilemmas concerning problems of the era, of the century, and of our decade.

a.   The era is reflected in a recent formulation, according to which "all through childhood a maturation process is at work which, in the service of an increasing knowledge and adaptation to reality, aims at perfecting (ego) functions, at rendering them more and more objective and *independent of the emotions* until they can become *as accurate and reliable as a mechanical apparatus"*. (6)

Obviously, the ego as such is older than all mechanization. If we detect in it a tendency to mechanize itself and to be free from the very emotions without which there is no experience at all, we may actually be concerned with a specific development underlying a historical dilemma. Today we face the question of whether the problems of the machine age will be solved by a mechanization of man or by a humanization of industry. Our child training customs, devised as yet by magic rather than by thought, have begun to standardize modern man, so that he may become a reliable mechanism prepared to "adjust" to the competition for the exploitation of the machine and its human manipulators. In fact, certain modern trends in child training seem to represent a magic identification with the machine, analogous to identifications of primitive tribes with their principal prey. If modern man's ego seems to crave mechanical adaptation and to sacrifice its privileges of ever wider experience and ever stronger reason, then we are not dealing with the nature of the ego, but with one of its historical adaptations, if not, indeed dysfunctions. The study of the ego's "nature", then, would lead to the investigation of conditions and forces which, in searching for material plenty for some, may be impoverishing the egos of all.

b.   The fact that Freud, for his first group-psychological discussions, quoted the post-revolutionary French sociologist Le Bon has left its mark on consequent psychoanalytic discussions of "multitudes" of men. As Freud recognized, Le Bon's "masses" were society on the rebound, shiftless mobs enjoying the anarchy between two stages of society and, at their best and worst, leader-led mobs. Such mobs exist; their definition stands. However, there is a considerable operational gap between this particular sociological material and the material secured by the psychoanalytic method—namely, individual history reconstructed from the evidence of transferences and counter-transferences, in therapeutic situations à deux. The resulting methodological gap has perpetuated in psychoanalytic thought an artificial differentiation between the individual-within-his-family (or seemingly surrounded by projections of his family constellation on the "outerworld") and the individual-in-the-mass, submerged in an "indistinct aggregate" of men. The phenomenon and the concept of social organization, and its bearing on the individual ego was, for the longest time, shunted off by patronizing tributes to the existence of "social factors"

A psychoanalyst with an outstanding historical orientation repeated even in 1943 that "each member of a large mass of people is an individual and a non-individual, a particle of a mass subject to many psychological laws different from those under which he primarily functions when alone, at home". (11)

If, for the moment, we accept as representative the image of a man who is geographically completely alone (and this, of all places, at home) it is questionable that any psychological laws governing his aloneness are really different from those which guide him in a "mass".[12] Would it not be more accurate to say: the situation differs— and with it the threshold of consciousness and of motility, the available channels of communication and the available techniques of expression and action? That a man could ever be psychologically alone; that a man, "alone", is essentially "better" than the same man in a group; that a man in a temporary solitary condition has ceased to be a political animal, and has disengaged himself from social action (or inaction) on whatever class level; these and similar stereotypes deserve to be accepted only in order to be further analyzed as ideological fiction.

c. While certain stereotypes, because they parallel a conservative economic trend, remain astonishingly constant, others lose or reverse their original connotations as they cross the boundaries of languages, nations, and continents. There was a post-romantic era in Europe when anything, by being traced to its origin in a "Trieb" became, as it were, knighted—if not deified; while today, and especially in this country, that which is called instinctual acquires thereby a kind of irreversible nuisance value. Instincts now demand "adjustment" where before they strove for sublimation on a "higher"

12. Maybe this is what is meant by Zilboorg's statement: "It is true, of course, that the laws of human psychology are the same wherever human individuals function as human beings."

plane. It would be a fascinating task to study the historical connotations of the basic psychoanalytic concepts on an international scale.[13]

d. As philosophers would predict, the concept of "reality" while
clear in its intended meaning, is highly corruptible in its usage.
According to the pleasure principle that is good which feels good at
the moment; the reality principle declares that to be good which in
the long run and with consideration for all possible outer and inner
developments promises most lastingly to feel good. Such principles,
established by scientific man, fall prey easily to economic man. The
reality principle, in theory and therapy, has taken on a certain individualistic color, according to which that is good which the individual
can get away with by dodging the law (insofar as it happens to be
enforced) and the superego (insofar as it causes discomfort). Our
therapeutic failures often define the limit of this usage: Western man,
almost against his will, is developing a more universal group identity.
His reality principle begins to include a *social principle* according to
which that is good which, in the long run, secures to a man what feels
good to him without keeping any other man (of the same collective
identity) from securing an analogous gain. The question that remains
is, what new synthesis of economic and emotional safety will sustain
this wider group identity, and thus give strength to the individual
ego.

e. In conclusion, I shall bring these notes up-to-date by a
reference to the undeniable power of popular methods and slogans
which seem to coincide with psychological terms. The popular use of
the word "ego" in this country has little to do with the psychoanalytic
concept of the same name; it denotes unqualified if not justified
self-esteem. Yet, in the wake of therapeutic shortcuts, this connotation
gradually creeps into psychiatric and even into psychoanalytic discussions of the ego.

When the present paper was read before the American Psychoanalytic Association in Chicago,[14] the discussion immediately abandoned the problem of society's role in the *strengthening* of the
infantile ego, and turned to the role of interested agencies in *bolstering* the ego of *adult* conscripts and workers. It was emphasized that
army and industry have gone about the job of ego-bolstering scien-

13. Siegfried Bernfeld (1) is doing some ground work for this task by elucidating
the scientific milieu in which Freud's concepts originated.

14. On May 26, 1946.

tifically and efficiently and that thus a convergence seemed to exist of the practice of "hardheaded business men" and of the theory of psychoanalysis.

Bolstering, bantering, boisterousness, and other "ego-inflating" behavior is, of course, part of the American folkways. As such it pervades speech and gesture and enters into all interpersonal relations. Without it, a therapeutic relationship in this country would remain outlandish and non-specific. The problem to be discussed here, however, is the systematic exploitation of the national practice of bolstering for the sake of making people "feel better", or of submerging their anxiety and tension so as to make them function better as patients, customers, or employees.

A weak ego does not gain substantial strength from being persistently bolstered. A strong ego, secured in its identity by a strong society, does not need, and in fact is immune to any attempt at artificial inflation. Its tendency is toward the testing of what feels real; the mastery of that which works; the understanding of that which proves necessary, the enjoyment of the vital, and the extermination of the morbid. At the same time, it tends toward the creation of a strong mutual reinforcement with others in a group-ego, which will transmit its will to the next generation.

A war, however, can be an unfair test to ego strength. During collective emergencies all resources, emotional as well as material, must be mobilized with relative disregard for what is workable and economical under more normal conditions of long range development. Ego bolstering is a legitimate measure in such days of collective danger; and it remains a genuine therapeutic approach in individual cases of acute ego-strain, i.e., wherever the individual is emotionally too young or physically too weak to meet a situation bearable to the mature and the healthy; or if a situation is too extraordinary to be met even by a relatively adequate ego. Obviously, a war increases the occurrence of both types of traumatic discrepancy between the ego and situations not included in its anticipations. Psychiatry, along with other delegated agencies, therefore was temporarily invested with omniscient power over masses of men. This power was largely based on the profession's monopolistic claim on the total subject matter of neurosis—including areas where neurosis is identical with psychosomatic and socio-economic facts which are beyond the grasp of any one discipline. The indiscriminate application of the philosophy and the practice of "ego bolstering" to peacetime conditions, however, would be theoretically unsound and therapeutically unwholesome. It is, furthermore, socially dangerous, because its employment infers that what causes the strain (i.e., "modern living") is perpetually beyond the individual's or his society's control—a state of affairs which would postpone indefinitely the revision of *conditions which are apt to weaken the infantile ego.* To deflect energy from such revision is dangerous. For American child-hood and other manifestations of the specific American freedom of spirit are but grandiose fragments striving for integration with the fragments of industrial democracy.

The effectiveness of the psychoanalytic contribution to this develop-ment is guaranteed solely by the persistent humanistic intention, beyond the mere adjustment of patients to limited conditions, to apply clinical experience to the end of making man aware of potentialities which are clouded by archaic fear.

2.

In studying his subject, the psychoanalyst (so Anna Freud points out) should occupy an observation point "equidistant from the id, the ego, and the superego" (7)—so that he may be aware of their functional interdependence and so that, as he observes a change in one of these sections of the mind he may not lose sight of related changes in the others.

Beyond this, however, the observer is aware of the fact that what he conceptualizes as id, ego, and superego are not static compartments in the capsule of a life history. Rather, they reflect three major pro-cesses the relativity of which determines the form of human behavior. They are:

1. the process of organismic organization of organ-systems in the time-space of the life cycle (evolution, epigenesis, libido-develop-ment, etc.),

2. the process of the organization of experience by ego synthesis (ego space-time, ego-defenses, ego-identity, etc.),

3. the process of the social organization of ego-organisms in geographic-historical units.

The order given follows the trend of psychoanalytic research. Otherwise, although different in structure, these processes *exist by and are relative to each other.* Any item whose meaning and potential changes within one of these processes, simultaneously changes in the others. To assure the proper rate and sequence of change, and to prevent or counteract lags, discrepancies and discontinuities of development, there are the warning signals of pain in the body, anxiety in the ego, and the panic in the group. They warn of organic dysfunction, impairment of ego mastery, and loss of group identity: each a threat to all.

In psychopathology we observe and study the apparent autonomy of one of these processes as it receives undue accentuation because of the loss of their mutual regulation and general balance. Thus psychoanalysis has first studied (as if it could be isolated) man's *enslavement by the id,* i.e., by the excessive demands on ego and society of frustrated organisms, upset in the inner economy of their life cycle. Next the focus of study shifted to man's *enslavement by seemingly autonomous ego (and superego) strivings*—defensive mechanisms which curtail and distort the ego's power of experiencing and planning beyond the limit of what is workable and tolerable in the individual organism and in social organization. Psychoanalysis completes its basic studies of neurosis by investigating more explicity *man's enslavement by historical conditions which claim autonomy* by precedent and exploit archaic mechanisms within him to deny him health and ego strength.[15] Only the reinterpretation of our clinical experience on the basis of this three-fold investigation will permit us to make an essential contribution to child training in an industrial world.

The goal of psychoanalytic treatment itself has been defined (12) as a simultaneous increase in the mobility of the id, in the tolerance of the superego, and in the synthesizing power of the ego. To the last point we add the suggestion that the analysis of the ego should include that of the individual's ego-identity in relation to the historical changes which dominated his childhood milieu. For the individual's mastery over his neurosis begins where he is put in a position to accept the historical necessity which made him what he is. The individual feels free when he can choose to identify with his own ego-identity and when he learns to apply that which is given to that which must be done. Only thus can he derive ego-strength (for his generation and the next) from the coincidence of his one and only life cycle with a particular segment of human history.

15. This basic plan was established, among others, in Freud's publication "Civilized Sexual Morality and Modern Nervousness" (10), and in his habitual references to the cultural and socio-economic coordinates of his own existence, wherever for the sake of his new science he published illustrations from his own life.

BIBLIOGRAPHY

1. Bernfeld, S. "Freud's Earliest Theories and the School of Helmholtz", *Psa. Quarterly*, **XIII**, 1944.
2. Bettelheim, B. "Behavior in Extreme Situations", *J. Abnorm. Soc. Psychol.*, 38, 1943.
3. Erikson, E. H. "Childhood and Tradition in Two American Indian Tribes", *this Annual*, I.
4. Erikson, E. H. "Hitler's Imagery and German Youth", *Psychiatry*, **V**, 1942.
5. Fenichel, O. *The Psychoanalytic Theory of Neurosis*, Norton, 1945.
6. Freud, A. "Indications for Child Analysis", *this Annual*, I.
7. Freud, A. *The Ego and the Mechanisms of Defence*, Hogarth, 1937.
8. Freud, S. "On Narcissism: an Introduction", *Coll. Papers*, IV.
9. Freud, S. "An Outline of Psychoanalysis", *Int. J. Psa.*, XXI 1940, p. 82.
10. Freud, S. "Civilized Sexual Morality and Modern Nervousness", *Coll. Papers*, II.
11. Hendrick, I. "Work and the Pleasure Principle", *Psa. Quarterly*, **XII**, 1943.
12. Nunberg, H. "The Synthetic Function of the Ego", *Int. J. Psa.*, XII, 1931.
13. Zilboorg, G. "Present Trends in Psychoanalytic Theory and Practice", *Bull. Menninger Clinic*, 8, 1944, pp. 3-17.

INCENTIVES TO DEVELOPMENT AND MEANS OF EARLY EDUCATION

By LILI E. PELLER, (New York)

"Hitherto education has only set itself the task of controlling, or, it would be more proper to say, of suppressing the instincts. The results have been by no means gratifying, . . . Nor has any one inquired by what means and at what cost the suppression of the inconvenient instincts has been achieved. Supposing now that we substitute another task for this one, and aim instead at making the individual capable of becoming a civilized and useful member of society with the least possible sacrifice of his own activity." (5)

I.

What are the effective means of early education? Wide disagreement as to the answer will be found among different schools of thought. Education is emerging from an empirical to a scientific discipline. When we find it hard to define basic concepts in education, we may turn to parallel areas in medicine in order to gain a frame of reference.

The function of therapy is to initiate, support and/or accelerate the healing process. As medical science progresses, the means of therapy necessarily change. In his diaries, kept during the epidemic of yellow fever towards the close of the eighteenth century in Philadelphia, Benjamin Rush accuses himself because he is unable to make the rounds of all afflicted who need blood-letting. Today we know that his qualms of conscience were unnecessary, because the blood-letting actually undermined the resistance of patients. If Dr. Rush had smoked his pipe with greater leisure, or slept an hour longer, more people might have had a chance to survive the fever.

The function of early education is to initiate, support and/or accelerate developmental processes leading from child- to adult-hood. Means of education considered of central importance yesterday, may be considered unnecessary or harmful today.

A specific educational measure or experience is frequently considered all-important in causing adjustment or maladjustment. As our case material broadens, emphasis may shift from a specific incident to a general condition. The father who remembers the spanking he incurred after stealing apples as a young lad attributes his development into a law-abiding citizen to this well-remembered incident. It may not be easy to persuade him of the possibility that he grew up to be honest mainly because he lived with, and was loved and cared for by honest parents. The corporal punishment which was comparatively harmless in his case may have under changed social conditions a humiliating effect that makes it dangerous.

In the early days of psychoanalysis the psychic trauma occurring once and suddenly was considered the cause of neurotic development. The search for the spectacular trauma has today been replaced by a patient and undramatic unravelling of early tensions and unbearable deprivations. Other changes in causal thinking are just appearing on the horizon. In many case histories of neurotic or delinquent maladjustment the emphasis is still placed on what the neurotic parents *did*. Yet we know that even if parents have insight on an intellectual level and do not *do* anything harmul to the child, but are highly neurotic, the child has but a small chance of normal development.

A historical perspective of changes in educational theory enables us to see in what direction we are moving today.

II.

The School of Habit Training

Representative of the view that good habits are the means of early education are the studies of Professor Blatz, of Toronto University. He is probably the most prolific writer of this school of thought. Most of his writings, including his recent book (2) are for parents. A systematic presentation of his principles can be found in the chapter "The Physiological Appetites" in Murchison's *Handbook of Child Psychology* (10). Those of his statements bearing on our topic can be summarized under three headings.

1) The young child has the tendency to continue his early behavior which it is up to the adult to change. The adult is active, he builds up in the child "habits of acceptance", he foresees future needs. If the adult fails to spur the child towards more mature forms

of behavior (discarding of bottle, feeding himself, etc.) the unfortunate child will remain a child for the rest of his life.

"A child could be kept alive and nutritionally well throughout a long life as bottle-fed. . . . If children were expected to be dependent all their lives upon someone else, then no harm is done in keeping them dependent. The difficulty arises, however, in the fact that as the child grows older he *must* accept more responsibility for *all* of his behavior, not only with respect to eating. Thus an early emancipation in eating habits is necessary not only *per se*, but because of its enormous influence on later behavior. . . . There is nothing except convenience in having the child learn to feed himself. . . ." (10, p. 738.)

2) All social restrictions are arbitary and conventional. Therefore the adult may well choose to impose such restrictions upon the child, as are most convenient for the adult.

"The social customs and traditions . . . are usually inhibitory in character, e.g., there are definite ways of using a knife and fork, there are definite times and places in which to urinate, there are restrictions upon sex activity and interest. These rules are indigenous to the social group in which the child lives and, needless to say, are usually quite arbitrary in form, differing from group to group." (10, p. 730.)

". . . if a child were permitted to obtain his gratification without conforming, he would later undoubtedly act anti-socially, and would eventually find it impossible to live comfortably with others because of the inevitable unresolved conflicts which would arise in social situations. During the first five years of life the habits of 'resolving conflicts' are built up. Such habits are often lifelong in duration. . . ." (2, p. 88.)

3) Through consistent early training the child's innate responses are recast. The need for food is a case in point. Not only does the child learn to wait when hungry, but after a short time he no longer feels hunger, except at the precise time when his training has taught him to expect his food.

"Now it does not matter at what time the child is born, the following day . . . routine is established and as far as results show it is not only adequate but far better biologically than the haphazard schedule of pre-pediatric days when a child was fed every time it cried (i.e., grew restless). There is no doubt that these 'children of freedom' were hungry every time they were restless and that their physiological background was similar to the present-day routinized child who, because of his training, is hungry only according to the clock. The important point, and it cannot be too greatly emphasized, is that, by this very training, the rhythm of the appetite's functioning is regulated and, furthermore, being regulated, the conscious aspect also is controlled.

"It must not be overlooked that this regulation is important, not only specifically as it affects the appetite of hunger. This control ushers in, perhaps, the first of the conflicting situations in which a child finds himself . . . in a few weeks . . . the conflict has been satisfactorily resolved . . . this type of resolution of a conflict is of course eminently satisfactory and satisfying. . . . The child accepts the routinized arrangement fully *by being hungry* at these times. . . . What better arrangement could be made? It is well to keep this in mind as true of all the appetitive activities because this phenomenon appears in connection with all of the appetites." (10, p. 737.) (According to Blatz there are six appetites: hunger, thirst, elimination, rest, change and sex.)

Blatz held the same doctrines in 1944: ". . . Physiological functioning has conformed to the social demands. Unless this arrangement is consistent, the child will be hungry at odd hours and will expect to be fed according to his whim." (2, p. 89.)

I do not know of any presentation of the goal and function of early restrictions, the all-importance of early and relentless habit-training, that is more clear.

Ad 1): Apparently Blatz is so preoccupied with hurrying the infant that it hardly occurs to him that a child would eventually protest with great vigor, if we should try to continue nursing beyond the fitting biological phase. The point is not that "he must accept more responsibility for his eating behavior"; but that there comes a time when he demands the right to hold the cup himself, to use a knife and fork, and all the other paraphernalia which represent for the child the prestige of adulthood. It is by no means correct to say that the adult's educational work consists in "thrusting more and more responsibility upon him", in chasing him out of the paradise of babyhood which he is reluctant to leave. The parent's work is not a continual pushing, it is rather a subtle guidance, which is the more successful the less direct pressure it uses.

Most parents and nursery teachers greatly overdo the phrase, "Only babies do that, big boys don't," because they know the magic this formula works. The child's desire to proceed towards grown-upness is so obvious that it is hard to refrain from exploiting it. But before the stage is reached when the child curtails his early satisfactions, he must have passed through two preceding stages: he must have reached a saturation point regarding his early pleasures, and must have traveled through the stage where he goes back and forth, refusing to do today what he did with pride or enjoyment yesterday.

Ad 2): Blatz feels strongly that all social rules and regulations are completely arbitrary. Accordingly, the educator cannot sit back and wait for social compliance to come. It is not a natural development; it must be planned first and then imposed upon the child. The earlier one begins to enforce rules, the stricter they are enforced, the quicker will the conflict between the child and society be resolved. If we accept the principles stated by Blatz, it follows that strict habit training is actually kinder to the child than a training permitting occasional slips.

It is true that the *form* of social restrictions is arbitrary and "differs from group to group" and "is most unstable, changing with each decade", but the *purpose* of the social restrictions has not changed in all the years of recorded history: the elementary and impulsive desires of the individual must be curbed in the interest of his fellow-beings. Of course, there are restrictions where this purpose is covered over by the traditional accretions. Furthermore, there are curbs which originated in concern for others, yet have lost their meaning today; and some restrictions seem to be only formal and unrelated to human happiness. Fortunately all of these can be kept out of the nursery.

Blatz states later on: "Some societies spurn human flesh, others do not. People of certain nations eat snails; others, plum pudding . . . It is unnecessary to comment on the *arbitrary nature*[1] of these choices." (10, p. 738.) We wonder whether Blatz takes his readers seriously when he labels the eating or spurning of human flesh as arbitrary.

By mixing restrictions of basic importance with those dealing with the amenities of life, and by confusing the *form* of social customs and restrictions with their *content,* he creates the impression of a complete ethnological relativism. His first contention, that the child takes no initiative in changing his early behavior; and his third, in that human appetites can be kneaded into any shape, and that this recasting completely obliterates the original form of the appetite,—create his educational credo: with early habit training you can remake the human being into the likeness of any image you choose. And he adds: when parents have tried it and failed, they should not blame the method, but themselves; they should try again, be prompter in applying displeasure, be adamant in wiping out exceptions, and they will succeed.

According to Blatz the secret of successful early education is to

1. Italics of this author.

make the child *practise* the right habit. If this has been achieved, the right habit "implanted", the child will continue with it. The child's desire to resemble a well-liked person, his at times ardent strivings to shed childish ways in order to become like that person, are not mentioned. The child's own judgment, his will, are not needed in the early education of his appetites.

The psychoanalytic school presents a very different picture as is indicated below. The child's own will is the *educator's most powerful ally*. Unless the child's will is activated, education can never succeed. The most determined and conscientious educator cannot educate a child who remains passive, a child whose imagination has not been set aflame with the picture of the kind of person he wants to become.

III.

The School of Developmentalism

The school of developmentalism, best represented by the work of Arnold Gesell, is in many respects the antipode of the habit training school. Whereas according to Blatz the child proceeds from one stage of development to the next, by dint of the educator's efforts, and thus strictness is the key to successful education, according to Gesell "It is better to do nothing at all than to be too severe with a young child." If a seed has good earth, the approximately right dosage of sunshine and rain, it will grow; in fact, it would be hard to prevent it from growing. After reading Gesell, a mother will get the impression that it is pretty much the same with a child's growth: the danger of doing too much is greater than that of doing too little. "The developmental outlook also tempers the almost irresistible desire to do something about everything and to do it immediately. In child care we fall prone to a certain kind of meddlesomeness—a tendency to set matters right with despatch." (7, p. 296.)

Some examples may help to illustrate the divergence between the two schools. Blatz says about the child's going to bed: Don't let him fool you at bedtime by letting him call you back with many excuses. See that he has been to the toilet, that he had his drink of water, etc., then close the door; if he reopens it, turn the key in the lock. The more frantic his crying becomes, the calmer you must be. Gesell, on the other hand, points out that while the child of twenty-one months goes to bed without too much ado, the child of twenty-four months may begin calling the mother back with all kinds of requests. He is more attached to her now, her company means more to him, thus he finds it harder to part with her. According to the developmental view, detours and pseudo-regressions are part of normal development. The increased dependence runs its course and subsides after a certain period.

Blatz warns parents not to fall for the child's trick when he throws up his food, as he does so deliberately, in order "to attain attention" or because he wants to shirk the responsibility of eating. Therefore, the remedy is not to pay attention to him or show any sympathy, lest he repeat the unsavory procedure. Gesell calls the child's vomiting "his form of hungerstrike". But a prisoner does not go on hungerstrike, unless he is in despair, and unless all other means of protest have been denied him. Neither does the child.

Development cannot be rushed by external pressure. Learning can take place only within the framework of developmental readiness. In the early thirties Hilgard (8), McGraw (9), et al, in experiments with pre-school children, again proved that "training cannot transcend maturation". The results helped to cement the principles on which the programs in progressive kindergartens and elementary grades were built. In nursery schools emphasis was placed on activities demanding gross muscular coordination. In the school the three R's were postponed by one or two years. While this principle — training predicated on maturation—was immediately applied to the child's "higher" learning, it was brought into no connection with the modification of the physiological processes, with his "lower" learning. While in a progressive nursery school and in the first grade the child was allowed to develop at his own pace, and the teacher was scrupulous in her "hands-off" policy, in the same decade a progressive mother worked hard to accelerate her baby's weaning and toilet training.

Anthropologists tell us that among primitives there is no thumb-sucking after the age of approximately eighteen months. The reason suggests itself, that as the infants have such abundant sucking enjoyment there is no need to return to it later. In this example we go one step further in our reasoning than Gesell, assuming that an unfulfilled basic need has a tendency to return, either in its original form or under some disguise. Educators in the past have had their eyes too often fixed on the goal, the civilized adult, and they have continually compared the child with this goal, measured him by his deficiencies in reference to it and judged their own efficiency in the yards and inches by which they pushed the child nearer to this goal.[2]

Gesell emphasizes that not every trait that appears in the child's behavior has come to stay. Educators need not get panicky and resort to stern measures when they notice developments or frailties that would be undesirable in the adult. Dewey has expressed the same principle succinctly: "It does not speak against the nutritional value of beefsteak that we don't feed it to infants."

A slightly different facet of developmentalism has been stressed by Montessori. According to her, the child passes through a series of differing "Sensitive Periods". In each period his interests, his main satisfactions, his sensitivities vary. For instance: the child of twenty-one or twenty-four months shows a strong interest in odors; the child of five and six years, a concern for counting, and if permitted, for weighing, measuring, arraying, etc. Montessori does not say why these interests come just at these periods, but psychoanalysis can explain their "dating": the child's interest in odors coincides with the final stage of his direct interest in defecation; his interest in counting and comparing marks the beginning of the latency period when children temporarily show some compulsive mechanisms, and in general, strive for an exactness and for conventional standards which are independent of personal variables. The impersonal repetitious precision of counting and weighing satisfies this need. The educator, says Montessori, should carefully study the *sensitive periods* and offer those experiences which the child apparently craves at the various stages of his growth. She criticizes our schools for either planning their program along traditional lines, or for bringing those things first which we adults consider easy. Yet learning that impresses us as difficult is easily assimilated by the child if its presentation coincides with developmental needs.

Gesell says we need not fear that without the parents' eternal vigilance and prodding the child will preserve infantile forms of satisfying his physical needs. Montessori has even asserted that the fullest acculturization is possible without direct pressure.

Gesell has a highly discerning and also a loving eye for the physical development of the child and some of its border areas. He shows, for instance, how concepts and thought processes are rooted in

2. This is not true of the great educators. According to Rousseau, who lived before the science of child psychology was born, the skill of the educator consists not in gaining, but in "losing time". In today's parlance, we would say he should protect his pupil from social pressures.

muscular experiences. The child cannot even count up to three until he has many times picked up and released objects one by one with eyes and fingers. This motor foundation is also required for such concepts as "up", "down", "in", "under". While Gesell presents certain aspects of the child's growth with so many significant details, he leaves huge areas uncharted. The child's body mastery, the interplay of body, space and motion, the physical gratifications (except masturbation) are discussed at great length; the child's ramified curiosity, his need for affection, his sensitivity for prestige, his social adjustments to peers are discussed. He fails, however, to include in his picture the child's type of pre-logic, his magical thinking, his crude ethos, his deep desire to become an adult, his anticipation of his adult role, his struggle with the problems of the coming and going of human beings (birth and death), his fear of injury, and all the rest of the fears that may beset the young child. Nor does he trace the devious ways in which the child comes to accept our differentiation of permitted and ostracized aggression, of clean and disgusting, decent and indecent. Gesell is so excellent an observer that he hardly can have missed the fact that the young child wrestles with so many problems not fitting into our traditional picture of childlike interests, that under the naive surface run deep and at times turbulent currents and counter-currents, shaping and re-shaping the young human being.

But, roughly speaking, Gesell acquaints his readers mainly with those facets of the child's development which can be observed when the charming young animal is put in a showcase and observed behind one-way screens, photographed simultaneously at different angles, or when his utterances, articulate as well as pre-articulate, are recorded. Gesell's records contain a wealth of cleverly and tenderly interpreted details. His vivid presentation of the child's locomotion, prehension and other muscular skills conveys to the reader a deep respect for the lawfulness, the power and the slow dignity of evolution. These are valuable counter-agents against the "start early and push hard" doctrines of yesterday and against the inevitable strain and friction a baby causes in a modern city apartment. Gesell's remarks on other aspects of the child's development have a static quality. There is no attempt to show the humble and the archaic, and thus at times shocking, beginnings from which his morals, his emotions and his inquisitiveness grow.

IV.

The School of Psychoanalysis

The child's physical growth is determined by inner factors. He himself indicates his need for food, exercise, rest, etc., and modern child care considers it its main task to answer these requests. Looking back only twenty or thirty years we realize that child care then tried much more to *shape* the child; this trend becomes even clearer if we go back a hundred years. The occasional cutting of the sublingual ligament to facilitate speech, tight swaddling clothes to force the child to stretch his knees, a contraption on wheels in which he was suspended by his arms and forced to "walk" when crawling was his desire, daily painful "cleaning" of the tender and easily injured inner tissue of his mouth,—all these preceded the rigid habit training. These are examples picked at random. Their common denominator is to change the child, to accelerate his development.

In modern child care our foremost goal is to interfere as little as possible with developmental trends. A recent attempt to do so concerns the skin of the neonate: since the days of antiquity midwives have carefully removed the vernix caseosa. Aldrich suggests that it be left untouched. The whitish smear is absorbed within forty-eight hours. Nature's handiwork sometimes appears sloppy and in need of improvement, yet when we step back and observe instead of rushing into action, the rather unpleasant-looking paste disappears without our help, leaving the skin excellently soft and clean.

While the main current in modern child care is to study the child's natural development and to follow along with ancillary measures, there are aspects of child care which certainly cannot be brought under this heading. Take the numerous inoculations against children's diseases: they have no counterpart in nature, they cause discomfort and real suffering to the baby—yet they are considered essential to good child care.

A good deal of the child's early intellectual and emotional progress as well as his physical development is maturational. Yet the greater part of his swift intellectual growth and of his ethical development does not follow the same model as his physical growth.

According to the psychoanalytic view powerful stimuli from the social world come into alliance with his innate tendency to develop.

There is nothing automatic about the child's emotional, intellectual and ethical progress. The main factors in his early development are his early attachment to his mother, his oedipal attachment to his parents, and the sequelae of this bond.

The child relinquishes childish satisfactions in order to please his mother. ". . . all (the children's) play is influenced by the dominant wish of their time of life: viz., to be grown-up and to be able to do what grown-ups do." (6) This wish is present in every child, but its power rises and falls with the depth of the child's attachment to an adult. In our culture the incentive to give up certain forms of behavior comes from the adult,—and from him comes the image which the child wants to resemble, but the metamorphosis itself is carried through by the child; no one else can do it for him. It is not true that the child is inert, while the adult is active, pulling out the weeds and implanting sundry virtues instead.

The simile of the gardener who "bends the twig" is not just a romantic phrase, old-fashioned and innocuous. It stands for a philosophy of education that is still widespread. It should be replaced by attitudes more in agreement with newer insight into the child's development. The gardener cares for an organism inferior to himself. Parent and child need deeply to realize that though separated by age, maturity and experience, *they are peers*. The parent who lacks this conviction will either be despotic or will treat the child as a toy or puppy. The latter is more likely to happen in our enlightened era, yet it is almost equally harmful. The child who fails to anticipate his future role has no motivation to identify with the adult.

The child's early attachment to his mother or mother-figure provides a powerful leverage for his education. In comparison with the child's later oedipal attachment its effect is limited. The baby's attachment to his mother changes but little. He might be compared to a person who likes to go about in an old, torn, and dirty garment, but has learned to throw a clean garment over it when visitors come, and moreover has acquired increasing skill in looking out for the approach of the visitors.

The conflicting emotions of the later oedipal attachment stir the child far more deeply. He goes through many storms, yet we should not be sorry for him, for without this apprenticeship in human relations he could never join the adult group. From these conflicts results the ardent wish to grow up and the first vague outline of his moral self. Their outcome determines his ability to form lasting and sincere attachments and spurs his intellectual development. In short, the oedipal passions, the structural changes which they initiate in the child's mind and their personal variables set the compass for his development in the next years, and, to a certain extent, for all his life. All the other known incentives of development seem small when compared with the oedipal attachment.

According to psychoanalytic thinking the individual undergoes several deep-reaching reorganizations before maturity is reached. The Sturm and Drang of puberty has been well known since Stanley Hall's studies. It took psychoanalysis to discover that the turmoil of early childhood surpasses it. The child experiences love, hate, jealousy, hope, despair, triumph and guilt in great intensity and rapid succession. Intellectually he wrestles with the riddles of sex, birth and death, although he is in no way equipped to understand them, even if the correct information is supplied. In the myth Oedipus solves the riddle of the sphinx, but the child can neither solve nor bypass it.

At the climax of the oedipal phase he strives for physical love satisfaction, for insight far beyond his years and for the exclusive possession of his love object. He attempts the downright impossible with the uniqueness of purpose characteristic of his age—and he fails.

The attachment to his parents survives this collapse and his desire to be like them is tremendously strengthened. So also is his interest in intellectual pursuits. He has tried a short-cut and failed. He is now eager to travel the long road and thus he is now ready for education in the academic sense of the word. He wants to learn and to acquire skills and is highly sensitive to prestige and status. A large share of his energy goes to pursuits unrelated to instinctual satisfactions. Emotional problems continue to hold a priority on his energy over intellectual concerns, but under favorable circumstances the most stirring emotional problems are temporarily solved as he enters latency.

To put it very simply: part of his early aspirations must fail, while the other part must be preserved. For his favorable development one is as indispensable as the other. His oedipal aspirations must collapse, but he must salvage his tender attachment to his parents, his admiration for them. He must be certain that they are fond of him and that he is a needed member of the family. It is highly desirable that he continue to live with them, day in day out, and that there is a wide range of shared interests. All these are incentives and aids to his development. The directly sexual part of his ambitions crashes—to this blow (in reality, it is a long series of blows) the child can adjust. But because this frustration and because confused feelings of guilt are inescapable, we, his educators, should keep other tensions and deprivations at a minimum. He cannot adjust to repeated changes in his parental figures.

In regard to the control of instincts the difference between his person three years ago and his present self is greater than the difference between a member of a primitive tribe and highly civilized man. This change was effected not by punishments and rewards. Cruelty has partly been transformed into concern for others, love of dirt into appreciation of cleanliness, the desire to exhibit his naked body into a sense of modesty. If one may use a simile, one may say that the fervor and passion of the oedipal conflicts has melted his early ego and forged a new structure. In these deeply revolutionary processes the child needs all the help which his attachment to stable and loving elders can provide.

Judging from the current literature of child welfare, the policy of preserving the child's emotional tie to his parents or parent-substitutes even under most trying circumstances, is being widely accepted. But how do we account for the fact that this need is more imperative than all the other needs of childhood? Outside the psychoanalytic school it can be explained only with the view that family ties are sacred. But as the child grows older a rupture of family ties becomes less harmful to him. Does this mean that family bonds become less sacred as the child approaches adolescence? If we take the oedipal situation for more than a figure of speech, then we have the explanation for his inability to advance in his education if his early attachment is broken several times: under normal conditions he already loses so much that he cannot bear losing more.

Leniency in early education is in various degrees practised by all pre-industrial societies and was postulated in our society long before psychoanalytic teaching was widespread, by educators such as Pestalozzi, Froebel, and Dewey. Permissiveness should be the keynote of early education, not because the young child cannot stand strain and frustrations, but because *inevitable* blows and sacrifices make heavy inroads on his resistance[3]. It may be said that this argumentation is idle and that only the permissive attitude is valid. However it seems to this writer that sometimes teachers waste their efforts trying to spare the child trials that should not and cannot be put out of his way; and that present day nursery education is honeycombed with sentimentalism. A child may be struggling with a piece of clothing, and the teacher's hands may be itching to help him; yet as long as he asks for no help there is no need to run to his rescue. A physician treats a man whom he knows to be frail in one way and prescribes a different regime to another who is strong and sturdy but recovering from a recent grave illness.

V.

Fenichel identifies as ". . . the basic means of all education . . . direct threat, a mobilization of the fear of losing love and the promise of special rewards." He defines "what education fundamentally desires . . . good behavior not only through fear of opposition from the grown-ups (who can after all, be deceived) but good behavior for its own sake . . ." (3, p. 285). As indicated above, the present author disagrees here, although she is in agreement with the main thesis of Fenichel's paper. Good behavior is too insignificant a goal of education. Good behavior is possible without initiative, without courage, without intellectual acumen, yet every society must expect these qualities in at least some of its subgroups or individuals. It seems doubtful whether good behavior includes the ability to form deep and lasting attachments, or the ability to enjoy mature sexual relations. To be kind and courteous, even towards those who cannot report on us, to be clean and industrious, to resist temptations even if there is no one to watch us—this is the essence of good behavior.

Freud defines as the task of education: "to make the individual capable of becoming a civilized and useful member of society with the least possible sacrifice of his own activity" (5). This purports "what education fundamentally desires" with more vision than Fenichel's statement, and it points to the two basic mistakes education can commit: failure to socialize the child, or the sacrifice of too much of the

3. A similar thought has been expressed by Whitehead (12): "It is not true that the easier subjects should precede the harder. . . . Some of the hardest must come first because nature so dictates, and because they are essential to life. The first intellectual task that confronts an infant is the acquirement of spoken language. What an appalling task, the correlation of meanings with sounds!"

child's spontaneous drive. Yet "good behavior" seems compatible with such a sacrifice.

For educators of the "old school" good behavior might be acceptable as the goal. Education for them is primarily restraint, achieved by external regulatory means. According to them intelligence is not connected with the fate of the child's emotions. Intellectual abilities are inborn and their development depends upon intellectual stimuli. In the sexual field the main concern is to bring the individual to the point where he will be unlikely to infringe upon moral laws and conventions. Punishments and rewards are regulatory measures and as such are able to bring about an increasing degree of restraint. But restraint, *even internalized restraint, can never be the main goal of education based on a dynamic theory of personality.*

There are limited areas where the child comes to modify his behavior on account of recurrent punishment. To take a time-honored example: he learns not to touch the hot stove because of the pain he has experienced. He learns to substitute caution for unreined curiosity. While such substitution and the prompt, rather mild, consistent displeasure that follows actions which he must learn to avoid, works in issues remote from his instinctual needs, it can never make the child travel the enormous distance he has to cover in order to become an adult. The displeasure which the child experiences may be a "natural" consequence of his action, or the educator may introduce it in order to make him change his behavior, sometimes to protect the child from serious harm (11). But in matters which lie in the path of direct instinctual satisfaction the punishment would have to be so painful that the child would be more bewildered than warned.

Threats and rewards are regulatory mechanisms effective in bringing about minor adjustments. The view that they can build the character structure which makes an adult out of a child, seems a replica of Lamarckian thinking. Lamarck explained the evolution of species by external, environmental regulation. If an organ is useful in a given environment it is retained and developed, if it is useless or harmful, it atrophies. The environment thus rewards or penalizes actions and their carriers, and thus creates new species. According to modern biology external regulatory influences could never lead to a new species. *Creative* processes, mutations, *are postulated,* although so far mutations producing new species have not been observed. Biology has thrown old concepts overboard, although for the time being there are no observational data supporting the new concept.

In the genesis of the adult from the child external pressure initiates many changes and regroupings within the child, but it cannot enforce them. In this case the *creative* factor is the child's attachment to his parents. It is this attachment, and not external pressure that generates the wish to relinquish childish satisfactions.[4]

Fenichel also states that "children (need) very deeply . . . love and affection from the persons of their environment."[5] This is correct but too general. The child's greatest need is for love from the persons to whom he is attached, and not merely from persons who chance to be near him. "Persons of his environment", his teacher or nurse or a kind-hearted aunt may offer this love amply to the child—yet he profits but little. We can assume that many foster-mothers appearing in the history of disturbed children have offered love and affection to no avail.

For the older child emphasis shifts from attachment to identification with the person in authority. The youngster will keep rules if he likes the person who gave them, understands why they are necessary, and is given a chance to support them actively. His intelligence must be stirred, his love and loyalty activated, and whatever helps in this is an important tool of education. This is true according to psychoanalytic thinking. According to traditional education the child who misbehaves should be punished harder and harder until he reforms.

4. It is tragic that Otto Fenichel cannot counter the above views. I want at least to add one remark, which is in line with his way of thinking. It concerns reaction-formations. The child who is especially fond of exhibiting his naked body may become especially modest; the child who is exceedingly cruel may develop deep and broad sympathies with those who suffer. This reaction-formation is initiated by the disapproval of a beloved adult, but its strength is derived from and will be proportional to the strength of the original drive. This is the classical view. On second thought we may conceive another possibility: it may be that the strength of the reaction-formation is determined by the differential which the child senses between his desire and the wishes of his beloved adults. In this case a child living in a highly prudish group or in a society abhorring uncleanliness would develop stronger reaction-formations than if he were living with the identical instinctual equipment in a less "civilized" group. External factors may have a greater weight than the classical psychoanalytic view assumed.

5. In a joking vein we may make the corollary statement: "Adults need love and affection from the young children of their environment." From personal experience I should say that for every child who asks to be kissed or taken on the lap, there are at least three adults who want to invade the reserve of a three-year-old and bestow unsolicited affection upon him. Children are highly selective in their quest for affection.

"What shall I do when I have tried every device that I can think of, and will fail?" (asks the young teacher). There is no explicit formula that will cover each specific case, but one general suggestion may be given: *get order.* Drop everything else, if necessary, until order is secured. . . . Pile penalty upon penalty for misdemeanors and let the 'sting' of each penalty be double that of its predecessor. Tire out the recalcitrants if you can gain your end in no other way." (1, p. 96.)

The attitude reflected in this old quotation is hardly found today in our schools, yet it still works great harm in some reform schools. The child without a bond to anyone cannot be reformed by punishment. Its only effect may be that he learns to use more cunning in reaching his goals and that he stores up resentment which may precipitate him into a criminal career. Has the education of the youngsters who fill the reform schools failed because they did not receive enough threats and rewards, or was some other means of education missing in their early history? It is far less harmful for a mature person to have promiscuous and shifting relations than for a young child. The personal bond leads a child towards a socialized existence; there is no "Ersatz" for it.

Anna Freud's work in the residential nurseries provides us with a fitting example. In the beginning all the children (about twenty-four) were cared for by all the nurses (about six). Later it was tried to group children and adults into "families". A very stormy period followed. Fights among the children multiplied, crying became more frequent, far more jealousy was observed; yet soon ". . . the state of frenzy subsided and gave way to a quieter, more stable and comforting attachment. At the same time the children began to *develop in leaps and bounds.*[6] The most gratifying effect was that several children who had seemed hopeless as far as the training for cleanliness was concerned, suddenly started to use the pot regularly and effectively . . . All the children in the group have greatly enlarged their vocabulary . . ." (4, p. 160.)

This may well be called an *experimentum crucis.* The same children, the same physical set-up, the same adults. No doubt they had love and affection for the children before and after the grouping in families. They showed approval and disapproval before and after. Yet after the establishment of the personal tie, the children's education made remarkable progress.

6. Italics of this author.

Those who attach greatest relevance to threat and reward make the implicit assumption that the instinct of self-preservation is stronger than any other desire. The child will comply with our demands in order to avert harm to himself. According to psychoanalytic thinking the need for self-preservation, though powerful, does not always rate priority. Under certain constellations a wayward adolescent will not be motivated towards "mending his ways" by increasingly severe and painful punishments. He rather develops an increasing ability to "take it" (plus a number of distorted attitudes like bitterness, masochism, hatred, etc.).

We are all familiar with the young child who is offered good food, yet in spite of his hunger does not eat well because the conflicts with his mother have been shifted to the food she is giving him. He is undernourished although offered tasty food at every meal. Here too emotional conflicts push self-preservation into the background.

Threats and rewards are the main means of education where education is conceived as external restraint. In some areas, such as in habit training, they can be important incentives. However, mechanical training, regardless of the child's understanding of what is being demanded of him, does not lead toward emotional maturity. The child's insight is as much a means of education as his mother's rewarding smile. On each age level a humanized education makes fullest use of the child's critical abilities.

In conclusion we return to the simile of the twig: the elastic young twig is bent into a certain position and held there by a cord and stick; after a year or two this support may be removed; the twig will not snap back, but continue of "its own" to grow as it was bent. External pressure has been "internalized". This well-known process *in horticulture* does not tell us anything about the child. To understand his way of internalizing we must consider his deep and contradicting emotions, his intellectual power, his fears, his ability for keen observation as well as for denying unpleasant facts, his reactions to frustrations, his anticipation of his adult role. Without this complex basis of reaction the child's development would not differ essentially from the results of animal training, and the child would not undergo a transmutation into an ethical and social being.

BIBLIOGRAPHY

1. Bagley, W. C. *Classroom Management,* New York, 1907.
2. Blatz, W. *Understanding the Young Child,* Morrow, 1944.
3. Fenichel, O. "The Means of Education", *this Annual,* I.
4. Freud, A. and Burlingham, D. T. *War and Children,* Internat. Univ. Press, 1943.
5. Freud, S. "Analysis of a Phobia in a Five-Year-Old Boy", *Coll. Papers,* III.
6. Freud, S. *Beyond the Pleasure Principle,* Hogarth, 1920.
7. Gesell, A., and Ilg, G. *Infant and Child in the Culture of Today,* Harper, 1943.
8. Hilgard, J. R. "Learning and Maturation in Pre-school Children", *J. Gen. Psychol.,* 1932.
9. McGraw, M. *Growth, A Study of Johnny and Jimmy,* Appleton-Century, 1935.
10. Murchison, C. *Handbook of Child Psychology,* Clark University Press, 1933.
11. Spencer, H. *Education,* New York, 1895.
12. Whitehead, A. N. "The Task of Infancy", *Aims of Education,* Macmillan, 1929; and earlier, in *The Rhythm of Education,* London, 1922.

J. B. FELIX DESCURET

By RAYMOND DE SAUSSURE, M.D. (New York)

Freud made such an impact on child psychiatry that all observations prior to his appear very superficial. However, the facts he elucidated oblige us to recall to memory physicians whom a classic era threw into oblivion. J. B. Felix Descuret, for one, was interested in psychosomatic medicine, like so many physicians of the eighteenth and nineteenth centuries; but he also observed the fact of children's conflicts.

Descuret was born at Châlons-sur-Saone on June 5th, 1795—a year rich in the birth of psychiatrists. Scipion Pinel, the eldest son of Philippe Pinel, who wrote a great number of books on the mentally ill; Jean Etienne Georget, Esquirol's best pupil; Alexandre Bottex, who wrote the first French treatise on Forensic Psychiatry (Lyon 1838); Ulysse Trélat, a good historian of Psychiatry; James Braid, the founder of hypnotism; all were born in the same year. Descuret studied in Paris, first literature, then medicine. He was very erudite and published a first book on Cornelius Nepos, followed by a bibliography of ancient and modern literature in thirty-one volumes. He was an active collaborator of *Bibliographie,* a magazine which completed the *Grand Dictionnaire des Sciences Médicales.*

A very active physician, he was in charge of the clinic for poor people in the Twelfth District of Paris, and in 1831 became officer of the Public Health Commission in the "Observatoire". Descuret did not belong to the Société Médico-Psychologique and therefore was never cited among the classical psychiatrists of his time. His philosophical interests were very different from those of his colleagues.

We do not know why he left Paris. He died in Châtillon d'Azergues near Lyon on November 27, 1872.

Among his works are: *Theory of Taste* (1847); *Les Merveilles du Corps Humain* (Paris, Labé, 1856), an anatomy for Catholic priests. His major work is *La Médecine des Passions considérées dans leurs rapports avec les maladies, les lois et la Religion* (Paris, Bechet et Labé, 1841; a second edition appeared in 1854). According to the *Dictionnaire Encyclopédique des Sciences Médicales* (Paris, 1883), he left the following manuscripts: "Le Médecin Moraliste", "L'Esprit de la Grammaire", "Les Mémoires d'un vieux Médecin". The whereabouts of the latter works are unknown.

During the eighteenth and nineteenth centuries, every psychiatrist knew that the emotions played a great role in the etiology of neuroses, but they had no clear idea of the relationship between a conflict and a neurotic symptom. They did not realize that the neurosis was the expression of the conflict.

Descuret saw this. More, he understood that many adult neuroses had deep roots in the unsolved difficulties of childhood. Even if he had no idea of the sexual origin of emotional troubles, he was, in many ways, a forerunner of Freud.

Not all the case histories of Descuret have the same value. He was a man who shared many prejudices of his time. He had an understanding of the psychosomatic medicine that was widely practised at that time, but he often judged the patient from the moral rather than from the psychological angle.

Miss Anne Williams has been kind enough to translate the following case histories of Descuret. She has retained the romantic and sometimes melodramatic flavor of his style, qualities which were common in the first part of the nineteenth century.

Medecine des Passions, Paris, 1841. Page 60 ff.

Jealousy in a seven-year-old child followed by a radical and unexpected cure

Young Gustave G., endowed with a good disposition, had enjoyed perfect health up to his seventh year when all of a sudden his appearance changed markedly. His complexion, usually fresh and rosy, lost its brilliance day by day. His eyes, formerly so full of animation, became dull, without expression, and seemed to lose themselves in their sockets. He lost weight, lost his former high spirits, and was unable to sleep.

The child's anxious expression and the frown which I noticed between his brows, made me suspect that he was suffering from jealousy, and I felt it my duty to warn his parents whom I met fairly often at one of my patient's homes. I had hardly uttered the word jealousy when Gustave's mother, a fairly witty woman but very frivolous, answered ironically that the child had no reason to be jealous, that she could attribute his trouble to boredom only, and that in consequence she was going to send him to school so that he would have more distractions than at home where he had no comrades to play with; his little brother, only eleven months old, being still at the breast.

But this solution, far from improving Gustave's health, undermined it from day to day. The poor little boy, after having spent several hours in the study hall, remained there while his schoolmates went out into the small garden adjoining the house to play. Several times his teacher found him sitting in a corner, head between his hands, back turned to the window. When she pressed him one day with kindly questions, the child finally broke down, letting tears and deep sighs escape him.

"I am so unhappy, teacher! I'm so very unhappy. If you only knew! No one loves me at home any more; they send me to school so that they can give everything to my little brother while I'm gone."

The wise instructor sent Gustave home immediately and wrote his parents what had happened, urging them not to send the child back to school if they did not wish to see him fall victim to the sickness which was eating him.

My diagnosis being all too well confirmed, Mr. and Mrs. G. wrote me immediately. They begged me to come and care for their child whose illness I had recognized from the start, and at the same time they told me the confessions which the teacher had dragged from him.

The boy whom I had not seen for almost two months seemed to me horribly changed. His face was extremely pale and his body painfully thin, save for the right spleen where the liver protruded considerably under the last short ribs. The color of the skin was slightly jaundiced; the tongue was red at the edges; and the pulse, fast. He was both constipated and abnormally thirsty. I began by being affectionate with the child and absolutely forbade his return to school for some time. Then, noticing that he frowned each time his eyes rested on his little brother, at this moment at his mother's breast, I turned to the woman and said:

"Madame, that little rascal drinking your milk is perfectly healthy while Gustave is sick and needs it. Your baby is over a year. You must wean him and breast-feed Gustave four times a day. In this way you will cure him very quickly."

"Mother would never let me nurse instead of my brother! She loves him too much for that!" cried Gustave.

"Darling," said the woman kindly, "I nursed you two months longer than this baby. But since you're sick and the doctor thinks that my milk will help you, I will wean him and let you take his place whenever you wish."

"Right now!" cried the child, and he threw himself on his mother and drank until she had not a drop of milk left.

From that moment on, Gustave fed at his mother's breast four times a day in the place of his little brother who was sent to the country to be weaned. His father and mother showered him with love and at the end of three weeks his health was perceptibly better. I had also prescribed light meals of chicken broth, tisanes, soothing poultices on the right spleen, two lukewarm baths a week, and short but frequent rides in the carriage.

Three months had barely gone by when the child was completely recovered. The following year, at my advice, his parents had the little brother brought home from the country. At first they showed him no affection in the presence of Gustave and pretended even to scold him when he cried or was naughty. Soon Gustave, whose heart was naturally kind, began to beg mercy for his younger brother. Satisfied with the victory which he had won, his young pride was still more flattered when his wishes were granted and not those of the baby boy. Finally, thanks to these innocent artifices which were kept up with great care for more than a year, Gustave felt the greatest affection for his brother, an affection that has not left him since.

Better than many medical men of his time, Descuret understood how frustration may create psychological conflicts and how important is the gratification of children's instinctual needs.

Ibid., page 615 ff.

A stepmother's jealousy

Mr. de S., a high-ranking officer, widower of a charming woman whom he had loved deeply and who had left him a young son, made a second marriage with a young Belgian girl who promised to be a mother to the child for whom she seemed to feel a genuine affection. The child was placed out to nurse only a short distance away from the town in which Mr. de S. lived. Every day the married couple went together to see the boy and they seemed to take equal delight in watching him grow in strength and intelligence. Nevertheless, his extreme likeness to his mother often threw Mr. de S. into deep thought which did not escape his young wife. He sometimes was imprudent enough to sing the praises of the one he had lost to his second wife, even to the point of admitting the emotions which the sight of the child whom she had contemplated with so much kindness had aroused in him. These confessions, however, did not seem to displease the one who heard them; quite often she even encouraged them, for the insight which love gave her taught her instinctively that in certain cases one must use in order to destroy, and she hoped to triumph over her husband's regrets in giving him the freedom to express them.

Nevertheless, it was a horrible conflict for her and one which was detrimental to her affection for the child whom she had adopted in such good faith. Already a clear-sighted observer would note that the gestures of affection she bestowed on the child in the presence of her husband sprang more from a sense of duty than from the heart. Finally she became a mother. It was then that the jealousy by which she was struck made sudden and rapid progress. Making numerous comparisons between Mr. de S.'s expressions of love toward the two children, she thought the son of the first wife better loved than hers, and, from that time on, she tried all means to take from him an affection she could no longer abide. Unfortunately, circumstances favored these erroneous thoughts. Orders forced Mr. de S. to leave his family. He went away with no inkling of his wife's frightful jealousy and left her, in complete confidence, his eldest son whom he had brought back home and who was then three-and-a-half years old.

Her husband had hardly gone when the cruel stepmother, weary of self-restraint, gave herself up to all the hatred which she felt toward the poor little boy entrusted to her. Reflecting first on how to destroy in him the happy disposition which had earned him his father's love, and constantly punishing him undeservedly, she forbade him even the tears which her cruelty brought forth. Thus she succeeded in suppressing in his young soul all spontaneity. Then she forced him to spend whole days in a room by himself where she gorged him with food but where she deprived him of all kinds of games and communication. So the poor little fellow, no longer receiving from outside the proper food to develop his intellectual faculties, soon loses his gaiety and last rays of intelligence. First taciturn and sulky, he suddenly becomes insensitive, stupefied, and feels only animal needs. As a finishing touch, the cruel woman, in her desire to make it impossible for him to complain about her to his father, if the latter should question him, made him forget French by addressing him only in Flemish. The child had spoken this language for a long time with his nurse. Soon he knew no other. He reached such a degree of idiocy that he ended by making sounds intelligible only to his stepmother.

It was in this state that, after two years, a friend of his father's found him. She had seen the child at birth and was extremely interested in him. Having examined very closely the stepmother's conduct, and having made numerous inquiries, she voiced her suspicions to Mr. de S. without hesitation. The latter came back and found his son in fair health and beautifully clothed. But when he discovered him to be deaf to his voice, unresponsive to his caresses; when he saw his eyes, dull and mournful, glancing around him with complete indifference, the father gave a cry that came from the depths of his heart. The truth had been revealed to him. For a moment he stared in cold fury at the guilty woman who was showing him his other son, and, pushing her back with horror, he snatched his poor firstborn in his arms and fled with him never to return.

Immediately placed in the care of a skilled physician, the boy regained his intelligence. But never did he recover his original gaiety. One might say that the dreadful jealousy to which he had almost fallen victim pursued him even in the midst of his happy youth and he spent many years before he could overcome the terrible after-effects.

This is the first observation of a case of pseudo-debility I know of that was successfully cured.

Ibid., page 716 ff.

A nostalgic nature, observed in a child of two

Eugene L., native of Paris, was sent to nurse in the outskirts of Amiens and brought home to his family when he was two years old. The strength of his limbs, the firmness and color of his skin, the vivaciousness and gaiety of his character—all showed him to be a child of vigorous constitution and the object of excellent care. During the fifteen days that his nurse stayed with him, Eugene continued to enjoy the best of health. But the woman had hardly gone when he grew pale, sad and morose. He showed himself unresponsive to his parents' love and refused the dishes which had been his favorites only a few days before.

Struck by this sudden change, the father and mother of Eugene called Dr. Hippolyte Petit who recognized immediately the first symptoms of homesickness and recommended frequent walks and all the childish distractions in which the capital abounds. These methods, ordinarily effective in similar cases, failed completely in this one. The little boy whose failing became increasingly apparent, spent whole hours in sad immobility, eyes fastened to the door through which he had seen pass the woman who had served him as mother. Summoned again by the family, the skillful doctor declared that the only way to save the child was to call the nurse back immediately. This was done right away. At her arrival, Eugene gave cries of joy; his melancholy expression gave way to one of rapture and, in the words of his father, "From that moment on he began to live again." Taken the following week to Picardie, he stayed there for about a year in perfect health.

On his second return to Paris, Dr. Petit gradually separated him from his nurse, first for only a few hours, then for a whole day, then for one week, until finally the child was accustomed to her absence. This tactic was crowned with complete success.

These conflicts between the nurse and the mother were probably numerous in the nineteenth century, when it was customary in the upper class to have the baby fed at the nurse's breast. Here Dr. Petit understood that the repression was due to a frustration and he acted like a good psychoanalyst.

Ibid., page 618 ff.

Jealousy complicated by envy and terminated by a fatal cancer

A woman of the middle class, having some means, had remained a widow with two little girls. The eldest, named Rose, had a quarrelsome nature and a figure so ungraceful that it was difficult, in looking at her, to suppress the gesture of repulsion which she inspired. The young Elise, on the contrary, was engaging, agreeable, and so kind that everyone delighted in showing her affection. All this turned her older sister into her bitterest enemy. This enmity, which time only increased, dated from Elise's birth. For the poor Rose, whose name seemed an insult, had not been able to see another child share the maternal cares of which she had been in sole possession, without suffering profound jealousy. The preference that her mother seemed always to show her over her younger sister, little though she deserved it, could not even soften this habitual emotion from which little Elise, in growing up, was forced to suffer the sad consequences. Every compliment, every show of friendliness accorded her by strangers, was to her ruthless sister a reason for abusing her. One day she bruised her face and pelted her with blows because a passerby had exclaimed over her attractiveness. The mother, through an unforgivable weakness, permitted Rose's bad treatment of her sister to go on, and sometimes added her own when the young victim dared to complain and ask for help.

Nevertheless, at the age of eighteen Elise got married and thus escaped the authority of an unjust mother as well as the unkindness of her enemy. But if the young woman had thought to rejoice in her deliverance, she could not escape her own heart which soon brought her back to the complete dependence of a profoundly-felt filial love. Her mother lost the little fortune she had accumulated, and from then on the generous Elise thought only to lighten by her own work the misery of the one who had given her birth. Care, thoughtfulness, absolute devotion—all these were lavished on her; and, more admirable yet, all was lavished also on the wicked sister who had never left home. All this without a single word or so much as a look of reproach. Such generous behavior which lasted over a long period of years should surely have been enough to disarm her wretched jealousy. But, on the contrary, her passion seemed to find new sustenance in these very kindnesses of which she was the recipient. It was for her a real torment to see her sister by her mother's side; she insisted that her mother never repay by so much as an affectionate word or a kindly smile the girl's loving and daily care. And, however much the weak mother gave in to her, Rose fell into excesses of rage and despair.

Such a long and continual conflict ended by developing in Rose a cancerous tumor of the breast. For several months her generous sister spared nothing in order to relieve her suffering; but, in the midst of the most cruel distress, Rose did not lose her dominant idea. Forced in 1838 to go to the hospital for an operation, she suffered less from the pain than from the jealousy and envy which devoured her soul. Soon she extended these two feelings to include her wardmates; with some, she envied them the interest which they roused, either on the part of the doctors during their visits or the nurses in their care; with others, she bitterly reproached the benign character of their illness, and finally almost all became for her objects of a hatred so profound that the hospital became unbearable and she wanted to be taken back to her family. Her wish was carried out. Shortly after, feeling the end draw near, she extracted from her mother the solemn promise never to go and live with Elise.

In spite of all the skill and patience which Dr. Robert showed in the removal of the cancerous tumor, the ganglions which it had been impossible to remove enlarged in the armpit, congested the upper arm and dragged the girl to her death. She succumbed at the age of forty-one on the 28th of March, 1838.

Had I known this unfortunate woman better, and had I perceived the moral evil by which she was consumed, I would assuredly have advised her not to run the risks of an operation, almost always followed by a fatal relapse, when the emotions have been for a long time vitiated by such unhappy diseases as hatred, chagrin, jealousy and envy.

It is interesting to see how deeply Descuret was convinced of psychosomatic medicine. He does not express the slightest doubt that a chronic repressed conflict could end in a cancer.

CONTENTS OF VOLUME I